CONSTRUCTION CONTRACTING

CONSTRUCTION CONTRACTING

Second Edition

Richard H. Clough

DEPARTMENT OF CIVIL ENGINEERING

THE UNIVERSITY OF NEW MEXICO

ALBUQUERQUE

WILEY-INTERSCIENCE

A DIVISION OF JOHN WILEY & SONS

NEW YORK • LONDON • SYDNEY • TORONTO

10   9   8   7   6

Library of Congress Catalogue Card Number: 79-84964
SBN 471 16105 5

Printed in the United States of America

PREFACE

In preparing this second edition of *Construction Contracting,* the essential approach to the subject has not been changed and the book continues to emphasize the management aspects and everyday workings of a construction contracting business. However, the text has been almost completely rewritten and the material has been extensively rearranged. New material has been added throughout and the subject matter has been regrouped into a more logical order of discussion. A special effort has been made to devise a format that will be useful as a classroom text and of value as a source of reference information.

The construction industry is a dynamic and ever-changing area of business, and much of significance has occurred since the first edition of this book came out in 1960. In this revised edition the subject material has been thoroughly modernized and the latest information has been included.

The book continues to be basic in its approach. Details are discussed when appropriate, but attention is concentrated on the essence of the matter. A number of new topics have been added and new groupings of associated subject matter have been created. The matter of unit-price estimates has been expanded considerably in the chapter on estimating, and an appendix discusses a probabilistic bidding strategy. "Hold-harmless" clauses and "wrap-up insurance" are among the new insurance topics. Another chapter is devoted to the important subject of project cost accounting with illustrative examples included, and Business Methods has been prepared from a regrouping of associated material which was included in the original edition. Construction Planning and Scheduling, an entirely new chapter, centers about a discussion of the critical path method and its associated applications of least-cost expediting and resource leveling. The chapter on labor law has been extensively modernized and includes information about the most recent federal legislation, NLRB rulings, and court decisions as well as matters pertaining to equal employment opportunity.

The second edition should serve well as a teaching text in conjunction with construction management courses, either within schools of engineering or architecture or in technology programs such as civil or construction technology. The subject matter and level of presentation make the book adaptable to a wide variety of teaching situations. In addition, the book is designed to serve as an information reference for people in general who are associated with the construction industry. Information concerning construction insurance, contract bonds, labor law, and other topics is sometimes difficult to find and a single source of such information can be of much use.

During the writing of this revision Mr. Tom Savage contributed invaluable information and advice on matters pertaining to insurance and contract bonds. Mr. Alva Coats provided help on a variety of topics. Much credit must go to my wife for her patient typing of the many revisions of the final manuscript.

RICHARD H. CLOUGH

Albuquerque, New Mexico
April, 1969

CONTENTS

CONSTRUCTION CONTRACTING

1

BUSINESS MANAGEMENT

1.1 THE MANAGEMENT FUNCTION

In any business, the management function may be divided into five distinct steps: organizing, staffing, directing, planning, and controlling. The skill with which these steps are carried out determines, in large measure, the success of the business venture.

Many effective techniques have been developed to assist the manager in carrying out his responsibilities. Business schools in the nation's colleges and universities emphasize the teaching of scientific management methods. The professional manager has emerged as an efficient and adroit manipulator of men, money, machines, and materials for the profitable production of goods and services.

The essential motivation underlying the use of good management practices by a business enterprise is the making of a fair and reasonable profit. A private enterprise must earn a profit or it will cease to exist. The need for better management has been sharpened by the highly competitive situation prevailing in business generally. Good management is a necessity for business success.

1.2 MANAGEMENT IN CONSTRUCTION

Construction contractors, generally speaking, have been slow in applying proven management methods to the conduct of their businesses. Specialists have characterized management in the construction industry as being "weak," "inefficient," "nebulous," "backward," and "slow to react to changing conditions." This does not mean to say that all construction companies are poorly managed. On the contrary, some of America's best-managed businesses are construction firms, and it may be noted with satisfaction that the list of profitable construction companies is a long one. Nevertheless, in the overall picture, the construction industry is at or near the top in the annual rate of business failures and resulting liabilities.

There are several explanations given as to why the construction industry has been slow in applying management procedures that have proven effective in other areas. Construction projects are unique in character and do not lend themselves to standardization. Construction operations involve many skills and are largely nonrepetitive in nature. Projects are constructed under environmental conditions of weather, location, transportation, and labor that are more or less beyond the contractor's control. The construction business is a volatile one, with many seasonal and cyclical ups and downs. Construction firms, in the main, are small operations, with the management decisions being made by one or two persons.

The conclusion cannot be drawn, however, that management problems in the construction industry are uniquely different from those in other industries. The complexity of the product and the lack of production standardization do indeed lead to difficult management problems, but these are not necessarily more complicated than those in other business fields. Many industries are characterized by a large number of relatively small firms. Many areas of business experience wide temporal variations in the demand for their products and services. Construction is certainly not the only industry experiencing keen competition. Ineffective management in construction is not, therefore, the inevitable result of pressures and demands peculiar to the industry. As a matter of fact, the presence of such pressures and demands emphasizes the need for the development of a management awareness in the construction industry.

It is a moot question as to how many construction firms are well managed and whether or not many enterprises enjoy any conscious management at all. It is an inescapable conclusion, however, that skilled management and business survival go together. That this maxim has not been recognized by all construction firms is amply demonstrated by the high incidence of financial failures in the industry.

1.3 BUSINESS FAILURES IN CONSTRUCTION

Studies over many years by Dun & Bradstreet show that contractor failures account for a disproportionate number of all business failures. Although failures of all kinds have risen during recent years, construction failures have increased at a considerably faster rate. In fact, the rate of construction business failures has grown faster than the rate at which contractors' ranks are increasing.

It seems to be anomalous that such a large number of construction firms go out of business each year at a time when construction volume remains at such high levels. Dun & Bradstreet lists the following as being the underlying causes of construction failures:

> Incompetence
> Unbalanced experience

Lack of managerial experience
Lack of experience in the line
Neglect
Reason unknown
Fraud
Disaster

The items in the preceding list appear in the order of their importance, and the first four account for over 90 percent of the failures. This fact makes it very clear that the financial success of a construction enterprise depends almost entirely upon the quality of its management. Many apparent causes can be given for business failure; for example, low profit margins, overextension, and inadequate accounting procedures are often cited as causing failure. It is obvious, however, that these business inadequacies are simply indicative of poor management.

1.4 THE CONSTRUCTION MANAGER

Organizing, staffing, directing, planning, and controlling have been cited as the five essential management functions. These functions must be performed by someone in every business venture. Performance of the managerial function is a necessary condition for the growth, development, and success of a construction company.

A large contracting concern, through its organizational structure, will subdivide the management function into a number of different areas with a manager in charge of each. In a small firm, one or two persons will carry out all such duties. In either case, the manager must meet his responsibilities through direction and control of the human effort. Management is associated, therefore, with the everyday operations and details of all phases and levels of the business.

Through judicious discharge of the management function, the management staff of a construction concern is expected to create and maintain a profitable enterprise. Although the manager does not normally carry out the construction operations with his own hands, he is nonetheless responsible for keeping the projects progressing efficiently and on schedule. He must oversee all of the many steps in the construction process from the preliminary estimates of job cost to the final inspection and payment.

Throughout this book, descriptive terms such as "contractor," "manager," and "administrator" are used to designate the person who supervises the process or procedure under discussion. Thus, these terms may refer to an owner, partner, officer, office manager, department head, or other individual who occupies the managerial position of immediate responsibility.

1.5 MANAGEMENT TOPICS

Between the inception and completion of a construction project lies an extensive panorama of management duties. The management functions, as they apply to the operation of a construction contracting firm, are considered in detail in various chapters, as described in the following.

Organizing. The organization of a construction business involves two different considerations. The business must first become legally established as a proprietorship, partnership, or corporation. The considerations involved in this important step are discussed in Chapter 3.

After the company is established, an organizational structure must be devised to carry on the business. Necessary activities must be identified, positions created to perform these activities, and the positions linked together into an operational whole. Chapter 4 discusses the principles of business organization.

Staffing. The staffing function of a construction manager also involves two, generally unrelated duties. One of these is concerned with the selection, compensation, training, evaluation, and retention of office and supervisory personnel. The general topic of staffing is discussed in Chapter 4.

Workmen on the projects are often temporary employees whose services are acquired and terminated by the foremen or superintendents in the field. Conditions of employment pertaining to such employees are usually dictated by labor contracts. Despite the almost casual nature of such employment, labor relations absorb a great deal of management's time and energies. Chapters 13 and 14 discuss matters pertinent to this topic.

Directing. Directing the activities of the firm involves primarily channeling and supervising the work of subordinates. Lines of authority and communication in the organization necessary for the manager to accomplish a proper job of direction are discussed in Chapter 4.

Direction of a contracting firm, or of any of its organizational segments, requires a business knowledge of its individual parts. The various considerations exerting an influence upon the business are so interrelated that each can affect the other. Hence, it is imperative that the manager have a broad acquaintance with the several business areas vital to construction. Chapters 5, 6, 7, 8, 9, 10, and 15 present detailed discussions of different aspects of the construction industry.

Planning. Planning is concerned primarily with the problem of choosing future courses of action through the evaluation of possible alternatives. In a construction company, planning involves both project planning and general planning for the future of the firm. The real focus of a construction company, however, is on its field projects. Despite the fact that the contractor's organizational departments operate relatively independently of one another, in the final analysis all of the various departments serve the same vital role of supporting the firm's field construction activities.

The construction manager's planning function is, consequently, associated almost entirely with project planning. This important topic is discussed in Chapter 12.

Control. The many forces that can affect his projects cannot always be predicted or completely controlled by the contractor. Although any good plan attempts to consider contingencies, even the most careful planning can never totally eliminate uncertainty. Once a project plan has been established, it is the control function to check continuously the adequacy and efficiency of the plan in the light of actual experience and to make needed adjustments as construction proceeds. Chapters 11 and 12 discuss the control function of a contractor's organization.

2

THE CONSTRUCTION INDUSTRY

2.1 ECONOMIC IMPORTANCE

Construction has great influence on the state of the nation's economic health. In fact, this industry is the keystone in the growth of the national economy. Times of prosperity are largely sparked by extensive private construction. In periods of recession, when construction volume suffers drastic cutbacks, government-sponsored public works are used to reduce unemployment. A high level of construction activity is an indispensable element for national prosperity.

Construction has been, for several years, the largest production activity in the nation. The total annual expenditure on construction now accounts for approximately 14 percent of the dollar value of our gross national product. Thus, approximately 1 of every 7 dollars spent for goods and services is a construction dollar. The Bureau of Employment Statistics of the U.S. Department of Labor currently indicates that approximately 3½ million persons are employed directly by the construction industry. If the production, transportation, and distribution of construction materials are taken into account, construction creates directly and indirectly about 16 percent of the total gainful employment of this country.

The figures given in the preceding paragraph are for all construction. Included are not only new construction of every category but also remodeling, maintenance, and repairs, which, during average times, account for roughly one-third of the annual volume of total construction.

2.2 DEVELOPMENT OF A CONSTRUCTION PROJECT

The development of a typical construction project involves four distinct steps. After the need for the project has been demonstrated, a feasibility study must be made to check the cost and scope of the facility against the economic or social benefits to be derived. The results of this study serve as the basis for approval or disapproval of the project.

When the project has been authorized, financing must then be arranged, the details of which depend upon whether the project is for a public or a private owner. After the financing is arranged, construction drawings and specifications are prepared. This step necessitates detailed planning and design of the project. Decisions are made concerning construction methods and materials, and the required contract documents are prepared. The fourth step is the actual construction of the project.

Of the four steps just described, the contractor is normally concerned only with the actual construction work. This fourth stage is usually performed by contract between the owner and the contractor.

2.3 CONSTRUCTION CATEGORIES

The field of construction is as diversified as the uses and forms of the many types of structures that it produces. However, construction can be divided into three main categories, although there is some overlap among these divisions and certain projects do not fit neatly into any one of them.

In general, contracting concerns specialize in one category of construction. Specialization is usual because of the radically different equipment requirements, trade and supervisory skills, and field procedures involved in each of the different types of construction. The three main divisions—building construction, engineering construction, and industrial construction—are defined in the following paragraphs.

Building Construction. Building construction covers buildings in the commonly understood sense, which are erected for habitational, institutional, educational, light industrial, commercial, social, and recreational purposes. Building construction is generally regarded as the mainstay of the industry and usually contributes about one-half of the total annual dollar volume of construction. In normal business years, private capital finances most of the projects in this category. The bulk of building construction is designed by private architectural or architectural-engineering firms and is erected by professional building contractors under contract with the owner. When public bodies or agencies are involved as the owners, they themselves sometimes perform the function of the architect and/or engineer.

A possible subdivision of the building construction category might be speculative construction, that is, projects that are designed, financed, and built by a speculator or developer for sale or lease. Housing projects constitute the majority of this subdivision, the distinguishing characteristics of which are that the developer acts as his own prime contractor and that he often builds for unknown owners. These so-called "operative builders" usually subcontract substantial portions, if not all, of their projects.

Engineering Construction. Engineering construction is a very broad category covering structures that are planned and designed by professional engineers. The actual construction is usually carried out by a contractor under contract with the owner and with engineer supervision. This category includes structures that are not primarily architectural in nature but that involve predominately engineering field materials such as earth, rock, steel, concrete, piping, and timbers. This broad category may be divided into two subgroups—highway construction and heavy construction.

Highway construction covers clearing, excavation, fill, paving, drainage, bridge structures, and other such items commonly associated with highway work. Heavy construction is usually construed to include sewage and water treatment plants, dams, waterways, levees, pipe and pole lines, marine structures, tunnels, bridges, reclamation projects, utility projects, and railroad work. Most engineering construction projects are publicly financed.

Industrial Construction. Industrial construction includes the erection of projects that are associated with the manufacturing or processing of a commercial product or service. Such structures are highly technical in nature and are frequently built by specialized contracting firms that do both the design and the construction under contract with the owners. Petroleum refineries, steel mills, chemical plants, smelters, electric-power generating stations, and similar installations are all examples of industrial construction.

2.4 THE COMPETITIVE-BID SYSTEM

The exact cost of a project cannot be known until it has been completed. However, costs can usually be estimated with considerable confidence if complete and detailed descriptions of the proposed work are available. These estimated costs, compiled in advance of the actual construction, are presented to the owner by several competing contractors as their proposals for doing the work. The owner then selects the bid that is the most advantageous from his point of view, the element of cost usually occupying a position of prominence in this decision.

Today, the overwhelming majority of construction is done by contractors who obtain their work in such bidding competition with other contractors. There are many different types of construction contracts (see Chapter 7), but the bulk of them pertain to this method of doing construction. The competitive method is standard procedure for federal and other public agencies, with an estimated 95 percent of all public construction work being done by this method.

The contractor occupies an essential position in the construction industry. His stock in trade is his equipment and know-how, and he acts as a broker for the necessary construction materials and labor. It is often said that contracting is the biggest gamble of the business world. When bidding a project, the contractor must estimate how much the structure will cost while it still exists only on paper. To this cost, he adds what seems to be a reasonable profit and guarantees to do the job for the given price. If his bid is selected, the contractor must complete the project for the contracted amount. If the actual costs of construction exceed this figure, the loss must be borne by the contractor.

A project awarded on a competitive-bid basis can be constructed under a single all-inclusive contract or by means of separate contracts.

2.5 THE SINGLE CONTRACT

Under the single-contract system, the owner awards construction of the entire project to a general or prime contractor. The distinctive function of the prime contractor is to coordinate and direct the activities of the various parties and agencies involved with the construction and to assume full, centralized responsibility for the delivery of the finished project within the specified time. Customarily, the contractor will construct certain portions of the job with his own forces and subcontract the rest to various specialty contractors. The general contractor accepts complete accountability, not only to build the project according to the contract documents but also to ensure that all costs associated with the construction are paid. His is the only contractual relationship with the owner, and he is fully responsible for the performance of his subcontractors and other third parties to the construction contract.

2.6 SEPARATE CONTRACTS

When separate contracts are used, the project is not constructed under the centralized control of a single prime contractor. Rather, several independent contractors work on the project simultaneously, each being responsible for his designated portion of the work. Separate contracts may be used by the owner for any one of several reasons. Natural division points of the work can allow the owner to let contracts for various portions directly to specialty contractors. A good example of this is bridge construction, where separate contracts are frequently awarded for the foundations and piers, the approach structures, the bridge superstructure, and the painting.

A few states have enacted statutes requiring that separate mechanical and electrical contracts be awarded on state public works. Many other public jurisdictions make the use of separate contracts optional under administrative authority. Recent experience would seem to indicate that public agencies might advantageously be left free to select a contract system appropriate to circumstances rather than be restricted by law to a specific contract system.

There is some dissension in the construction industry concerning the single-contract system versus the use of separate contracts. The general contractor organizations favor the single contract, whereas certain large specialty subcontractor groups prefer separate contracts. Proponents of both methods present valid arguments in support of their views. Nevertheless, in the absence of a legal requirement, the choice of contract method is the prerogative of the owner.

From the viewpoint of the owner, one of the principal advantages to be derived from the use of separate contracts is the saving of the markup on certain subcontracted work that the general contractor will otherwise include in his bid. This markup is in the nature of a fee for his management and coordination of the subcontractors.

When separate electrical and mechanical contracts are awarded, an extra burden is placed upon the owner, or more commonly on his agent, the architect-engineer, because one party or the other must carry out the managerial and coordinative function normally performed by the general contractor. The American Institute of Architects cautions its members concerning the added burdens and responsibilities occasioned by the use of separate contracts and recommends that the architect charge an additional fee for his coordination of the job under these circumstances.

If neither the owner nor the architect-engineer provides strong, centralized control over the separate contractors, the amount of real savings accruing from the use of this system can be somewhat problematical. Failure or refusal on the part of a contractor to keep his work up to schedule and to coordinate it with that of the others can cause expensive delay to the owner and subject the other contractors to serious financial involvement. This matter becomes particularly difficult when liquidated damages (see Section 7.22) are involved.

2.7 THE NEGOTIATED CONTRACT

Rather than follow the competitive-bid process, the owner may choose to select a contractor on the basis of his dependability, experience, and skill. After a study by the owner of the qualifications, previous experience, and facilities of one or more candidates, a contract is negotiated between the owner and the contractor of his choice. During normal times, this type of construction contract is limited to privately financed work because competitive bidding is required by law for public-work projects.

There are no restrictions on the form of contract that can be negotiated. Normally, however, the owner reimburses the contractor for the actual costs of construction and pays him a fee for his services. This is a cost-plus form of contract, and it is only in the fee arrangement that such contracts differ appreciably from one another.

2.8 CONSTRUCTION BY FORCE ACCOUNT

Rather than have his work done by a contractor, the owner may elect to do the construction with his own forces. This method of work accomplishment is called the force-account system. Under this method, the owner acts as his own contractor. He provides the supervision, materials, equipment, and labor.

Many studies have been made, mostly by public agencies, to compare construction costs by competitive bid and by force account. Generally speaking, it has been clearly demonstrated that for all but very small projects the force-account system is more expensive than the competitive-bid method. In addition, the quality of the work is usually better when done by a contractor.

There are several good reasons why contract construction is usually cheaper and better than that done by force-account means. A qualified contractor is an experienced construction manager who is intimately familiar with materials, equipment, and methods. He maintains a force of competent supervisors and workmen and is equipped to do the job. Construction is his business, and he must be good at it in order to survive. All of these factors lead to efficiencies of cost and time that an owner will find difficult to match unless his organization already includes a trained construction force.

Normally, as mentioned previously, a public project must be contracted out on a competitive-bid basis. Force-account work by a public agency is generally limited to maintenance, repair, or cases of emergency. Some important public works have been built by force-account means, however; the Panama Canal and some projects for the Tennessee Valley Authority are examples.

2.9 SUBCONTRACTING

The prime contractor usually subcontracts portions of his work, the type and amount depending greatly upon the nature of the project and his own organization. He may do the excavation, concrete forming and pouring, reinforcement steel placing, masonry, and carpentry and subcontract the remainder. It is common practice for him to subcontract the structural steel erection, pile driving, plumbing, heating and ventilating, electrical work, roofing, elevator installation, plastering, glazing, painting, and other such specialties. General contractors are usually glad to leave the increasingly complex specialty work to concerns that concentrate along these lines.

Construction contracts frequently limit the proportion of the contract amount that the prime contractor may subcontract. For example, the Bureau of Public Roads, the Public Buildings Service of the General Services Administration, and the U. S. Corps of Engineers have set such limitations. Also, some states have enacted statutes that impose a similar restriction on the general contractors of public works in those states. Such restrictions on subcontracting are intended to circumvent well-recognized drawbacks associated with having a prime contractor subcontract an excessive proportion of the work. This condition can prevent the effective scheduling of job operations, lead to a serious division of authority, fragmentize responsibility, make the coordination of construction activities difficult, weaken communication between management and the field, foster jurisdictional disputes between the construction unions, and be generally detrimental to job efficiency. However, the extent to which these difficulties may occur is dependent upon the experience and administrative ability of the prime contractor.

Everyday economic facts have confirmed the subcontract system to be efficient and economical in the use of available resources. The operations of the typical general contractor are not usually sufficiently extensive to permit full-time employment of skilled journeymen in each of the several trade classifications. Hence these contractors are able to keep only a limited nucleus of full-time employees and must be able to draw from the local pool of skilled labor as additional needs arise. By subcontracting, the general contractor can obtain men with the requisite skills when they are needed, without the necessity of maintaining an unwieldy and expensive full-time organization. By the same token, the subcontractor is able to provide substantially full-time employment for his workers, thereby affording an opportunity for the acquisition and retention of the most highly skilled and desirable journeymen.

When the prime contractor engages a specialty firm to execute a particular portion of his overall construction program, the two parties enter into a contract wherein their mutual responsibilities are defined and the consideration involved is designated. No contractual relationship is established thereby between the owner and the subcontractor. The prime contractor, by the terms of the general contract with the owner, assumes complete responsibility for the direction and control of the construction program. An important part of this responsibility is coordinating and supervising the work of his subcontractors.

2.10 LICENSING OF CONTRACTORS

Several states require that any and all contractors doing business within the state be licensed. Some of the licensing statutes are solely revenue-raising measures. Under these laws, the payment of the license fee confers the right to conduct a construction business with no further conditions. Generally, however, the statutes provide that the contractor pay a fee and meet certain qualifications. Such laws are designed to protect the public health and safety and to guard against contractor incompetence and fraud. These statutes establish a Board of Registration or other regulatory body that administers the law, accepts applications for registration, gives examinations where required, issues the licenses, and enforces the provisions of the registration act.

Licensing requirements vary widely among the states that have such laws. Most of these laws require licenses only for contractors whose annual volume of business exceeds certain designated amounts. Almost all require that a license be obtained in advance of any bidding within the state with certain minor statutory exemptions. Some states exclude from licensing contractors doing work financed by federal funds or performed for the federal government on government-owned land.

Certain states issue various classes of licenses differentiated in accordance with maximum size of contracts or annual volume of business. In addition, licenses may be issued that pertain only to specific classifications such as general engineering construction, general building construction, or specialty work. A few states require that applicants must pass an examination before issuance of the license.

It is very important that a contractor be properly licensed when this is a legal requirement of the state in which he is working. Most licensing statutes provide that acting or offering to act in the capacity of a contractor without a valid license is a misdemeanor. Also important is the fact that the unlicensed contractor is operating illegally, a factor that may render unenforceable any construction contracts to which he is a party in the state involved. A possible result can be that the contractor cannot force payment from an owner who refuses to pay for work done under the contract. In addition, the contractor may have no right to file or claim a mechanic's lien against the owner's property.

2.11 REGULATED SPECIALTY CONTRACTORS

Contracting firms engaged in structural or finishing work are not subjected to any particular regulation beyond that of being licensed where required. However, this is not the case for contractors who are engaged in the mechanical and electrical trades and whose work is intimately associated with public health and safety. Every state and/or certain of its political subdivisions now impose licensing and other special regulations upon electrical, plumbing, and gas-fitting contractors. Mechanics in these fields must pass examinations before being allowed to assume the role of journeymen. Many city governments have enacted their own requirements in addition to those of the state in which they are located.

In a similar manner, the installation of elevators is regulated in varying degree. The American Society of Mechanical Engineers publishes the *American Standard Safety Code for Elevators, Dumbwaiters, and Escalators,* which has been widely used as the basis for local codes. Most manufacturers of elevator equipment require that subcontractors who install their products conform to this code, in the absence of any more stringent regulations. Many states and most of the principal cities have enacted into law elevator codes that establish minimum standards of design and installation and that make provision for field inspection and licensing of elevator contractors. Examinations for elevator constructor journeymen are administered by their craft union.

2.12 THE ELECTRICAL CONTRACTOR

The National Board of Fire Underwriters, under the procedural rules of the United States of America Standards Institute, sponsors the *National Electrical Code.* This code has no force of law and is recommendatory only. However, it has been widely accepted in its essential form by various states and municipalities over the country. Changes, where made, have been generally of a nature that make the requirements more stringent than provided for by the national code itself. States and other political entities have enacted legislation giving their codes legal status and making compliance with them mandatory, establishing at the same time electrical administrative boards or designating building departments to administer the provisions of the law.

These public bodies oversee all electrical construction work within their jurisdiction and administer the various provisions of the act or ordinance under which they were created. Journeymen electricians are required to pass an examination that tests the applicant's training and knowledge of the code. Electrical contractors and other persons doing electrical construction work, such as elevator contractors and sign erectors, are required to have an electrical contractor's license, which they obtain from the board upon passing a contractor's or master electrician's examination. An application fee is required, together with an annual license renewal charge.

The administrative board also carries out the important function of job inspection in order to ascertain compliance with the applicable electrical code. A contractor doing electrical work is required to have designated phases of his field installation checked by authorized inspectors. Upon notification by the contractor that certain portions of his work are ready for inspection, a representative of the board visits the job site and certifies acceptance or rejection of the electrical work involved. In cases of willful violation of the electrical code, the board has the power to revoke the contractor's license.

2.13   THE MECHANICAL CONTRACTOR

The mechanical contractor undertakes work associated with plumbing, piping, gas fitting, heating, and air conditioning. In many respects, mechanical contracting is subject to the same kinds of rules and regulations as is electrical contracting. The United States of America Standards Institute sponsors the *National Plumbing Code,* which, like the electrical code, has no force of law but is widely recognized as a standard over the entire country. Codes have also been compiled by other organizations that represent the plumbing industry within designated geographical areas. The Western Plumbing Officials and the Southern Building Congress are two examples of regional bodies that have promulgated plumbing codes. These various codes do not differ greatly from one another and have served as models for the codes of the various states and municipalities, with changes made here and there to fit local needs.

The statutes or ordinances enacted to give plumbing codes the effect of law typically provide for the establishment of a plumbing administrative board. This board inspects field plumbing installations, gives examinations, and generally administers the provisions of the law. It is a usual requirement that all journeymen plumbers and gas fitters pass an examination and be licensed by the board. A master plumber's or master gas fitter's examination, which is given by the board, must be passed in order to obtain a plumbing contractor's license.

2.14   CONTRACTOR'S BOND

A few states and many cities require that all contractors, including subcontractors, who operate within their jurisdiction post a permanent surety bond with the state or city. This is in the nature of a performance and payment bond, a subject discussed more completely in Chapter 8, and serves for the protection of the public. It functions as a guarantee of the financial integrity and technical ability of the contractor. An owner or other party may bring process against the bond in the event of alleged malpractice or malfeasance on the part of the contracting concern.

It is, perhaps, a somewhat more common practice to require bonds of only selected contractors whose work is intimately associated with public health and safety. A representative listing of bonded specialty contractors is as follows:

Gas fitting
Plumbing
Electrical
Curb, gutter, and sidewalk (on public property)
House moving
Sign erection
Boiler installation
Elevator installation

Firms proposing to do such work must post bond with the designated authority in the required amount before commencing operations.

2.15 CONTRACTOR ORGANIZATIONS

There are many associations of contractors throughout the country, some being local in character and others being chapters of large national organizations. The Associated General Contractors of America, the National Constructors' Association, and the Associated Builders and Contractors are countrywide organizations representing primarily general contractors. The National Association of Home Builders is a national group representing the housing industry.

These associations perform a number of valuable services for their members such as providing a united basis for labor negotiations, monitoring both local and federal legislation, sponsoring safety and apprenticeship programs, providing tax information, holding conferences, and serving as a clearinghouse for construction information. These organizations strive to maintain the business and ethical standards of contracting at a high level and to establish the integrity and responsibility of their members in the public mind.

Both local and national specialty contractor organizations also function to promote the mutual benefit of their members and to bring their combined resources to bear upon common problems. These associations usually parallel the craft jurisdictions of the unions and are represented by aggregations of specialty contractors such as electrical, lathing and plastering, painting, and roofing. Generally speaking, there will be several such groups functioning within a city or other local area. These regional groups are frequently affiliated with national organizations such as the National Electrical Contractors' Association or the National Association of Plumbing, Heating, and Cooling Contractors.

3

FORMS OF BUSINESS OWNERSHIP

3.1 ALTERNATIVE FORMS

The forms of business ownership used by construction contractors are the individual proprietorship, the partnership, and the corporation. Selection of the proper type depends upon many considerations and is a matter deserving of careful study. Each form of business organization has its own legal and financial implications, which must be thoroughly appreciated and understood. Advice of legal counsel should be obtained when setting up a new business or changing the form of a going concern.

Of the approximately 800,000 construction companies in the United States, slightly over 80 percent are individual proprietorships. The rest are about equally divided between partnerships and corporations.

3.2 THE INDIVIDUAL PROPRIETORSHIP

The simplest business entity is the individual proprietorship, sometimes called "sole ownership." It is the easiest and least expensive procedure for the establishing of a business and enjoys a maximum degree of freedom from governmental regulation. No legal procedures are needed to go into business as the sole owner except the obtaining of required insurance, registration with appropriate tax authorities, and possible licensing as a contractor.

The proprietor owns and operates the business, provides the capital, and furnishes all of the necessary equipment and property. All business transactions and contracts are made in his name. The individual proprietorship is usually small in size because the scope of the enterprise is entirely dependent upon the resources and personal credit of the owner. This mode of doing business has many advantages to offer, such as possible tax savings, simplicity of organization, and freedom of action of the owner.

As an individual proprietor, however, the owner is personally liable for all debts, obligations, and responsibilities of the business. This unlimited liability extends to all of his personal assets, even though they may not be involved in his contracting business. Although management is immediate and direct, the owner must shoulder alone all of the burdens and responsibilities that accompany this function. A proprietorship has no continuity in the event of the death or incapacitation of the owner. Finally, the owner must pay income taxes annually on the full earnings of the business whether or not he withdraws them.

3.3 THE PARTNERSHIP

A partnership is an association of two or more persons who, as co-owners, carry on a business for profit. The principal benefits to be gained by such a merger are the concentration of assets, equipment, facilities, and individual talents into a common course of action. The pooling of financial resources results in the increased bonding capacity of the business, offering the possibility of a greater scope and volume of construction operations than would be possible for any partner alone. Each partner customarily makes a contribution of capital and shares in the management of the business. Profits or losses are usually shared in the same proportion as the distribution of ownership. If no such agreement is made, each partner receives an equal share of the profits or bears an equal share of the losses, regardless of the amount that he has invested.

A partnership is not considered as being a separate legal entity apart from the individual partners. For example, a partnership pays no income tax, although it must file an information return. Earnings of the partnership are divided annually according to predetermined ratios established in the partnership agreement. Partners usually receive drawing accounts against anticipated earnings or annual salaries that are considered to be operating expenses of the partnership. In any event, each partner must pay annual income tax on his salary and on his allocated share of the partnership profits whether or not these are actually withdrawn.

A partnership can own property, with the possible exception of real estate, in its own name. An individual partner cannot sell or mortgage partnership assets. Neither can he sell, assign, or mortgage his interest in a functioning partnership without the consent of the other partners.

3.4 ESTABLISHMENT OF A PARTNERSHIP

State laws regarding partnerships vary, but the basic provisions are similar in all states. It is customary and preferable to draw up written articles of partnership, although a binding partnership can, in certain instances, be formed by oral agreement. Ruling out statutory requirements, these articles may include almost anything that the partners believe to be desirable. It is usual that articles of partnership, signed by the parties in interest, contain complete and explicit statements concerning the rights, responsibilities, and obligations of each partner. Although such articles must be individually tailored for each specific case, the following list indicates the types of provisions typically included in partnership agreements:

1. Names and addresses of the partners.
2. Business name of the partnership.
3. Nature of the business.
4. Location of the business.
5. Date on which business operations will commence.
6. Contribution of each partner in the form of capital, equipment, property, contracts, goodwill, services, and the like.
7. Any statement requiring partners' full-time attention to partnership affairs.
8. Division of ownership as it affects allocation of profits and losses.
9. Voting strength of each partner.
10. Drawing accounts or salaries of the partners.
11. Duties or restrictions pertaining to management of the business.
12. Specification of majority or unanimous decision on management questions.
13. Payment of expenses incurred by a partner in carrying out partnership duties.
14. Rental or other remuneration for use of a partner's personal property or for personal services.
15. Arbitration of disputes.
16. Record keeping and inventories.
17. Right of each partner to full access to books and audits.
18. Rights and responsibilities of the individual partners upon dissolution.
19. Extraordinary powers of surviving partners, such as option to purchase interest of deceased or withdrawing partner.
20. Termination date of the agreement, if any.

By mutual consent of all the partners, any provision of a partnership agreement can be modified or deleted or new provisions can be added.

3.5 LIABILITY OF A PARTNER

The law of agency applies when one person represents another or acts as his agent in certain types of business transactions. An agency relationship exists by agreement, and an agent can be appointed by the principal to do any act which the latter might lawfully do. When the agent acts within the scope of his actual or apparent authority, the principal is liable for all contracts made in his name by his agent as well as for the torts, misdeeds, and negligent acts of the agent. A general agent is one empowered to transact all of the business of his principal. Correspondingly, each member of a partnership is a general agent of the partnership and has full authority to make binding commitments, enter into contracts, and otherwise act for his fellows within the scope of the business.

Each partner assumes unlimited personal liability to third parties for the full amount of all debts of the partnership. Each partner is individually liable for any act of fraud or misrepresentation perpetrated by another partner in the ordinary conduct of the partnership's business affairs. Under the usual rule, each partner is jointly liable with the others for meeting contractual partnership obligations. A creditor of a partner can attach the latter's interest in the profits of the business but cannot proceed against partnership property unless the partnership is being dissolved. Under the agency principle, notice to any one partner is considered to be notice to all.

It is apparent from the foregoing that careful judgment should be exercised in the selection of business partners. Each partner accepts unlimited financial responsibility for the acts of his fellows, and he underwrites the debts of the enterprise to the full extent of his personal fortune. If a partner withdraws from a going partnership, he remains personally liable for the partnership obligations outstanding as of the date of his withdrawal. To protect himself from future partnership debts, the retiring partner should give personal notice to firms doing business with the partnership and publish public notice of his leaving.

3.6 DISSOLUTION OF A PARTNERSHIP

One of the major weaknesses of the partnership form of business organization is its automatic dissolution upon the death of one of the partners. However, this possibility can be circumvented by making provision in the partnership agreement that the business will continue and that the surviving partners will purchase the decedent's interest. Dissolution may also be precipitated by bankruptcy, duration provision in the original partnership agreement, decision of a partner to withdraw, insanity of a partner, court of equity decree, or mutual consent of all parties. Dissolution is not a termination of the partnership, but simply a restriction of the authority of the partners to activities necessary for the conclusion of the business. It has no effect upon the debts and obligations of the enterprise.

In the settlement of partnership debts, outside creditors enjoy a position of first priority. If partnership assets are insufficient to satisfy the outstanding obligations, the partners must personally make up the difference. After the creditors have been satisfied, partnership assets are used to repay any loans or advances that were made by partners above and beyond the capital contributions stipulated. Then follows the return to each partner of his capital investment. If further assets remain, these are treated as profits and are distributed accordingly. When construction contracts involving considerable time for their completion are involved, the clearing of partnership accounts and the settlement of the decedent's estate are often subject to considerable delay pending payment of all debts, receipt of all accounts receivable, and discharge of all contract obligations of the partnership.

3.7 LIMITED PARTNERSHIP

A general partner is a recognized member of his firm, is active in its management, and has unlimited liability to creditors. The general partnership has been the basis of discussion in the preceding sections. A limited partner is one who holds part ownership of the business and shares in the profits or losses but has no voice or vote in matters of management. Unlike the general partner, the limited partner is liable for partnership debts only to the amount of his investment in the partnership. However, a limited partner can be held fully liable if the nature of his participation in the partnership has been withheld from creditors.

Under the Uniform Limited Partnership Act, a limited partnership may be formed by two or more persons, at least one of whom must be a general partner and the rest limited partners. The various states have enacted legal requirements that control the establishment of limited partnerships, and such arrangements must be formed in accordance with the applicable statute. Articles of partnership must be filed in a designated public office and be published as required by state statute. The operation of a limited partnership, as well as its establishment, must be in strict accordance with the laws of the state in which it is formed. The partnership is not automatically dissolved by the death of a limited partner, as in the case of a general partner.

The limited partnership is used principally as a means of raising capital for the enterprise. Bringing in additional general partners, each of whom shares in the management, can result in serious problems of business administration. The addition of a limited partner, however, is sometimes preferable to borrowing from a bank or other source.

3.8 SUBPARTNERSHIP

A general partner can enter into an agreement with an outsider, called a "subpartner," whereby the latter will share the general partner's profits or losses derived from the partnership's business activities. The subpartner is not a member of the firm. Consequently, he performs no active function, has no voice in the management of the partnership, and has no contractual relationship with the partners other than the one with whom he made the profit- or loss-sharing arrangement. Because the subpartner has contracted to participate in the individual partner's share only, he is not personally liable to creditors of the partnership.

3.9 THE CORPORATION

A corporation is an entity, created by law, that is composed of one or more individuals united into one body under a special or corporate name. Corporations have certain privileges and duties, enjoy the right of perpetual succession, and are regarded by the law as separate and distinct from their members. A corporation is authorized to do business, own real and personal property, and incur debts in its own name and on its own responsibility. It sues and is sued in its corporate name. The principal advantages of this form of business organization are the limited liability of its owners (stockholders), perpetual life of the company, ease of raising capital, easy provision for multiple ownership, and economic benefit in that owners pay taxes only on profits (dividends) actually received.

A corporation is created by the obtaining of a charter granted by the state in which the corporation is to be domiciled. The powers of a corporation are limited to those enumerated in its charter and to those that are reasonably necessary to implement its declared purpose. These powers include the drawing up of bylaws pertaining to the day-to-day conduct of the business.

Corporations are regulated and controlled by the various states, each having a corporation code that prescribes the formal process that must be followed by the organizers in obtaining a charter. These legal requirements differ somewhat from state to state, and it is always important to secure competent legal guidance when establishing a new corporation or modifying an existing one. In any case, fees must be paid and substantial quantities of information filed with the proper officials. Certain detailed requirements must be satisfied regarding the incorporators, residence, and financial structure.

A corporation is dissolved by the surrender or expiration of its charter. Dissolution of a corporation merely means that the corporation ceases to exist. State laws govern the means by which the business affairs of a dissolved corporation may be settled.

3.10 FOREIGN CORPORATIONS

A corporation is created under the laws of a specific state and is considered to be a foreign corporation by every other state. The incorporated contractor who wishes to extend his operations beyond the borders of his home state must apply for and receive certification to do business within each additional state. Usual requirements for the certification of a foreign corporation are the filing of a copy of the corporate charter, designation of a local state resident as an agent for the service of process, and the payment of a filing fee. In some states, acts of a foreign corporation are considered to be unlawful until the corporation has duly complied with certification requirements. Hence the incorporated contractor must make certain that he has complied with the state corporation laws before he enters into a contract for construction work in a particular state. Otherwise, he may find that the contract is unenforceable. Additionally, an uncertified foreign corporation may not have access to the state courts.

3.11 STOCKHOLDERS

The ownership of a corporation is exercised through shares of stock that entitle the owners thereof to a portion of the business profits and of the net assets upon liquidation. This does not mean that the shareholders own the corporate assets because the corporation itself holds legal title to its own property. However, each share of stock does represent a share in the ownership of the corporation. Under the Uniform Stock Transfer Act, accepted by most states, a stock certificate is negotiable and stock ownership may be transferred merely by endorsing the certificate and delivering it to the purchaser. For this reason, any restrictions on the ownership or transfer of stock should be printed on the stock certificate. It is to be noted that many corporations are wholly owned and controlled by one individual. A clear distinction between the individual and his corporation is recognized by the courts.

When a corporation is established, its articles of incorporation authorize the issuance of a certain dollar value of stock (the authorized capital stock). The actual capital stock is the amount actually paid to the corporation for its outstanding stock and does not necessarily equal the authorized capital stock. The stock may be common or preferred, or both. Preferred stock is subject to less risk than is common stock, because it has a certain preference as to dividends and distribution of assets upon liquidation of the corporation. However, preferred stock usually carries no voting privileges. Common stock generally is entitled to one vote per share and presents the possibility, at least, of greater ultimate profits to the owner. Stockholders have certain rights and privileges that are based upon state statute, the charter of the corporation, and the terms of ownership as stipulated on the stock certificate. These rights include the preemptive right to subscribe new stock issues, to carry out reasonable inspection of the corporation's books and records, to bring suit against the corporation, to share ratably in the declared dividends, to receive a share of net assets upon dissolution, and to enact bylaws.

The profits of a corporation are subject to federal and state income taxes at the corporate rate. Such taxes are paid by the corporation before any profits can be distributed as dividends to the stockholders. The stockholders are then taxed individually on any such dividends distributed on a cash basis. Dividends can only be paid out of earned surplus and may be declared only if such action does not impair the position of corporation creditors. Such dividends, or surplus distributions, are declared as a fixed sum per share of outstanding stock. This payment is generally made quarterly but may be declared at such intervals as decided upon by the board of directors. Special rules apply to stock dividends.

An outstanding advantage of the corporate system is the privilege of owner immunity from personal liability for corporate debts. Although the stockholder assumes the risk of losing his investment, his private and personal resources cannot be jeopardized by any action or failure of the corporation. In the same vein, a stockholder is not an agent for the corporation and cannot act in any way for or on behalf of the organization.

3.12 CORPORATE DIRECTORS AND OFFICERS

The shareholders elect a board of directors that exercises general control of the business and determines the overall policies of the corporation. The directors must conduct the firm's affairs in accordance with its bylaws and are ultimately responsible to the stockholders. A director has no authority to act individually for the corporation or to act as its agent. His administrative functions may be exercised only through the majority actions of the board. Directors occupy the position of fiduciaries and are required to serve the corporation's interests with prudence and reasonable care.

The president, vice-president, secretary, and treasurer are the corporate officers, normally appointed by the board of directors, who carry out the every-day management functions. The officers are empowered to act as agents for the corporation. The president is authorized to act for the firm in any proper way, including contract making, whereas the lesser officers generally have more limited authority. Officers also serve in the capacity of fiduciaries and may be held personally liable for corporation losses caused by their neglect or misconduct.

3.13 THE JOINT VENTURE

As a means of spreading risks and pooling resources for certain projects, it is common for two or more contracting firms to unite forces through the medium of a joint venture. The members of a joint venture can be sole proprietorships, partnerships, or corporations, but the joint venture itself is a separate business entity. Although there are some technical differences in law between a true partnership and a joint venture, a joint venture may be described as a special-purpose partnership. The determination of the relationship depends upon the particular facts and the agreement upon which the joint relationship is created. Properly used, joint ventures are well-proved devices for pooling abilities and facilities and for spreading construction risks.

A joint venture relates only to a single project, even though its completion may take a period of years. Normally, the contractors submit to the owner a joint venture proposal in which all of the interested parties are named and in which all, separately and severally, are directly bound to the owner for the performance of the contract. Each coventurer is thereby legally liable for the performance of the entire contract and for the payment of all labor, material, equipment, and other obligations.

A joint venture serves to combine the resources, assets, and skills of the participating companies. Such a combination offers the multiple advantages of pooling construction equipment, estimating and office facilities, personnel, and financial means. Each joint venturer participates in the conduct of the work and shares in any profits or losses. Many of America's largest structures have been built by joint ventures. Hoover Dam, constructed by an association of six companies, was an early example. Succeeding years have seen joint ventures develop into standard practice in the construction industry.

The participants in a joint venture enter into a written agreement with one another that defines the aims and objectives of the association and clearly delineates such matters as the advance of working capital, percentage interest of each participant, division of profits and losses, specific responsibilities and contributions of the individual parties, details of contract administration, project management and any fidelity bond requirement, supervision of accounting and purchasing, procedure in case a coventurer defaults on his commitments, and termination of the agreement. The writing of a joint venture agreement is an important and technical job requiring the assistance of expert tax counsel. Such an agreement may be subject to the approval of the owner of the project being bid.

4

MANAGEMENT ORGANIZATION

4.1 BASIC CONSIDERATIONS

The establishment of an effective operating organization is one of the principal functions of management. The main task of a contractor's organization is to plan, direct, and control the elements associated with the construction of the projects so that the best combination of operational economy and time efficiency is obtained. In order to implement this function, the contractor must create an organizational structure that is particularly suited to his needs. The organizational framework must be sufficiently stable to assure action but yet be flexible and adaptive. It is very important to relieve from detail those who shoulder the decision-making responsibilities of the company. Administrators cannot be left to struggle with masses of routine work and still be expected to fulfill the all-important functions of management.

"Authority," "responsibility," and "duty" are terms useful to the discussion of organization principles. Authority may be defined as the ability to act or to make a decision without the necessity of obtaining approval from a superior. Authority may be delegated to others. Responsibility implies accountability for an assigned function or duty. Although responsibility may be assigned to subordinates, this in no way serves to relieve the supervisor of his prime accountability. A duty is a specifically assigned task that cannot be relegated to another. When devising a company organization plan, the individual positions of authority and responsibility must be identified and the duties of each participant be defined.

Management must protect against both under- and overorganization. A balance must be struck between overhead salaries and the monetary benefit actually realized therefrom. It is a serious organizational failing to burden too few with too much. It is equally undesirable to tolerate an organization top heavy with half-productive administrators and supervisors.

4.2 PRINCIPLES OF ORGANIZATION

No business is so small that well-recognized principles of organization cannot be profitably applied. The mere act of making a formalized analysis of the necessary tasks, how they relate to the company as a whole, and who is responsible for each task, creates a clear understanding of who, what, when, and how. An organizational plan removes confusion, indecision, buckpassing, duplicated efforts, and neglected duties. The following steps should be followed in the development of an effective organization plan:

1. List every duty for which someone must be made responsible.
2. Divide the duties listed into individual positions.
3. Arrange these positions into an integrated functional structure showing lines of supervision.
4. Staff the organization.
5. Establish lines of communication.
6. Put the entire plan in writing in the form of a manual of procedure.
7. Review the plan with everyone concerned.

4.3 LIST OF DUTIES

The conduct of a contracting business involves certain duties regardless of whether the business is large or small. These duties will be carried out by only a few persons in a small organization, whereas several people will be involved in a larger company. In making up a list of company duties, the question immediately arises as to how detailed such a list should be. The best answer, presumably, is that the more detailed the thinking concerning all of the requirements for sound operation, the less likely it is that something essential will be overlooked. The following list of duties will be used for illustrative purposes and is not intended to be complete:

EXECUTIVE
 Banking
 Construction loans
 Financial structure
 Legal matters
 Business organization
 Management organization
 Auditors and audits
 Public relations
 Industry associations

Labor negotiations
Contract negotiation and execution
Investment
Personnel relations and policies
Long-range planning
Salaries, bonuses, pensions, and profit sharing
Legislative matters
Capital improvements
Scope of operations
Approval of major expenditures
Operating procedures and policies

ACCOUNTING AND PAYROLL

General books of account
Subsidiary records
Cost records and reports
Financial reports
Tax returns and payments
Payments of invoices
Billing
Collections
Assignments
Bank deposits
Personnel records
Payrolls and records
Wage and personnel reports to public agencies
Office services

PROCUREMENT

Requisitions
Purchase orders
Subcontracts
Change orders
Inventories
Ordering and control of stores
Expediting
Routing shop drawings
Licenses
Insurance, project and company
Subcontractors' insurance
Owners' contract bonds
Bonds from subcontractors
Releases of lien
Guarantees and warranties
Routing and scheduling materials
Building permits
Checking and approval of invoices

Information on prices and sources of supply
Verification of quantity and quality of deliveries

ESTIMATING
Decision to bid
Visiting the site
Obtaining bidding documents
Mailing out bid invitations
Pre-bid conferences
Quantity take-off
Subcontract and material quotations
Pricing
Checking estimate
Preparation of proposal
Bid bond
Delivering proposal
Bills of materials and subcontractors

ENGINEERING
Project planning
Construction schedules
Project monitoring
Project cost breakdowns for pay purposes
Periodic project pay requests
Checking shop drawings
Project cost reports
Field and office engineering
Safety policies and procedures
Accident reports to insurance companies
Relations with owners and architect-engineers
Labor relations

CONSTRUCTION
Hiring and firing labor crews
Supervision of construction
Coordination of subcontractors
Timekeeping
Project cost data
Project accident reports
Safety program
Project progress reports
Construction methods
Storage of materials on project sites
Scheduling construction equipment

YARD FACILITIES
Receipt, storage, and warehousing of project materials

Maintenance and repair of construction equipment
Storage of construction equipment
Maintenance and issue of stores
Issue, receipt, and repair of hand tools
Transportation
Equipment rental
Prefabrication and subassembly
Spare parts

4.4 DIVISION OF DUTIES

After the duties have been listed, the next step in the development of an organizational plan is to subdivide them into groups, the duties in each group to become the assigned responsibilities of a single individual. To illustrate, suppose that the business is a small partnership consisting of two partners and an employed bookkeeper. One partner is in charge of the office, and the other supervises the field operations. The three persons concerned must, in a collective way, carry out all of the pertinent duties listed in Section 4.3. The executive duties would normally be carried out by both partners acting together. The bookkeeper would perform the accounting and payroll tasks. The office partner could do all duties related to procurement and estimating and be responsible for the bookkeeper. The field partner's duties could include those associated with engineering, construction, and yard facilities. It is obvious, however, that the duties can be distributed among the three participants in any way desired. The important thing is that every duty be covered and, conversely, every position created be made responsible for a specific list of duties. This list of duties for each position is known as a "job description."

Considerably more subdivision of duties will be involved for a larger firm. There might be several departments, each with a manager in charge. For example, an estimating department would be headed by a chief estimator. Take-off men and cost estimators, under the chief estimator and in conjunction with him, would carry out the estimating duties listed, with specific tasks being assigned to each individual involved.

4.5 ORGANIZATIONAL STRUCTURE

The organizational procedure followed thus far ensures that, in combination, the employment positions established will accomplish each and every duty that has been listed. It is now desirable to link these positions together into an integrated operational structure. It is common practice in the construction industry to establish jurisdictions or departments, each roughly equivalent in authority, which, although interrelated, operate semi-independently of one another. This is a functional form of organization in which semiautonomous departments each perform a specialized function. How far this horizontal division is carried depends upon the size of the company involved and the wishes of its management. Each department is assigned a specific area of responsibility, estimating for example, and is headed by a manager who possesses training, experience, and skill in that particular aspect of the business.

Each department thus created is then divided vertically. Vertical division refers to the establishment of lines of supervision, each individual along a line being accountable to the person above him and acting in a supervisory capacity to those below. Generally speaking, the further down that a position appears on the organizational ladder, the more limited is the responsibility and authority of the person concerned.

4.6 ORGANIZATION CHARTS

Organization charts present the company's organizational structure in pictorial form, showing every position of responsibility and all lines of supervision and authority. They provide an understanding of the company's structure at a glance. The organization chart is a particularly efficient way in which to clearly establish in the mind of each individual involved his position within the overall company, the identities of his supervisor and those whom he supervises, and the exact nature of his duties. It constitutes an established, permanent reminder of job responsibilities. Such a chart also underscores to employees the fact that the business is well organized and that top management knows at all times who is responsible for what.

Figure 4.1 shows a typical organizational structure of a small contracting company being operated as an individual proprietorship. The organization chart for a small partnership is presented in Figure 4.2. Figure 4.3 shows a typical organization chart for a moderately large corporate firm. The organizational structure and the assignment of duties shown in these charts are for illustrative

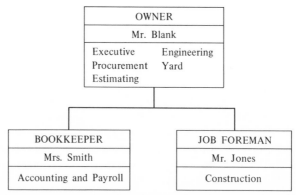

Figure 4.1 Organization chart for small individual proprietorship.

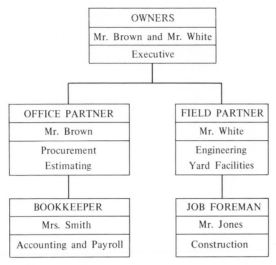

Figure 4.2 Organization chart for small partnership.

purposes only, and the allocation of duties in Figure 4.3 is not intended to be complete. The reader should note that, for each position shown, a person's name appears together with a list of his clearly defined duties. In addition, each member of the team reports to only one superior.

4.7 STAFFING

The organizational structure devised must now be staffed; that is to say, a person must be assigned to each of the positions created. In the construction industry, supervisory personnel are typically selected on the basis of their job knowledge or technical ability rather than on management training or experience. The reasons for this are obvious, but it should be pointed out that the selection of an individual for a supervisory position only on the basis of his technical competence is no guarantee that the most effective man will thereby be obtained.

Admittedly, detailed knowledge of the construction process is an important attribute for the construction manager, but other qualifications are also required. Positions on the lower rungs of the organizational ladder are preoccupied primarily with specific and technical details. Correspondingly, it is entirely appropriate that people be selected for such positions largely on the basis of their job knowledge because their management function is quite limited. However, in selecting individuals for progressively higher positions, more and more attention should be paid to managerial ability and general industry experience. Many examples can be cited to show that technical ability alone does not assure managerial success.

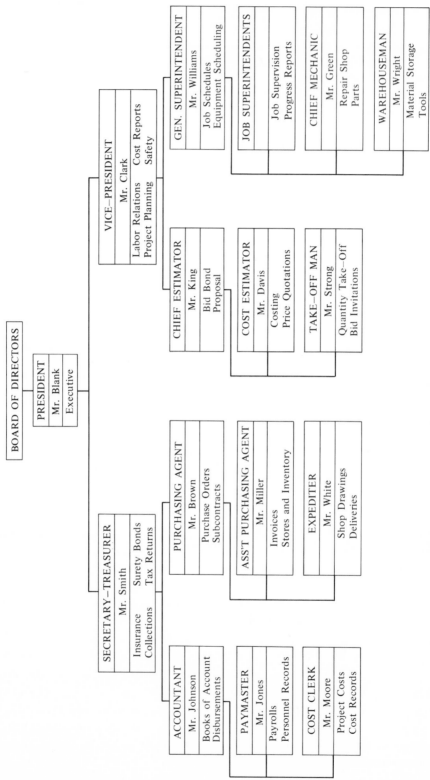

Figure 4.3   Organization chart for moderately large corporation.

4.8 AUTHORITY AND RESPONSIBILITY

The person who is responsible for the work of a segment of the company does not necessarily do personally everything for which he is accountable. Responsibility implies making sure that tasks are done, regardless of who actually performs them. This means that in Figure 4.3 the president is responsible for every action necessary to the proper operation of the company. He must be given, by the board of directors, full authority over the operating departments of the business. Otherwise, he cannot be held responsible for results since, without full authority, he cannot control what occurs.

According to the organization chart in Figure 4.3, the president has delegated appropriate responsibilities to the secretary-treasurer and the vice-president. In turn, these two officers have delegated parts of their responsibilities to those under their supervision. However, such downward delegation does not relieve the original person of his prime responsibility. To illustrate, the expediter is responsible for the duties specifically assigned to him. The purchasing agent is responsible for his own duties as well as those of the expediter and the assistant purchasing agent. The secretary-treasurer is responsible for his own work plus that of the accountant, paymaster, cost clerk, purchasing agent, assistant purchasing agent, and expediter.

Authority commensurate with responsibility must apply at all operating levels. When the president delegates responsibility for departmental operation to others and they, in turn, delegate parts of their responsibilities to their subordinates, adequate authority must be delegated at the same time. In each instance, authority must be given the individual concerned to do his job in any way that he chooses as long as the results are satisfactory and his procedures conform to established company policies.

4.9 COMMUNICATION

The proper functioning of the business depends upon an intraorganization exchange of information of many kinds. A good system of company communications is essential for smooth and profitable operation. Top management must be kept apprised of job costs and job progress. Procurement people must receive purchasing information concerning materials and subcontractors required for a new project. The project superintendents must be kept advised of contract changes such as drawing revisions and change orders. Subcontractors must be consulted about project planning and be informed of their part in the construction schedule. Procurement people must keep the yard and the projects aware of the delivery status of materials and be told of the nature and extent of delivery shortages or damage. Information about job accidents must be conveyed from the projects to company management. Payroll must be informed concerning hirings and layoffs. Information on back charges against material suppliers and subcontractors must get to accounting. These are only a few examples of many such company communications.

Communicative needs that are repetitive and routine in nature, such as the examples cited in the preceding paragraph, can be met by the establishment of set procedures. The next section discusses the manual of policies and procedures, which has, as one of its principal purposes, the description of routine communicative processes.

Periodic meetings of various groups of the company management are a necessity. For one reason, there are many aspects of a company's operations that are confidential and that must be kept within a limited circle. These meetings serve to exchange ideas, resolve misunderstandings, and decide upon future courses of action. Also, this mode of communication helps to establish team spirit and a feeling of esprit de corps. Brainstorming sessions of such groups have proven to be extremely effective in the production of new ideas and management innovation.

To disseminate company information of general interest, bulletin boards and a company publication are very effective. Issued periodically, the publication can contain matters such as the firm's safety record, new projects, personnel changes, company policies, and other pertinent information.

4.10 POLICIES AND PROCEDURES

Once the organizational structure has been established, written company policies and operating procedures can be prepared that augment the organization chart and work in conjunction with it. These policies and procedures should be set forth in manual form and be made available to all company personnel concerned. Company policies gradually evolve from experience with operating problems that occur with relative frequency. If a loose-leaf manual is used, it is easy to make revisions and add new sheets.

The operating procedures establish general rules governing communications, the flow of paper work, and other routine company operations. Such rules remove the element of decision making from office routine and allow duties to be assigned to the lowest practical management level. The very act of reducing these procedures to writing helps to clarify ambiguities, removes areas of overlap, and reveals discrepancies and other shortcomings in the organizational plan. The written procedures ensure uniformity of action, are valuable in training new personnel, and reduce the need for close supervision. The first step in the writing of any such set of company procedures is generally accomplished by having the supervisor of each department consult with his personnel and then write down the procedures that apply to his own area of responsibility. These various procedures are then incorporated into a single set of rules through a series of interdepartmental meetings in which the proposed procedures are coordinated and adjustments made.

The manual must be explicit concerning the keeping of records. Governmental agencies require that certain kinds of records be kept, and the contractor soon finds that records pertaining to project costs, shop drawings, equipment maintenance, inventory, job progress, estimating, personnel, and other aspects of his business are of real importance. Although too few records can be costly, excessive record keeping can become equally expensive. It makes no sense to keep records that are not actually used and whose potential value does not at least equal their cost of preparation. The type and form of records should be carefully selected to yield a maximum of information with a minimum of effort and clerical time. The manual should include samples of all standard record forms with explanations and illustrations of their use. Printed forms for records and communications are great labor savers. They simplify the task of adhering to company policies and procedures and make it possible to use incompletely trained people with less supervision. Information repeatedly presented in the same format can be quickly understood by all who use it.

Another matter to be covered by the operating manual concerns routine company reports—who prepares them, when they are prepared, and to whom they are to be routed. Such reports are intended primarily for the use of top management in its direction of company affairs. Effective decision making depends to a large degree upon the timely and continuous flow of needed management information. Reports on project costs, accident experience, current financial status, profit projections, and similar matters present vital operating information in condensed and summary form.

The development of an effective manual of policies and procedures requires time and constant re-evaluation. The manual evolves gradually over a period of time, additions and changes being made as needed. For effective standardization, the policies and procedures must be firmly established, and this generally requires a period of adjustment as improvements are found. In a large organization, manuals are usually issued in parts, each section pertaining to the operation of a single department.

4.11 PROJECT ORGANIZATION

The form of a contractor's project organization depends upon the extent and the type of the construction work being done. A firm whose jobs are not particularly extensive will have almost all office functions, such as accounting, payroll, purchasing, and engineering, concentrated in its main or area office. Only larger projects can justify the additional overhead necessary to carry out the required office tasks in a field office on the job site. Large projects frequently support a substantial field management team, the extent of this depending upon the nature of the work, its geographical location, and the type of contract. For example, a large cost-plus contract might well have all associated office functions performed at the project site. A project management staff is customarily developed along much the same lines as the contractor's main operating organization.

5

DRAWINGS AND SPECIFICATIONS

5.1 THE ARCHITECT-ENGINEER

Some large industrial firms and many public agencies maintain their own construction design departments. The average owner, however, engages the services of a licensed professional architect or engineer to plan and design his project. In any event, several documents must be prepared before the actual construction process can begin. These documents, which include the instructions to bidders, proposal form, general and special conditions, drawings, technical specifications, and agreement, will be considered in this chapter and the ones that follow.

As a general rule, building construction requires primarily the services of an architect, whereas highway, heavy, and industrial projects are predominately of an engineering nature. Recent years have seen the formation of many concerns designated as architect-engineers, which do planning and design work of both classifications. Within this text, "architect-engineer" is used to designate the owner's agent, whether he be architect or engineer or a combination of both.

On private work, the owner is free to select an architect-engineer of his choice, basing his selection on personal acquaintance, reputation of the firm, or recommendation by an associate. On public works, if the contracting agency does not maintain its own design staff, several architect-engineer firms are invited to present information concerning their experience, qualifications, capacity, and amount of work currently on their boards. In either case, a firm is selected by the owner, and a contract is entered into by the two parties. This contract may involve only the preparation of drawings and specifications or may also entail the approval of shop drawings, job inspection, supervision, and other services by the architect-engineer.

Contracts for architect-engineer services establish the fee in a variety of ways, such as a percentage of the cost of the work or a lump sum. Fees of 4 to 8 percent of the project cost are typical, but the exact figure is a matter of negotiation and depends upon the nature of the work involved as well as the overall size of the project. Architect-engineer fees on publicly financed projects may be subject to statutory or administrative regulation.

5.2 RESPONSIBILITY OF THE ARCHITECT-ENGINEER

The architect-engineer is an agent of the owner during the construction process and is required to exercise ordinary care and diligence in carrying out his responsibilities. Learning, skill, and experience are expected to the degree customarily regarded as being necessary and sufficient for the ordinary practice of the profession. By his contract of employment, the architect-engineer implies that he possesses ordinary skill and ability and that he will carry out his duties with promptness and a reasonable exactness of performance. It is not expected that the architect-engineer produce a perfect design or flawless set of contract documents. Nevertheless, if he allows errors to occur because of his negligence or lack of ordinary skill, he can be liable for damages to the owner or injured third persons. Although the architect-engineer can be held responsible for his lack of care, diligence, or skill, he is not considered to be negligent because of errors in judgment.

The architect-engineer must prepare his drawings and specifications carefully and accurately and present them in a form readily understood by contractors skilled in the trade. The plans and specifications are expected to produce a structure that has reasonable fitness for its intended purpose. The architect-engineer also bears the responsibility for preparing documents that are in conformance with applicable building codes and zoning regulations.

Recent years have seen a large increase in the number of claims against architect-engineers because of alleged malpractice or negligence. Historically, the courts have held that, if a purchaser of a product were injured by or because of it, he could recover against the builder or designer only if a direct contractual relationship existed between the two parties. However, in a 1947 New York case, the court held that architect-engineers and builders could be sued by a person injured because of a design or construction shortcoming without the usual privy of contract existing between them. This removed the legal barriers to third-party suits. Thus, people with no contractual relationship with the architect-engineer, such as workmen on the job, can sue him for damages alleged to have been caused by his negligence or malpractice. In addition, there seems to be a trend in the courts toward expecting a much greater degree of perfection and foresight of the architect-engineer.

5.3 PROJECT DESCRIPTION

The nature and extent of the construction to be done, the materials to be provided, and the quality of workmanship required are described by the drawings and specifications. Very close complements, the two present a complete description of the work. The drawings portray pictorially the extent and arrangement of the components of the structure. The specifications describe verbally the materials and workmanship to be required.

If a conflict exists between the drawings and the specifications, it is usual that the specifications be followed. In some cases, it may be provided that the architect-engineer shall determine which is to prevail. Should a construction requirement appear only in the specifications and not on the drawings, or vice versa, the contractor must provide the requirement just as though it were included in both places.

When competitive bids are being solicited, the drawings and specifications must be in a complete and detailed form before the time of bidding. When a cost-plus contract is under consideration, the documents may be more rudimentary. In such cases, detailed drawings and specifications must still be provided, but they can follow as needed during the construction period. As a general rule, it is preferable to have the drawings and specifications in as complete and detailed condition as possible before costs are discussed. When incomplete and preliminary drawings and specifications form the basis for cost quotations, subsequent development of the design nearly always adds complicating features that result in greater costs than were originally contemplated.

Ownership of the drawings and specifications and their possible reuse can be a matter of considerable importance. Even though the architect-engineer has a common-law right of ownership of these documents, the courts have not been entirely consistent in their decisions concerning this matter. During their preparation, the drawings and specifications are the personal property of the architect-engineer. However, some courts have ruled that the filing of the plans with a building department terminates any common-law copyright the architect-engineer might have had. Normally, the contract between the owner and the architect-engineer makes explicit provision regarding ownership. Documents of The American Institute of Architects provide that the drawings and specifications remain the property of the architect-engineer. However, agencies of the federal government and many other public and private owners require a clause in the design contract with the architect-engineer that conveys ownership of the documents to the owner upon completion of the work.

5.4 THE DRAWINGS

The drawings are instrumental in the communication of the architect-engineer's intentions concerning the structure that he has conceived and designed. They portray the physical aspects of the structure, showing the arrangement, dimensions, construction details, materials, and other information necessary for estimating and building the project. Drawings are individually prepared for almost every project. A job covered by drawings that are complete, intelligible, accurate, detailed, and well correlated can be bid much more realistically than one described by sketchy, poorly drawn, ambiguous, and incomplete documents. When well-prepared documents are provided, disputes and disagreements during construction are minimized and the owner is likely to get a much better finished product at a lesser cost.

From original drawings prepared by the architect-engineer, booklets or rolls of drawings are reproduced. Custom and usage have evolved more or less standard classifications of drawings and a prescribed order in which they appear in a set. To illustrate, the drawings for a building typically include subgroups such as plot plan, structural, architectural, plumbing, mechanical, and electrical in that order. The sheets of each category are designated by an identifying capital-letter prefix and are numbered separately and consecutively. The drawing format varies with the type of construction, however, the make-up of the drawings differing considerably among building, industrial, heavy, highway, and utility construction.

5.5 STANDARDIZED DRAWINGS

The use of standardized drawings is quite widespread in certain areas of the construction industry. Such drawings are usually standard design details, showing materials, dimensions, arrangement, configuration, and other information. Designs for sewer and street work and other municipal construction are common applications. Street and alley paving, street inlets, manholes, curb and gutter, drop inlets, catch basins, sewer connections, valve chambers, hydrant and motor settings, and gate wells are familiar examples of municipal work readily susceptible to the standardization of design. Many engineering aspects of bridge and highway construction are also illustrated by standard design details, which may be physically incorporated into the project drawings or included by reference only. The development of such details is of considerable convenience to the contracting agency and is conducive to construction economies.

5.6 THE SPECIFICATIONS

Specifications are written instructions concerning project requirements. Generally speaking, the drawings show what is to be built, and the specifications describe how the project is to be constructed and what results are to be achieved. Historically, the word "specifications" has referred to specific statements concerning technical requirements of the project, such as materials, workmanship, and operating characteristics. However, it has become customary to include contractual provisions of a nontechnical nature with the technical specifications, referring to the entire aggregation simply as the specifications.

A substantial number of nontechnical contractual clauses must be included in a construction contract. These provisions normally appear as "general conditions" and "special conditions." Although there is some variation in practice, the general conditions and special conditions typically appear as initial sections of the specifications.

The specifications, as well as the drawings, serve three necessary functions in the construction of a project. First, they serve as a description of the proposed work so that bids may be compiled. Second, they act as a guide or book of rules during the construction period. Third, they are a contractual document that can serve as evidence in case of litigation or arbitration. It is important, therefore, that the drawings and specifications be carefully examined by the contractor during his bidding of a project.

5.7 SPECIFICATION DIVISIONS

Specifications are issued by the architect-engineer in duplicated form, usually on 8½ × 11 inch paper and bound with stiff paper covers. For large projects, these specifications can assume the dimensions of a good-sized catalog and may be issued in more than one volume. It is usual practice for the specifications to be segmented into standardized divisions generally used by the construction industry. The Construction Specifications Institute has developed a standard specification format that is widely used.

As mentioned previously, the initial divisions of the specifications normally contain the nontechnical provisions of the contract. The succeeding divisions, which constitute the bulk of the specifications, contain the technical provisions that describe the workmanship and materials for each of the individual construction segments such as excavation, concrete work, painting, and plumbing.

5.8 SPECIFICATION OUTLINE

The divisions that appear within a set of specifications depend upon the nature of the project and the general category of construction. Specifications covering the construction of a building, for example, will have only a general resemblance to those for an engineering work such as a highway, water treatment plant, or marine structure. To illustrate this point, Appendix A presents specification outlines that are typical for building construction and for engineering construction. The building construction specification outline was prepared as a model by a joint committee of architects and building contractors and includes many more items than would normally appear for any one specific project. The engineering construction specification outline is substantially that used by the State of California for its public works.

5.9 GENERAL CONDITIONS

The general conditions set forth the manner and procedures whereby the provisions of the contract are to be implemented according to accepted practices in the construction industry. These conditions are intended to govern and regulate the obligations of the formal contract; they exert no effect on any remedy at law that either party to the contract may possess. They are not intended to regulate the internal workings of either party to the agreement, except in so far as his activities may affect the rights of the other party or the proper execution of the work.

Although the headings and topics included within the general conditions can vary, there is a certain similarity of subject matter. The general conditions will typically include the following items:

1. Definitions.
2. Contract documents.
3. Contractor's rights and responsibilities.
4. Architect-engineer's authority and responsibilities.
5. Owner's rights and responsibilities.
6. Separate contracts.
7. Time.
8. Payments and completion.
9. Changes in the work.
10. Insurance and bonds.
11. Disputes.
12. Termination of the contract.

5.10 STANDARDIZED GENERAL CONDITIONS

Standardized sets of general conditions have been developed by various segments of the construction industry. The American Institute of Architects, various branches of the federal, state, and municipal governments, and others have compiled standardized sets of general conditions. The general conditions compiled and published by The American Institute of Architects have found wide acceptance by the building construction industry and constitute a part of the specifications of most private and many public building projects. These conditions are reproduced in full as Appendix C.

Standard forms of general conditions have the advantage that their record of usage has proven them to be workable. In addition, they have evolved into a form that has stood the test of time and experience and have become familiar to contractors, who clearly understand their meanings and implications.

5.11 MODIFICATIONS TO STANDARDIZED GENERAL CONDITIONS

Any standard set of general conditions is intended to apply to construction in general and correspondingly must be modified at times to conform to the peculiarities of a given project. Such revisions to the standard general conditions are presented as modifications. A list of modifications that might appear in the specifications when the general conditions of The American Institute of Architects are used is presented in Appendix D.

5.12 SPECIAL CONDITIONS

The special conditions are usually located in the specifications directly after the general conditions or their modifications. Setting forth regulations and procedures peculiar to the project, they embody extensions of the general conditions. Conditions of location, order of procedure, time during which the work will proceed, owner-provided equipment, other contracts, unusual administrative relationships, details of remodeling, time of completion, liquidated damages—all constitute special factors whose relationship to the contract must be controlled and defined. Appendix E, which contains a representative list of special conditions, illustrates the distinctively individualistic nature of this division of the specifications.

5.13 TECHNICAL SPECIFICATIONS

The technical provisions of the specifications are presented in the same general sequence as the construction operations in the field and are subdivided in accordance with the usual construction craft jurisdictions. It is customary that a separate division of the specifications be devoted to each major type of construction operation that will be involved, such as excavation, concrete, structural steel, piping, insulation, and electrical work.

Many projects, buildings for example, include elements of such a nature that it is impossible or not feasible to prove the adequacy of the structure by field tests after completion of construction. Under such circumstances, the technical specifications are quite explicit concerning the materials required and the conditions governing their installation.

It is possible with other construction elements to measure, test, or otherwise verify the service performance of the finished product. In such cases, specifications frequently specify only the desired end result. Such "performance-type" or "end-result" specifications are now widely used.

5.14 PERFORMANCE SPECIFICATIONS

A performance specification is one that describes the required performance or service characteristics of the finished product without specifying in detail the methods to be used in obtaining the desired end result. This type of specification makes the contractor responsible for obtaining the results expected, and he is required to produce an end product that will meet the acceptance tests and standards specified. The selection of construction methods and procedures is left up to him. Normally, the contractor must warrant the adequate performance of his work for some time period after completion of construction.

When service requirements can be established and measured by means of some practical test procedure, the use of the end-result type of specification can be advantageous. The contractor is made responsible for obtaining a satisfactory result. By leaving him free to exercise his ingenuity, skill, and experience to the fullest extent in achieving the desired result the cost of construction may well be reduced.

5.15 MATERIAL AND WORKMANSHIP SPECIFICATIONS

Material specifications describe the kinds and types of materials that are to be provided, their physical and performance properties, requirements concerning handling and storage, and inspection and tests required for verification of quality. When possible, specifications also prescribe performance standards or material properties that can be verified by measurement or test. It is common practice that a specific brand name or names be listed with model numbers and other data to establish the standard of quality desired. The use of substitute materials or equipment by the bidding contractors is discussed further in Section 5.16.

It is not usual practice for the architect-engineer to stipulate detailed construction methods except with reference to the quality of workmanship; for example, matters of finish, appearance, tolerances, clearances, noise, and like properties of the finished product are indicative of workmanship standards and are made subject to final approval by the architect-engineer. Occasionally, it is necessary that detailed installation methods or fabrication procedures be specified to ensure obtaining a desirable result. Although this procedure becomes necessary in certain special cases, it is to be noted that the architect-engineer is responsible for the adequacy of the procedure he specifies.

5.16 STANDARD BRAND SPECIFICATIONS

On private work it is possible to use a closed material specification in which only one manufacturer is named as acceptable. This procedure, however, is not generally considered to be in the best interests of the owner because it eliminates the several advantages of open competition. It is more common practice to name two or three manufacturers, the product of any one of which will be acceptable.

On public works, the architect-engineer cannot ordinarily write a closed material specification because of laws pertaining to the expenditure of public funds. In order to establish a standard of quality, the architect-engineer will sometimes specify a brand name or names, followed by the term "or approved equal." The equality of substitutes for the brand name specified is decided by the architect-engineer. This provision has been very troublesome for both the architect-engineer and the contractor. A preferable procedure might be the use of a performance-type specification, the listing of several brand names with a statement that any of them will be acceptable, or a base-bid material specification.

A base-bid material specification is one in which items of equipment and materials are identified in the technical specifications by a manufacturer's name, model, catalog number, or other specific data. The words "or equal" do not appear. The intent is that only those items listed are to be used in preparing the base bid. However, the bidding contractors may offer alternate items, either on the proposal form or as an attachment to the proposal. These alternate proposals are accompanied by full descriptions and technical data, together with a statement of the cost additional to or deductive from the base bid if the substitution is approved. The architect-engineer does not approve or disapprove such alternates before the bid opening, and the submission of material or equipment alternates is voluntary with the contractor. The low-bidder is determined on the basis of the base bid, with approved substitutions being made by subsequent change orders to the contract.

Materials for federal government projects are designated by federal specification number. Agencies of the federal government use a standardized system of specifying desired materials, each specification bearing a distinctive identification number and being listed in the federal catalog of standard specifications. When no federal specification exists, it is usual practice to specify a standard brand or brands with provision for the substitution of alternate products of equal quality or performance.

5.17 MASTER SPECIFICATIONS

Standardized specifications, including both the technical and nontechnical provisions, are used by some segments of the construction industry. These are designated as "master specifications" and have found considerable application in highway and bridge construction. These master specifications are issued by the contracting agency and may be obtained by any interested party. Though they often do not form a physical part of the specification booklet for the individual projects, the master specifications are made a part thereof by reference. The issued specifications for the individual projects consist merely of the proposal, bond, and agreement forms, together with necessary modifications and special provisions to the master specifications.

Similar master specifications in other fields of construction have been prepared, covering the work of the various trades. Many government, state, and city agencies utilize these master trade specifications, augmenting them with modifications in order to make them conform to the peculiarities of the project under consideration. However, to date, the use of master specifications by the construction industry has met with only limited acceptance, with the notable exception of the highway and bridge categories.

5.18 CONTRACT DOCUMENT FORMS

It is customary for the required bidding and contract document forms to be included with the specifications. Large projects or those involving an unusual number of legal formalities may have a separate booklet of these forms and instructions. These document forms are as necessary to the prospective bidders as are the drawings and specifications. By terms of the bidder's guarantee, the successful bidder will be required to enter into a contract with the owner. The contractor cannot be expected to guarantee that he will execute a contract without first having seen the proposed forms of the several contract documents. The following forms are customarily presented to the bidding contractors along with the drawings and specifications:

1. Bid bond.
2. Proposal form.
3. Payment bond.
4. Performance bond.
5. Agreement.

All of these forms might not be included for a given project; for example, most private owners will accept the usual form of bid bond that is in common usage by the established surety companies. This is also true for the payment and performance bonds. The bid bond and proposal form are discussed further in Chapter 6. Construction contracts, including the agreement form, are the subject of Chapter 7, and Chapter 8 takes up contract bonds.

5.19 ADDENDA

During the bidding period any changes, modifications, corrections, or additions to the contract documents as submitted to the bidding contractors are made by means of addenda issued by the architect-engineer. These addenda serve to notify the bidders of changes in the owner's requirements, corrections of detected errors or oversights, clarifications or interpretations of the various provisions of the contract documents, changes in the design, and similar matters. Changes in the drawings are accompanied by the submittal of revised sheets.

The general conditions require that such corrections, changes, interpretations, and clarifying answers on the part of the architect-engineer be in writing. It is the responsibility of the architect-engineer to see that copies of all addenda reach promptly the parties who received plans and specifications. Addenda are made a part of the contract documents and must receive the full attention of all parties who are preparing bids covering any or all portions of the project.

5.20 SHOP DRAWINGS

The drawings as prepared by the architect-engineer show only the general design of the structure and contain just enough details to enable the bidding contractors and suppliers to estimate costs. However, for the purposes of producing the necessary materials and job equipment when construction is actually underway, the contract drawings must be amplified by detailed shop drawings.* Such drawings are prepared by the manufacturers or fabricators of the equipment or materials and are submitted to the general contractor and architect-engineer for approval before the item is supplied. This procedure also applies to materials and equipment provided by subcontractors, in which case shop drawings are submitted to the general contractor through the subcontractor. Shop drawings are required for almost every product that is fabricated away from the building site; for example, in building construction, shop drawings must be prepared for everything from reinforcing steel and glazed tile to millwork and finish hardware. The general contractor himself must sometimes prepare shop drawings covering work that he has designed.

5.21 APPROVAL OF SHOP DRAWINGS

When shop drawings are first received from a supplier, the contractor must check them carefully against the contract drawings and specifications. The shop drawings are then forwarded to the architect-engineer for his examination and approval. The production and supply of shop drawings is the responsibility of the contractor or his supplier. The checking and certifying of these drawings, however, is properly the responsibility of the architect-engineer, since they are basically a further development and interpretation of his design and the final verification is the designer's responsibility. Courts consider shop drawings that are approved and signed by the architect-engineer to be a part of the contract documents.

A sufficient number of copies of each drawing must be provided so that there are enough for distribution to all interested parties. After the approved drawings have been returned by the architect-engineer, the contractor notes the nature of any comments or corrections and routes copies as necessary, including one copy that is returned to the supplier. Because the material supplier must receive a copy of the approved shop drawings before he will place the order into production, it is important that the submittal-approval-return process be expedited as much as possible. Otherwise, materials may not be delivered to the project by the time they are needed. It is usual for the contractor to establish some form of check-off and reminder system with regard to shop drawings to guard against oversight or delay in the approval process.

It is important to note, however, that the architect-engineer generally checks only the manufacturer, style, capacity, quality, and other specification require-

---

* The term "shop drawings" includes such fabrication, erection, and setting drawings; manufacturer's standard drawings or catalog cuts; performance and test data; wiring and control diagrams; samples; and descriptive data pertaining to material, equipment, and methods of construction as may be necessary to carry out the intent of the contract drawings and specifications.

ments of the material or job equipment when approving shop drawings. Thus only qualified approval is given because quantities and dimensions are not normally verified by him. In addition, approval of shop drawings by the architect-engineer does not usually relieve the contractor from his responsibility for errors or inadequacies in the shop drawings nor for his failure to perform the requirements and intent of the contract documents. Consequently, approval of shop drawings is an important responsibility of the contractor as well as of the architect-engineer. For this reason construction contracts often include a condition that requires the prime contractor to check and approve all submissions before sending them on to the architect-engineer.

6

ESTIMATING AND BIDDING

6.1 GENERAL

Construction estimating is the compilation and analysis of the many items that influence and contribute to the cost of a project. Estimating, which is done before the physical realization of the work, requires detailed study of the contract documents. It also involves a careful analysis of the results of the study in order to arrive at the most accurate estimate of the probable cost consistent with the bidding time available and the accuracy and completeness of the information submitted.

Much of the credit for the success or failure of a contracting enterprise must be ascribed to the skill and astuteness of its estimating staff. On the one hand, a contractor must be the low bidder on a sufficient number of the projects he bids in order to stay in business. On the other hand, the jobs that he obtains must not be priced so low that it is impossible to realize a fair profit from them. In an atmosphere of intense competition, the preparation of realistic and balanced bids requires the utmost in good judgment and estimating skill.

In a general way, only the lump-sum and unit-price contracts are subject to estimation and bidding in the usual sense. Negotiated cost-plus contracts lack the competitive element usually associated with the bidding of construction projects. Nevertheless, accurate estimates of costs constitute an important element in such contracts and provide the owner with indispensable advance cost information. The estimation of costs is a necessary part of any construction operation.

The management staff of a contracting concern must appreciate the fact that construction estimating bears little resemblance to the compilation of industrial "standard costs." By virtue of standardized conditions and close plant control, a manufacturing enterprise can arrive at the total cost of a unit of production in an almost exact way. Construction estimating, by comparison, is a very approximate and crude process. The absence of any appreciable standardization of conditions from one job to the next, coupled with the inherently complicating factors of weather, materials, labor, transportation, locale, and a myriad of others, makes the advance computation of exact construction costs a matter more of accident than of design. Nevertheless, the estimator must still strive to accomplish the best results possible.

There are probably as many different estimating procedures as there are contractors. In any process involving such a large number of intricate manipulations, innovations and variations naturally result. The form of the work sheets, the order of procedure, the mode of applying costs—all are subject to considerable diversity, procedures being developed and molded by the individual contractor to suit his own needs. Rather than attempt any detailed discussion of estimating procedures, this chapter presents only the general aspects of construction estimating.

6.2 LUMP-SUM ESTIMATES

Cost estimates in the field of building construction are customarily prepared on a lump-sum basis. Under this procedure, a fixed sum is compiled for which the contractor agrees to construct a specified structure in full accordance with the drawings and specifications. Lump-sum estimates are applicable only when the nature of the work and the quantities involved are well defined by the bidding documents.

Lump-sum estimating requires that a detailed quantity survey, or materials take-off, be made. This is a complete listing of all of the materials and items of work that will be required. Using these quantities of materials as a base, the contractor computes the costs of the materials, labor, equipment, subcontracts, taxes and insurance, overhead, and contract bond. The sum total of these individual items of cost constitutes the anticipated overall cost of the construction. Addition of a markup yields the lump-sum estimate that the contractor submits to the owner as his bid for doing the work.

6.3 UNIT-PRICE ESTIMATES

Highway and heavy construction projects are generally bid, not on a lump-sum basis, but as a series of unit prices. Unit-price estimates can be compiled when quantities of work items may not be precisely determinable but the nature of the work is well defined. The unit-price schedule of Appendix G shows a typical list of bid items. It should be noted that an estimated quantity is shown for each item. These quantity estimates are those of the architect-engineer and are not guaranteed to be accurate. When unit-price proposals are involved, a somewhat different estimating procedure from that described in the previous section must be followed.

A detailed quantity survey is made, much as for lump-sum estimates, but a separate survey is needed for each bid item. This survey not only serves as a basis for computing costs but also checks the accuracy of the engineer's estimated quantities. A total project cost, including labor, equipment, materials, sub-contracts, overhead, taxes, insurance, markup, and contract bond, is compiled just as in the case of a lump-sum estimate, but all costs are kept segregated according to the individual bid item to which they apply. More information on this process is presented in Section 6.33.

In making up his unit prices, the contractor must keep several important factors in mind. The quantities as listed in the schedule of bid items are estimates only. The contractor will be required to complete the work specified in accordance with the contract and at the quoted unit prices, whether quantities greater or less than the estimated amounts are involved. This requirement is often modified, however, by contract provisions for the adjustment of unit prices when more than 20 or 25 percent variation is experienced from the quantities listed by the architect-engineer. All items of material, labor, supplies, or equipment that are not specifically enumerated for payment as separate items, but are reasonably required to complete the work as shown on the drawings and as described in the specifications, are considered as subsidiary obligations of the contractor. No separate measurement or payment is made for them.

6.4 APPROXIMATE ESTIMATES

The only way to ascertain project costs with reasonable certainty is by means of the detailed procedures described in Sections 6.2 and 6.3. However, for a variety of reasons, a contractor may wish to compute approximate construction costs by means of various short-cut methods. Architect-engineers and owners often seek the assistance of a contractor in getting preliminary approximations of cost. Also, the contractor may wish to obtain an approximate cost for purposes of his own, such as to check roughly the costs estimated by more accurate methods or to compare the costs of similar structures. Negotiated contracts with owners are often consummated while the plans and specifications are still in a rudimentary stage. The contractor, in such cases, must compute a "target estimate" for the owner by some approximate method.

Fundamentally, all approximate methods are based upon some system of unit costs. For example, preliminary costs of engineering projects are computed on the basis of making educated guesses as to the probable costs of concrete in place, per cubic yard; structural steel erected, per ton; excavation, per cubic yard; hot-mix paving in place, per ton; and the like. Approximate cost estimates for buildings are commonly established on the basis of the square-foot-of-floor-area method or the cubic-foot-of-volume method. Each of these methods is based on multiplying the square footage or cubic footage of the building in question by an assumed unit cost per square foot or per cubic foot. Obviously, buildings of different types, of different kinds of construction, and in different geographical areas vary widely in their unit costs. However, the contractor has several sources of information available to him when establishing such unit costs. His own experience is, of course, the principal criterion. In addition, trade journals regularly publish such information and local architect-engineers can supply valuable guidance.

6.5 ADVERTISEMENT FOR BIDS (PUBLIC CONTRACTS)

In all jurisdictions, statutes regulate and control the award of public construction projects. These legal requirements start with the first step in the construction process; that is, notice must be given to interested and qualified members of the construction industry in advance of the bidding of any project financed by public funds. In addition, all bidders must be treated alike and be afforded an opportunity to bid upon the same terms and conditions.

Public agencies must conform with applicable regulations relating to the method of advertising for bids. The contracting agency customarily gives notice of the proposed bidding by posting notices in public places or by placing advertisements for bids in newspapers, magazines, and trade journals. How often and over what period of time notices must appear vary from jurisdiction to jurisdiction. Weekly notices for two, three, or four consecutive weeks are common.

The advertisement describes the nature, extent, and location of the work and the authority under which it originates, together with the time, manner, and place in which bids are to be received. The place where bidding documents are available is designated, and information is listed concerning bond requirements, dates when the work is to be started and completed, terms of payment, estimate of cost, and the owner's right to reject all bids. Statements concerning minimum wage rates and applicable labor statutes are also commonly included. Figure 6.1 is a typical example of such an advertisement.

Federal projects utilize a standard form of bid invitation in addition to published advertisements. The form is mailed to interested general contractors and conveys essentially the same information as the advertisement. Figure 6.2 illustrates a typical invitation covering a construction project for the Bureau of Indian Affairs, U. S. Department of the Interior.

6.6 ADVERTISEMENT FOR BIDS (PRIVATE CONTRACTS)

Private owners may proceed in any manner they choose to select a contractor. Nevertheless, public advertising is widely used on private projects in order to obtain the advantages of open and free competition. When specialty work is involved or when the owner has had prior dealings with a particular contractor,

ADVERTISEMENT FOR BIDS

Sealed bids for the construction of a Municipal Airport Terminal Building at Portland, Ohio, will be received by the City of Portland at the City Manager's Office, Portland, Ohio, until 2:30 P.M. (E.S.T.), Wednesday, May 19, 19—, and then publicly opened and read aloud. Bids submitted after closing time will be returned unopened. No oral or telephoned proposals or modifications will be considered.

Plans, specifications, and contract documents will be available April 16, 19—, and may be examined without charge in the City Manager's Office, in the office of Jones and Smith, Architect-Engineers, 142 Welsh Street, Portland, Ohio, in Plan Services in Cleveland, Akron, Toledo, and Youngstown, Ohio; Pittsburgh, Pennsylvania; Detroit, Michigan; Chicago, Illinois; and Buffalo, New York. General Contractors may procure five sets from the Architect-Engineer upon a deposit of $100.00 per set as a guarantee for the safe return of the plans and specifications within 10 days after receipt of bids. Others may procure sets for the cost of production.

A cashier's check, certified check, or acceptable bidder's bond payable to the City of Portland in an amount not less than 5% of the largest possible total for the bid submitted including the consideration of additive alternates must accompany each bid as a guarantee that, if awarded the contract, the bidder will promptly enter into a contract and execute such bonds as may be required.

The Architect-Engineer's estimate of cost is $3,800,000.00.

Full compliance with applicable Federal, State, and Municipal Wage Laws is required and not less than the rates of wages legally prescribed or set forth in the Contract, whichever is higher, shall be paid.

Proposals shall be submitted on the forms prescribed and the Owner reserves the right, as its interest may require, to reject any and all proposals; waive any formalities or technicalities. No bidder may withdraw his proposal after the hour set for the opening thereof, or before award of contract, unless said award is delayed for a period exceeding thirty (30) days.

CITY OF PORTLAND, OHIO
By John Doe, City Manager

April 15, 19 — .

Figure 6.1 Advertisement for bids.

however, he may decide against putting his job out for competitive bidding and negotiate a contract with the contractor of his choice. This procedure is widely followed in residential construction and in industrial construction where highly technical work involving special skills and equipment is involved. It is somewhat more common, however, for the owner to select a few prime contractors, each of whom he considers to be reputable and capable, and invite them to bid on his project. This procedure is known as "invitational bidding" and assures the owner the advantages of competitive bidding while restricting the potential contractors to a selected group.

When there is no advertising, a "Notice to Bidders" is given to each contractor who receives plans and specifications. This notice assures uniformity in the dissemination of bidding information and circumvents the possibility of inadvertent misunderstandings or mistakes. It assumes the same general form as the advertisement and conveys essentially identical information. On public projects the advertisement, sometimes designated as a "Notice to Bidders," is often reproduced in the specifications as a matter of record.

STANDARD FORM 20 JANUARY 1961 EDITION GENERAL SERVICES ADMINISTRATION FED. PROC. REG. (41 CFR) 1-16.401	REFERENCE Serial No. BIA-0150-65-1
INVITATION FOR BIDS (CONSTRUCTION CONTRACT)	DATE July 7, 19___

NAME AND LOCATION OF PROJECT Rosebud Quarters Rosebud, South Dakota	DEPARTMENT OR AGENCY Department of the Interior Bureau of Indian Affairs

BY (*Issuing office*)   Bureau of Indian Affairs
Branch of Plant Design & Construction
P. O. Box 8327
Albuquerque, New Mexico

Sealed bids in   one copy only   for the work described herein will be received until

2:00 P.M., M.S.T., August 19, 19___,

at the office of the Bureau of Indian Affairs, 5301 Central
Ave., N.E., First National Bank Bldg., East (5th Floor),
Albuquerque, New Mexico

and at that time publicly opened.

Information regarding bidding material, bid guarantee, and bonds

Drawings and Specifications will be available after July 15,
19___, and may be obtained only from the "Issuing Office" above
upon application without deposit. All drawings and specifications shall be returned to the above address after opening
of the bids. Drawings and Specifications will be on file after
July 15, 19___, and may be reviewed at the "Issuing Office" at
the following address:

Branch of Plant Design & Construction, Bureau of Indian
Affairs, 5301 Central Ave., NE, First National Bank Bldg.,
East (5th Floor), Albuquerque, New Mexico.

A bid guarantee equal to 20% of the bid price will be
submitted with any bid in excess of $2,000. If the contract
exceeds $2,000, a performance bond equal to fifty (50%)
percent of the contract price and a payment bond in amount
required by the Miller Act of August 24, 1935, will be
required.

Description of work

The work will consist of the following construction:
Two 2-Bedroom Houses with attached garages, two 3-Bedroom
Houses with attached garages, and one 4-Unit Apartment
Building. The buildings will have concrete floors in
basements and garages, wood framed first floor, trussed
roof, asphalt shingles, wood siding, and drywall construction
on wood studs. Plumbing and heating systems and light and
power are included. Outside work consists of water, sewer,
power, fuel systems, streets, parking areas, sidewalks, and
clotheslines.

Rosebud, South Dakota, is approximately 13 miles
southwest of Mission, South Dakota.

20-104   U.S. GOVERNMENT PRINTING OFFICE : 1960—O-572728

Figure 6.2   Invitation for bids.

6.7 REPORTING SERVICES

Contractors find the advance notices of construction projects that appear in the trade publications and those of the various reporting services to be an additional source of bidding information. The F. W. Dodge Company, Division of McGraw-Hill, Inc., is one well-known national reporting service. Separate "Dodge Bulletins" are issued that announce new jobs and biddings within defined localities over the country. Prime contractors, subcontractors, material dealers, and many others find such reports to be a valuable source of up-to-date information. The reporting services also maintain plan rooms, where drawings and specifications of current projects are kept on file for use by interested parties.

6.8 THE DECISION TO BID

After learning that proposals are to be taken on a given construction project, the contractor must ascertain whether or not he is interested in bidding. The decision to bid involves a study of many interrelated factors, such as bonding capacity considerations, location of the project, the architect-engineer, the nature of the project as it relates to company experience and equipment, amount of work on hand, probable competition, and the availability of a capable project superintendent. In short, the contractor does not always bid every job that comes along. Rather, he does a considerable amount of picking and choosing.

It is possible, of course, that the contractor may not be eligible to bid on a particular project; for example, under regulations of the Small Business Administration, certain federal construction projects can be "set aside" for small contractors. In such an instance a contractor must satisfy certain business measures to be eligible to bid on such a project.

6.9 QUALIFICATION

Many states have enacted statutes that require a contractor wishing to bid on public work in those states to be adjudged qualified before he can be issued bidding documents or before he can submit his proposal. Other states require that the contractor's qualifications be judged after he has submitted his proposal. The first method is called "prequalification" and the second is called "postqualification." Many other public bodies, including agencies of the federal government, require some form of qualification for contractors bidding on their construction projects. The relative merits and drawbacks of the process have been debated for many years, but qualification in some form has become almost standard practice in the field of public contracts. The obvious purpose to be served by qualification is to eliminate the incompetent, overextended, underfinanced, and inexperienced contractors from consideration.

Prequalification requirements apply principally to highway construction, although all projects financed with public money require contractor prequalification in certain jurisdictions. In states in which licenses are required the contractor must be licensed before application for prequalification. In order to prequalify, he must submit a statement of detailed information concerning his equipment, experience, finances, current jobs in progress, references, and personnel. Evaluation of these data results in a determination as to whether the contractor will be allowed to submit a proposal. Highway contractors usually submit qualification questionnaires at specified intervals and are rated as to their maximum contract capacity. Their construction activities are reflected in their "current ratings," with proposal forms being issued only to those qualified to bid on each project. The prequalification certificate may also limit the contractor to certain types of work such as grading, concrete paving, or bridge construction.

In jurisdictions having postqualification, the contractor is called upon to furnish certain information along with his bid. The information is much the same as that required for prequalification, but it serves the qualification purpose only for the particular project being bid.

6.10 DEPOSITS

After a contractor has decided that he wishes to bid, he must obtain the necessary sets of drawings and specifications from the architect-engineer or the contracting authority. The number of sets needed depends upon the size and complexity of the project, the time available for the preparation of the bid, and the distribution that the architect-engineer has made to subcontractors, material dealers, and plan services. Table 6.1 presents one group's ideas as to the number of plan sets required by general contractors to bid on different classes of building construction. In general, more sets will be required for shorter times of bidding and for more complex projects. It is customary for architect-engineers to require a deposit for each set of plans as a guarantee for its safe return. This deposit, which may range from $5.00 to over $100.00 per set, is usually refundable.

6.11 AVAILABILITY OF PLANS AND SPECIFICATIONS

Undue restriction of the number of sets of plans and specifications made available to the various bidders is shortsighted. Admittedly, the reproduction of these documents is expensive, and certainly no more sets should be provided than are necessary. However, there can be no argument that a reasonably thorough coverage of subcontractors and material suppliers is necessary to obtain the best competitive prices, particularly for large and complex projects. The plan services in large cities perform a valuable function in this regard, making drawings and specifications readily available to interested bidders.

Many subcontractors and material suppliers, particularly those who are concerned with significant portions of the project, obtain their own drawings

TABLE 6.1   Recommended Bidding Period and Plan Distribution Schedule*

Type of Building Project	Estimated Project Cost in Dollars											
	Under 25,000		25,000 to 75,000		75,000 to 150,000		150,000 to 500,000		500,000 to 1,000,000		Over 1,000,000	
	Sets	Days	Sets	Days	Sets	Days	Sets	Days	Sets	Days	Sets	Days
1. Garages, warehouses, factories, mills	2	14	3	14	3	18	4	21	4	28	4	28
2. Commercial buildings, schools, banks, office buildings	2	14	3	18	3	21	4	26	4	28	4	28
3. Hospitals	2	14	3	20	3	22	4	26	4	28	4	35
4. Churches, theaters	2	14	3	18	3	22	4	25	4	28	4	35
5. Motels, residences, apartments, hotels	2	14	3	21	3	24	4	26	4	28	4	35

Notes: 1. The foregoing recommendations should be considered as minimal.

2. The foregoing distribution chart presupposes an average of five general contractors responding to an invitation to bid. When less than five general contractors have been invited to bid or do not respond to an invitation to bid, the redistribution of plans to subcontractors (by general contractors) is proportionately reduced. In such instances, the distribution of plans to general contractors should be correspondingly increased.

* Reproduced by permission of Joint Cooperative Committee of the New Mexico Chapter, American Institute of Architects, and the New Mexico Building Branch, Associated General Contractors of America.

and specifications directly from the architect-engineer. Nevertheless, the prime contractor almost always finds it necessary to lend his drawings in order to obtain quotations. In this regard he will find it advisable to stamp each set of drawings and specifications with his name and to establish a check-out system.

A word of caution should be injected regarding the lending of drawings and specifications. Care must be exercised that all contract documents in their entirety, including addenda, are made available. This foresight will eliminate later complaints by subcontractors or material suppliers that they bid on the basis of incomplete information and hence did not tender a complete proposal. The general contractor, if possible, should set aside a well-lighted plan room for the use of the estimators of subcontractors and material dealers. When such facilities are available, the drawings and specifications need never leave the office and can be made to serve a wider range of bidders in a considerably more efficient manner.

6.12 THE BIDDING PERIOD

The estimating process takes considerable time and must be dovetailed into the contractor's current operations. Hurriedly prepared bids are generally poor ones. Careful study and analysis of the plans and specifications usually result in lower bid prices and substantial savings for the owner. The more complicated and extensive the project, the bigger the dividends that additional bidding time will pay to the owner. Unless the work is truly of a rush or emergency nature, it is sound economy for the owner to allow sufficient time for the bidding contractors to make a thorough study and examination of the proposed work. When an insufficient bidding period is allotted, many of the best prices will not be received by the contractor in time for him to pass the savings on to the owner. Table 6.1 represents a typical cross section of opinion as to minimum bidding periods for building projects of varying type and cost.

From the contractor's point of view, the architect-engineer should avoid setting any day following or preceding a weekend or holiday as the date for receiving bids. Morning hours are also highly undesirable. Such times impose undue hardships upon the contractors and other bidders and greatly restrict the availability of prices and other information. As far as is practicable, the architect-engineer should schedule bidding dates that do not conflict with other openings.

6.13 INSTRUCTIONS TO BIDDERS

When competitive proposals are requested, a considerable amount of information concerning the technicalities of the bidding process must be communicated to the contractors involved. This information usually comprises the first division of the specifications and is designated as "Instructions to Bidders." These instructions review the requirements that the owner or contracting authority has set up for the form and content of the bids and also prescribe certain procedures with which the bidding contractors are expected to conform. Failure to comply may result in a contractor's bid not being accepted.

Clauses are commonly included that give the owner the right to reject all bids, to postpone the date of bid opening, and to exercise many prerogatives in the selection of the successful bidder. A typical list of instructions to bidders is contained in Appendix B. Federal construction projects utilize a standard form that contains essentially the same information as Appendix B.

6.14 PRELIMINARY CONSIDERATIONS

Before starting the detailed estimating procedure, the estimator must become familiar with all of the contract documents such as the instructions to bidders, proposal form, alternates, general and special conditions, drawings, specifications, addenda, and form of contract. Such familiarity is equally as important for the quantity take-off men as it is for the cost estimator. The form and arrangement of the quantity surveys can be dictated by the requirements of the foregoing documents. For example, alternate proposals often require tnat the quantity surveys of certain portions of the project be compiled separately. When bidding large projects, it is desirable to hold a prebid meeting between the estimators and the men who will occupy the principal supervisory positions on the project if the bid is successful. The purpose of this meeting is to explore the alternative construction procedures that might be followed and to make tentative decisions regarding methods, equipment, personnel, and time schedules.

After preliminary examination of the drawings and specifications, the construction site should be visited. Information must be obtained concerning the following:

1. Project location.
2. Probable weather conditions.
3. Availability of electricity, water, telephone, and other services.
4. Access to the site.
5. Local ordinances and regulations.
6. Conditions pertaining to the protection or underpinning of adjacent property.
7. Storage and construction operation facilities.
8. Surface topography and drainage.
9. Subsurface soil, rock, and water conditions.
10. Underground obstructions.
11. Transportation and freight facilities.
12. Conditions affecting the hiring, housing, and feeding of workmen.
13. Material prices and delivery information from local material dealers.
14. Rental of construction equipment.
15. Local subcontractors.
16. Other matters that pertain to the proposed construction.

An experienced man should perform this site inspection, particularly in locations that are relatively new or strange to the contractor's organization.

6.15 BID INVITATIONS

Early in the bidding period, the contractor should mail out bid invitations to all material dealers and subcontractors whom he believes would be interested and whose bids he would like to receive. This mailing, by post card or form letter, informs of the project under consideration, the deadline for receipt of proposals by the prime contractor, the place where bids will be accepted by him, the place where contract documents are available, and any special instructions that may be necessary. Specific reminders concerning the status of addenda, alternates, taxes, and bond are desirable. Contractors customarily maintain a card file that lists addresses and other pertinent information about material suppliers and subcontractors. These cards are filed both by geographical area and by specialty.

6.16 QUANTITY SURVEYS

The quantity survey is the only accurate and dependable procedure for compiling either a lump-sum or a unit-price estimate. Although the bid documents for a unit-price project customarily provide the contractor with estimated quantities of each bid item, these are approximate only and the architect-engineer assumes no responsibility for their accuracy or completeness. For this reason, the contractor customarily makes his own quantity take-off even on projects for which estimated quantities are given.

The quantity take-off man must have had sufficient experience and training to visualize and plan the detailed steps of the construction process. When alternative procedures are possible, he must investigate each of them to determine which will be the most advantageous. The most propitious procedure is based not only upon the immediate cost but also on the time needed, equipment and labor requirements, geographical location, labor union policies, and other such factors. The adequate consideration of alternative procedures always proves to be time well spent. When the estimator makes major decisions regarding equipment, methods, or procedures, he should make appropriate notes concerning the details of his assumptions.

The take-off man uses pads of standard forms that provide suitable spaces for the entry of dimensions, numbers of units, and extensions. Allowances for the waste of materials such as lumber, portland cement, brick, sand, and gravel are made as the take-off proceeds. In large organizations in which there are several take-off men it is usual practice for each man to specialize, more or less, along certain lines; for instance, one man may take off only the masonry work, whereas another will concentrate on excavation, concrete, and forms. Although this system has many obvious advantages, it also has the disadvantage that there is always the possibility of overlooking items or duplicating them. This possibility can be minimized, however, by careful coordination and checking.

The prime contractor does not concern himself with making quantity surveys for all work categories but limits his take-off to items that he may reasonably expect to carry out with his own forces. The specialized categories that are done by subcontractors are not usually investigated in detail by the prime contractor. However, at times he may analyze any or all of these categories as a check against the possibility that he may be able to do the work for less money than the best available subcontract bid.

6.17 CONSULTANT QUANTITY SURVEYORS

It is standard practice in competitive bidding for each bidding contractor to make his own quantity take-off. Thus, there is considerable duplication of effort. In this regard it is interesting to note that there are many firms, commonly called "consultant quantity surveyors," whose business is the making of quantity surveys. This service provides an independent take-off and list of quantities for contractors, owners, architect-engineers, and other interested parties.

Ordinarily, however, most contractors prefer to prepare their own quantity surveys, in which they have a sense of confidence. They maintain a staff of experienced estimators whose reliability and accuracy have been well established. During the take-off process, the estimator must make many decisions concerning procedure, equipment, sequence of operations, and other such matters. All of these decisions must be considered when costs are being applied to the quantity surveys. In addition, work classifications used in quantity surveys must conform with the contractor's established cost accounting system.

Nevertheless, it seems possible that at some future date bids may be solicited from contractors on the basis of a single, prebid, material take-off furnished by the owner and prepared for him by a consultant quantity surveyor. Proponents of this procedure claim that it would enable each bidder to concentrate more fully on the techniques of construction and other job features that best utilize a contractor's experience and capabilities.

6.18 SUMMARY SHEETS

Upon completion of the quantity surveys, all multiplications are done, and these extensions are added for each work classification. The totals are then transferred to summary sheets that list and classify the several items of work. As an example, Figure 6.3 presents one form of summary sheet and illustrates typical subdivisions of concrete and form work. Similar summaries are prepared for all of the other work items.

It should be noted that each work classification is assigned a designating number. These are the company's standard cost account numbers, which are basic to its cost accounting system. Each estimate is broken down in accordance with the cost system, the extent to which each work classification is subdivided depending upon whether or not it is performed under subcontract or by the contractor's own forces. Chapter 11 discusses the essentials of a contractor's cost accounting system.

6.19 MATERIAL COSTS

Although manufacturer's price lists may occasionally be used, it is customary for the contractor to solicit and receive special quotations for all materials required for the job being bid. Written quotations from the various material dealers are desirable to serve as a matter of record concerning such important considerations as the quoted prices, status of freight charges, inclusion of taxes, and delivery schedule and to specify exactly what material is included. Most suppliers tender their quotations on printed forms that include stipulations pertaining to terms of payment and other considerations.

Material costs as entered on the summary sheets should all be on a common basis, for example, delivered to the job site and without tax. These costs will

Summary Sheet

Concrete and Forms

Cost Account Number	Item	Unit	Total Quantity	Material Cost		Labor Cost		Total Cost
				Each	Total	Each	Total	
240	CONCRETE							
.01	Footings	C.Y.	1,240	$18.50	$ 22,940	$2.70	$ 3,348	$ 26,288
.05	Grade beams	C.Y.	1,055	19.50	20,572	3.90	4,115	24,687
.07	Slab	C.Y.	3,072	18.50	56,832	3.30	10,138	66,970
.08	Beams	C.Y.	608	19.50	11,856	3.30	2,006	13,862
.09	Bond beam and lintels	C.Y.	62	19.50	1,209	6.00	372	1,581
.11	Columns	C.Y.	102	19.50	1,989	5.80	592	2,581
.12	Walls	C.Y.	566	19.50	11,037	3.90	2,207	13,244
.16	Stairs	C.Y.	417	19.50	8,132	5.20	2,168	10,300
.19	Sidewalks	C.Y.	420	18.50	7,770	3.30	1,386	9,156
.20	Expansion joint	L.F.	44,060	0.10	4,406	0.08	3,525	7,931
.40	Screeds	S.F.	163,000	—	—	0.06	9,780	9,780
.50	Float finish	S.F.	27,000	—	—	0.05	1,350	1,350
.51	Trowel finish	S.F.	156,320	—	—	0.10	15,632	15,632
.52	Stair finish	L.F.	2,200	—	—	0.50	1,100	1,100
.60	Rubbing	S.F.	3,700	0.02	74	0.25	925	999
.91	Curing, slab	S.F.	192,400	0.01	1,924	0.01	1,924	3,848
					$148,741		$60,568	$209,309
	Indirect labor cost					20%	12,114	12,114
	Total concrete				$148,741		$72,682	$221,423
260	FORMS							
.01	Footings	S.F.	1,420	$ 0.21	$ 298	$0.40	$ 568	$ 866
.05	Grade beams	S.F.	5,240	0.26	1,362	0.40	2,096	3,458
.08	Beams	S.F.	2,165	0.30	649	0.52	1,126	1,775
.11	Columns	S.F.	2,378	0.27	642	0.76	1,807	2,449
.12	Walls	S.F.	3,640	0.30	1,092	0.40	1,465	2,557
.17	Risers	L.F.	1,100	0.20	220	0.85	935	1,155
.45	Chamfer	L.F.	510	0.04	21	0.05	25	46
.60	Oil, ties, and nails	S.F.	14,933	0.03	448	—	—	448
.63	Anchor slot	L.F.	3,600	0.08	288	0.03	108	396
					$ 5,020		$ 8,130	$ 13,150
	Indirect labor cost					20%	1,626	1,626
	Total forms				$ 5,020		$ 9,756	$ 14,776

Figure 6.3   Summary Sheet

ordinarily include freight, transportation, storage, and inspection. It is common practice to enter material prices without sales or use tax, adding this as a lump-sum amount on the final "recap" sheet. Figures 6.4 and 6.5 illustrate this procedure.

RECAP SHEET MUNICIPAL AIRPORT TERMINAL BUILDING PORTLAND, OHIO				
Item	Material	Labor	Sub	Total
Clearing and Grubbing	$ 1,150	$ 8,620	$ --	$ 9,770
Excavation and Fill	14,060	15,780	--	29,840
Concrete	148,741	72,682	--	221,423
Forms	5,020	9,756	--	14,776
Masonry	--	--	472,000	472,000
Carpentry	19,120	13,640	--	32,760
Millwork	54,060	20,211	--	74,271
Steel and Miscl. Iron	321,890	73,340	--	395,230
Kitchen Equipment	--	--	59,981	59,981
Insulation	--	--	22,280	22,280
Caulk and Weatherstrip	--	--	4,980	4,980
Lath, Plaster, and Stucco	--	--	210,600	210,600
Ceramic Tile	--	--	19,333	19,333
Roofing and Sheet Metal	--	--	182,770	182,770
Resilient Flooring	--	--	22,624	22,624
Acoustical Tile	--	--	28,019	28,019
Painting	--	--	83,340	83,340
Glass and Glazing	--	--	62,319	62,319
Terrazzo	--	--	84,108	84,108
Miscellaneous Metals	61,228	11,315	--	72,543
Finish Hardware	43,600	4,430	--	48,030
Plumbing, Heating, Air-Cond.	--	--	600,000	600,000
Electrical	--	--	338,768	338,768
Clean Glass	--	--	2,800	2,800
Paving, Curb and Gutter	--	--	79,330	79,330
Equipment Expense	26,000	33,800	--	59,800
Job Overhead	39,550	94,260	--	133,810
	$ 734,419	$ 357,834	$2,273,252	$ 3,365,505
Sales Tax, 3%				100,965
				$ 3,466,470

Changes	(+)	(-)	Changes (-)	90,428
Plumbing, Heating, Air-Cond.	$ --	$ 86,958		$ 3,376,042
Ready-Mix Concrete	--	5,170	Markup, 8%	270,083
Metal Doors	1,700	--		$ 3,646,125
	$ 1,700	$ 92,128	Bond	22,736
			Total	$ 3,668,861

Figure 6.4 Recap sheet for lump-sum bid.

RECAP SHEET

Project: __Holloman Taxiways and Aprons__   Bid Date: August 9, 19___

Bid Item	Unit	Quantity	Total Labor Cost	Total Equip. Cost	Total Material Cost	Total Sub Cost	Total Direct Cost	Bid Unit	Bid Total
1 Clearing	ls	Job	$ 500	$ 10,331	$ --	$ --	$ 10,831	$13,000.00	$ 13,000
2 Demolition	ls	Job	250	7,894	--	--	8,144	9,800.00	9,800
3 Excavation	C.Y.	127,000	2,625	55,613	--	--	58,238	0.55	69,850
4 Base Course	S.Y.	160,000	16,878	88,014	41,800	--	146,692	1.10	176,000
5 Concrete Pavement, 9 in.	S.Y	90,000	52,111	139,229	157,466	--	348,806	4.65	418,500
6 11 in.	S.Y.	70,000	45,338	140,267	164,515	--	350,120	6.00	420,000
7 Asp. Conc. Surface	ton	150	195	729	779	--	1,703	13.60	2,040
8 Concrete Pipe, 12 in.	lf	1,000	1,122	1,207	3,333	--	5,662	6.80	6,800
9 36 in.	lf	300	929	1,166	2,079	--	4,174	16.70	5,010
10 Inlet	ea	2	206	26	271	--	503	300.00	600
11 Fiber Duct, 4 way	lf	600	301	1,843	849	--	2,993	6.00	3,600
12 8 way	lf	1,200	1,719	9,800	4,503	--	16,022	16.00	19,200
13 Electrical Manhole	ea	6	--	--	--	2,000	2,000	400.00	2,400
14 Underground Cable	lf	34,000	--	--	--	28,330	28,330	1.00	34,000
15 Taxiway Lights	ea	120	--	--	--	12,000	12,000	120.00	14,400
16 Apron Lights	ea	70	--	--	--	8,750	8,750	150.00	10,500
17 Taxiway Marking	ls	Job	1,273	350	1,728	--	3,351	4,000.00	4,000
18 Fence	lf	26,000	7,466	411	6,209	--	14,086	0.65	16,900
Totals			$130,913	$456,880	$383,532	$51,080	$1,022,405		$1,226,600

Job Overhead   35,342
1,057,747
Sales Tax, 3%   31,732
1,089,479
Markup, 12%   130,738
1,220,217
Bond   6,383
Total Project Bid $1,226,600

$$\text{Factor} = \frac{1,226,600}{1,022,405} = 1.200$$

Figure 6.5   Recap sheet for unit-price bid.

6.20   LABOR COSTS

Labor costs are subject to considerable variation and cannot be determined with the same degree of exactness as can most other elements of construction cost. Labor costs, together with equipment costs, represent the largest areas of uncertainty in the bidding process. Nevertheless, reasonably reliable labor costs can normally be estimated after a careful analysis of job conditions and with reference to good cost records from past operations. An activity of primary importance to the contractor is the accumulation of accurate labor costs on his projects. This information constitutes one of the most valuable trade secrets of a contracting organization.

The basic unit of labor cost information is the labor time of various categories required to do a certain piece of work. As an example, 7 hours of carpenter time and 7 hours of carpenter-tender time may be required to assemble, oil, erect, plumb, brace, strip, and clean 100 square feet of rectangular concrete column forms using adjustable steel form clamps. To obtain the estimated labor cost for a quantity of such work, the labor-hours required per unit of work can be multiplied by the appropriate wage scales per hour and again multiplied by the total number of units of work of this category as given by the quantity survey. By following the same procedure for all such categories, the total labor costs associated with the overall project can be determined.

Most cost estimators prefer to work with a labor cost per unit of work. For example, if carpenters earn $6.35 per hour and a carpenter-tender's wage scale is $4.50 per hour, the rectangular column forms cited previously will cost $0.76 per square foot. These "labor units" enjoy the advantage of ease of application as illustrated by Figure 6.3. However, the cost estimator must exercise care that his labor units are kept up to date and that they reflect the actual levels of production and current wage rates.

6.21   INDIRECT LABOR COSTS

The inclusion of indirect labor costs is an important part of the estimating process, such costs amounting to appreciable percentages of the direct labor costs. One category of indirect labor costs is payroll taxes and insurance. Employer contribution to social security, unemployment insurance, workmen's compensation insurance, and public liability and property damage insurance are all based upon payrolls. The premium rates of workmen's compensation insurance depend upon the classification of labor involved.

Fringe benefits constitute another category of indirect labor cost. Labor agreements in the construction industry typically provide for various kinds of fringe benefits such as health and welfare funds, employee insurance, paid vacations, pension plans, and apprenticeship programs. Contractor contributions to these funds are customarily computed on the basis of an amount per hour worked by each employee covered. Fringe benefits and their costs differ from one craft to another.

One way in which these indirect labor costs can be included in the bid is to add a percentage to the estimated total direct labor cost for the entire project. However, because of the variation of indirect costs from one classification of work to another, it is preferable to add these costs to the labor total of the individual summary sheets. The 20 percent addition in Figure 6.3 represents the total indirect labor cost associated with both concrete forming and placing.

6.22 EQUIPMENT COSTS

Equipment is an important item of expense in most construction operations. The cost of equipment ownership and operation is a major element of total cost for heavy and highway projects but is less significant for buildings. When the nature of the work requires major items of equipment such as earth-moving machines, concrete plants, and pile drivers, detailed studies of the associated costs must be made. Costs associated with minor equipment items—power tools, wheelbarrows, concrete vibrators, and the like—are not normally subject to detailed study but are included as a lump sum on the job overhead sheet (Section 6.27).

Equipment costs can be computed in a variety of ways. A scheme sometimes found to be expedient is for the contractor to purchase all new or renovated equipment for a project and sell it at the cessation of construction activities. The difference between the purchase price and the estimated salvage value is figured into the job as a direct cost. This procedure has the advantage of ensuring the use of modern and properly functioning equipment and can be economically desirable when the service life of the equipment will be about equal to the duration of the construction period.

Rental or lease of equipment, another procedure frequently used, can be appropriate when equipment is involved of a type or capacity that the contractor does not own and for which he anticipates little or no future need. Rental is particularly advantageous when the job site is far removed geographically from the contractor's other operations. Lease agreements for construction equipment extend for periods of one year or more, while renting is usually of shorter term. Equipment costs are computed by applying the lease or rental rates to the time periods that the equipment will be on the project. To this figure must be added move-in, operating, and move-out expenses.

The most common procedure is for the contractor to use his own equipment. In order to estimate reliable costs, the contractor must keep accurate records of his equipment expenses. The keeping of such records is an integral part of a contractor's cost-accounting system and provides the most dependable source of cost data.

Equipment costs are customarily expressed as the sum of ownership expense and operating costs. Ownership expenses are those of a fixed nature and include depreciation, interest, taxes, insurance, and storage. Operating costs include on-the-job costs, such as tire replacement and repair, repair parts and labor, fuel, oil, grease, maintenance, and operating labor. The cost of equipment overhauls and major repairs can be capitalized, and thus are treated as an ownership expense. However, it is believed that the most common practice is to charge such costs to a specific project and treat them as operating costs. Ownership expense and operating costs are usually expressed as a total cost per unit of time or per unit of production. In the following section an illustrative example is given that is typical of how these costs are computed.

6.23 OWNERSHIP AND OPERATING COSTS

For illustrative purposes let us compute the ownership and operating costs for a bottom-dump hauler, a common example of earthmoving equipment. Earthmoving equipment is commonly assumed to operate 2,000 hours per year. In our example, we assume that the useful life of the hauler will be 10,000 operating hours or a total of 5 years, with no salvage value to be realized at the end of that period. Most heavy construction equipment has a life of only 4 to 8 years, either because it wears out or because it becomes obsolete.

In the following cost figures, the original price of the bottom-dump hauler is depreciated out over a period of 5 years. Depreciation is equipment expense caused by wear and obsolescence and allows the recovery of the invested capital over the useful life of the equipment. In this example, depreciation expense is computed on the basis of the cost per operating hour, assuming 2,000 operating hours per year. Depreciation methods are discussed in Chapter 10.

Interest, taxes, insurance, and storage are customarily based upon the average annual value of the equipment. The example assumes taxes as 2 percent, insurance and storage as 2 percent, and interest on investment as 6 percent, for a total annual cost of 10 percent of the average yearly value. When salvage is not considered, the average annual value may be obtained by the equation

$$A = \frac{C(n + 1)}{2n}$$

where A = average annual value,
C = original cost, and
n = number of years of useful life.

In the example following,

$$A = \frac{\$25,226(6)}{10} = \$15,135.60$$

Operating costs such as tire replacement, repairs, and oil and grease are estimated on the basis of company cost accounting records. A new set of tires is assumed to have a life of 5,000 operating hours.

It should be pointed out that ownership expense goes on whether or not the equipment is working. If the bottom-dump hauler actually works 2,000 hours per year, the owner recovers this cost. If the hauler works less, the contractor does not recover all of his annual ownership costs and the difference comes out

Estimated Hourly Ownership and Operating Costs for Bottom-Dump Hauler

OWNERSHIP COSTS

1. Depreciation:

Purchase price	$24,690	
Freight	536	
Delivered price	$25,226	
Less tires	6,446	
Amount to be depreciated	$18,780 $\div$ 10,000 hrs $=$	$ 1.88

2. Interest, taxes, insurance, and storage:

$$\frac{\$15,135.60 \times 0.10}{2,000} \qquad = \$\ 0.76$$

Total hourly ownership cost $= \$\ 2.64$

OPERATING COSTS

1. Tire replacement cost:
   Value of original tires, $6,446 $\div$ 5,000 $= \$\ 1.29$
2. Tire repairs (15% of hourly tire costs): $= \$\ 0.19$
3. Repairs and labor, parts, supplies (90% of depreciation): $= \$\ 1.69$
4. Fuel, 4 gal per hr @ 16¢: $= \$\ 0.64$
5. Oil and grease, including labor: $= \$\ 0.20$
6. Operator, including payroll taxes and insurance: $= \$\ 6.10$
   Total hourly operating cost $= \$10.11$
   Total estimated hourly ownership and operating cost $= \$12.75$

of general company profits. Operating costs are, of course, incurred only when the equipment is actually being used.

As the preceding example illustrates, ownership expense is distributed over the anticipated service life of each piece of equipment. A service life in terms of operating hours is normally used for earthmoving equipment, ditching machines, and the like. However, there are many other classes of construction equipment for which it is more appropriate to express service life in other terms. For example, hoists and scaffolding are required at the job site on a continuous basis during particular phases of the work whether actually being used continuously or not. Operating hours are meaningless in such cases, and the service life of equipment of this type must be expressed in terms of more meaningful time units such as months. The essential features of computing ownership and operating expenses, however, remain unchanged.

6.24 PRODUCTION RATES

On a lump-sum job, once the estimator has established rental rates or ownership and operating costs for the equipment to be used, he must determine the length of time that the equipment will be needed on the job. The total equipment expense is then easily established as the product of the appropriate rate and the necessary time on the construction site. When a unit-price estimate is involved, the estimator must obtain equipment expense per unit of production, such as total equipment cost per cubic yard of excavation. Move-in, erection, dismantling, and move-out costs are also included whenever these expenses are to be incurred.

In any event, some form of production rate of the equipment is usually required. Production rates of equipment in the field depend upon many factors such as equipment capacity and operating characteristics, soil types, terrain, weather, and operator skill. The estimator has to consider and evaluate these variables when he is bidding a new project. A production rate is needed that will approximate a time-average of useful work accomplishment during the equipment's stay on the job. The best source of information in this regard is advice from the equipment operators themselves and records from past projects of a nature similar to the one being bid. Otherwise, rules of thumb and formulas available from equipment dealers have been found to give reasonable results.

The "50-minute hour" is commonly used with regard to excavating and other forms of operating equipment. This term means that, on the average, the equipment is producing a net time of 50 minutes of each hour. The remaining time is consumed by necessary but nonproductive actions such as greasing, fueling, minor repairs, maintenance, and shifting position, and by operator delays and waiting.

If we continue to use the bottom-dump hauler as an example, the estimator must combine his analysis of field conditions with knowledge of the equipment to arrive at an estimate of the bank cubic yards of earth material that it can haul and place per hour. Suppose that his analysis of earth material to be hauled, characteristics of the loading shovel, haul road length and grade, rolling resistance, turning and dumping conditions, and other relevant factors discloses that our bottom-dump hauler can move 95 bank cubic yards per hour. With an hourly ownership and operating cost of $12.75, the equipment cost will be 13.4 cents per bank cubic yard.

6.25 SUBCONTRACTOR BIDS

Quotations from subcontractors are an important element in the compilation of a project estimate. Unfortunately, many of these bids may not be submitted to the prime contractor until shortly before closing time, a factor that makes it difficult to study and analyze these bids. Submission by telephone of bids by subcontractors, together with the practice of making last-minute deductions, makes the final bid compilation a difficult matter during that hectic period immediately before bid opening. The submission of written quotations by subcontractors with sufficient time to allow the general contractor to analyze the bids is to be preferred. Stipulations regarding the use of hoisting facilities, the supply of electricity, water, and heat, conditions to be met before starting work, delivery and storage of materials, and others are commonly attached to and made a part of subcontract bids. Because subbid stipulations usually require some commitment on the part of the prime contractor, they must receive his careful attention during the bidding period so that all costs pertaining thereto can be included in his estimate.

The estimator must be sure what each subbid includes and what it does not cover, a matter that can require considerable checking when several subbids are involved. Inclusion of taxes and surety bond and acknowledgment of addenda must either be stipulated by the quotation or determined by the general contractor. On building construction in particular, many items of work must be checked with the bidding subcontractors to be sure of their incorporation. For example, the prime contractor should check with the plumbing and electrical subcontractors to see whether their bids include an allowance for connecting up temporary water, sanitary, and electrical services.

6.26 ALLOWANCES

On occasion, the architect-engineer will designate in his specifications a fixed sum of money that the contractor is to include in his estimate to cover the cost of some designated item of work. This practice is common on building construction for items such as finish hardware, brick, landscaping, and electric light fixtures. Generally speaking, the allowance amount is for the invoice cost of materials only, and the contractor must add the necessary labor, taxes, insurance, profit, and bond.

The architect-engineer may also state that a given sum must be included within the estimate to act as a contingency for extras that might prove to be necessary as the work progresses. Such contingency provisions are commonly utilized for remodeling and other types of work that have many uncertainties associated with them.

Occasionally, allowances are used for subcontracted work. For example, the owner himself may solicit bids from specialty contractors for specific portions of his project in advance of the date for the opening of the prime proposals. After the owner has made his selection, he advises the bidding prime contractors of the amounts and nature of the subbids that are to be included within their estimates. Instead, the specifications may merely indicate a sum of money to serve as an allowance for certain subcontracted work that will be let at a date subsequent to the award of the prime contract. In either case, however, the prime contractor must become cognizant of all conditions pertaining to the award of the subcontracts and the exact nature of the work covered by them.

The inclusion of an allowance in his proposal does not necessarily mean that the contractor is entitled to receive payment in the same amount. The contract documents provide that after the completion of construction an adjustment in the contract amount will be made equal to the difference between the specified allowance and the actual cost associated with it.

6.27 PROJECT OVERHEAD

Overhead expenses are costs that do not pertain directly to any given construction work item but are nevertheless necessary for ultimate job completion. Project overhead refers to costs of this type that are incurred on the project itself. Office overhead is discussed in the next section. Job overhead costs can be estimated with reasonable accuracy and are compiled on a separate overhead sheet. This overhead is an appreciable item of expense and will generally run from 4 to 10 percent of the total project cost, depending somewhat upon where certain costs are included.

Job overhead expense should be computed by listing and costing each item of overhead individually rather than by using an arbitrary percentage of project cost. This is true because different projects can have widely varying job overhead requirements. The only way to arrive at an accurate estimate of job overhead is to analyze the particular and peculiar needs of each project.

Typical items of job overhead are listed below. This list is not represented as being complete, nor would all of the items necessarily be applicable to any one project.

Project manager	Timekeepers
General superintendent	Watchmen and guards
Gang foreman	Engineers
Heat	Job sign
Electricity	Temporary lighting
Water	Drinking water facilities
Storage buildings	Badges
Sanitary facilities	Worker transportation
Field office supplies	Worker housing
Job telephone	Legal expenses
Small tools	Surveys
Temporary enclosures	Field office
Temporary stairs	Parking areas
Permits and fees	Security clearances
Special insurance	Load tests
Builder's risk insurance	Temporary roads
Photographs	Storage area rental
Barricades	Travel expense
Winter operation	Protection of adjoining property
Concrete and other tests	First aid
Cutting and patching	Storage and protection
Drayage	Workmen's subsistence
Clean up	Temporary partitions

6.28 OFFICE OVERHEAD

Office overhead includes general business expenses such as office rent, office insurance, heat, lights, office supplies, furniture, telephone and telegraph, legal expenses, donations, advertising, travel, association dues, and salaries of executives and office employees. The total cost of this overhead expense generally ranges from 3 to 8 percent of a contractor's annual business volume. This percentage represents inescapable costs of doing business, and the contractor must include in his cost estimate of each project an allowance for his office overhead expense.

From the preceding, it is easy to see that office overhead includes costs that are incurred in support of the overall company construction program and that generally cannot be charged to any specific project. For this reason, office overhead can be included in a job estimate only as a percentage of total estimated job cost. Details of how the contractor does this vary, but the net effect is the same. A percentage of the total estimated cost of the job can be added as a separate cost item, or a suitable "markup" percentage can be applied that will include office overhead as well as an allowance for profit.

6.29 CONSTRUCTION TIME

The bidding documents usually stipulate the length of time in calendar days within which the construction must be completed. On the other hand, these documents sometimes require the contractor to indicate on the proposal form his own time requirement for completing the project. In either case, construction time is a binding contract provision, and failure to complete on time is a breach of contract that can subject the contractor to the costs of liquidated damages or to litigation. Because of the importance of time, the contractor cannot simply accept at face value the construction period stipulated by the bidding documents. Not only because the completion date is a contract provision but also because many items of job cost are directly related to the length of the construction period, the contractor must make his own independent assessment of the construction time that will actually be required.

In cases where the contractor believes the stipulated contract time to be inadequate for project completion using normal construction procedures, he may request the owner and the architect-engineer to reconsider and allow a longer construction period. Otherwise, he must figure into his estimate the additional costs associated with overtime or multiple-shift work. If liquidated damages will be assessed against the contractor for his failure to complete the project within the designated period, he may decide simply to add the anticipated amount of damages to his estimate of job cost.

When the contractor's estimated construction time is called for on the bid form, its determination should receive due consideration because this figure becomes a contract requirement in the event of the owner's acceptance of the proposal. Contractors too often insert a time that they believe will be attractive to the owner but that is not realistic. When the stated time has elapsed and completion has not yet been attained, the owner is inconvenienced and litigation may result.

6.30 MARKUP

Markup, an allowance for profit plus possibly other items such as office overhead or unforeseen contingencies, is added at the close of the bidding process.

This item, which may vary from 5 to more than 20 percent of project cost, represents the contractor's considered appraisal of a whole series of imponderables that may influence the probability of his being the low bidder and his chances of making a reasonable profit if he is. The percentage added is dependent upon many factors, among them being the size of the project, its complexity, the contractor's evaluation of the risks and difficulties inherent in the work, the provisions of the contract documents, the contractor's desire for the work, the competition, and many other intangibles associated with his judgment and experience.

The contractor is required to bid under a form of contract that has been designed to protect the owner. The contractor is rightfully held responsible for his interpretation of the bidding documents. However, in their attempts to afford the owner the protection that he needs and deserves, the writers of contract documents sometimes force the contractor to assume all risk for any variances from the drawings and specifications that may be found in the field and to assume liability for every conceivable contingency, some of which involve risks for which he rightfully should not be made responsible. For example, provisions are found in some contract documents that absolve the owner from all claims for damages caused by project delay, even though caused by his own fault or negligence. Contractors are frequently made to assume full responsibility for any and all unknown physical conditions, including subterranean, that may be found at the construction site. Such contract clauses have resulted in much litigation. When such severe language is used in private contracts, the contractor can sometimes protect himself by inserting protective language on his proposal form or by submitting a qualifying letter with his bid. This is not usually possible on public contracts because of the risk of disqualification. It suffices to say that the markup figure selected must reflect the contractor's evaluation of the risks created by such contract provisions.

The contractor's objective when he selects his markup figure is to include the maximum possible profit while at the same time keep his bid at a competitive level. Stated another way, he wants to be the low bidder but with minimum spread between his low bid and that of the second-low bidder. Procedures have been developed to assist the contractor in selecting markup figures that will maximize his profits over the long term. These "bidding strategies" are based on a study of the past bidding record of the contractor and of his competitors. The application of certain principles of probability to the analysis of such data has produced some interesting and potentially valuable bidding models for the determination of optimum markup percentages. Appendix L discusses a simple bidding strategy that is based upon the concept of mathematical expectation and elementary probability.

6.31   THE LUMP-SUM BID

All costs associated with a project estimate are brought together and summarized on a recapitulation or "recap" sheet. Figure 6.4 illustrates a typical recap sheet for a lump-sum bid. The costs associated with work items that the contractor proposes to carry out with his own forces are posted from the take-off summary sheets and entered in the material and labor columns. All subcontract bids are shown under the subheading. Equipment and project overhead costs are entered, with wages placed under the labor heading and the total of all other expenses in the material column. The total of the material, labor, and subcolumns must equal the sum of the total column and affords a useful check on the accuracy of the additions. The bid price is arrived at by the final inclusion of taxes, markup, and bond.

Taxes applicable to construction projects vary with locality and can differ substantially between public and private projects. A common tax provision requires the contractor to pay sales tax on his business volume, less the cost of materials that are purchased by him. The contractor, of course, pays the sales tax on his materials at the time of their purchase. Consequently, under such an arrangement, he pays sales tax on the aggregate amount of his materials, labor, and subcontracts. Figure 6.4 includes such a sales tax in the amount of 3 percent.

6.32 CHANGES

When subbids and material prices are still being received and changed right up until bid time, the general contractor must devise some method to include last-minute changes in his final quotation. Figure 6.4 illustrates one such procedure. Referring to this figure, let us suppose that no subbid covering plumbing, heating, and air conditioning has been received up to within 2 or 3 hours before the opening of bids. Under these circumstances, the estimator makes an educated and conservatively high guess of $600,000. This permits all columns to be totaled and taxes to be computed and added in. Upon receipt of the best subbid covering the mechanical work, $515,575 in our example, a deduction is shown under "changes" in the amount of ($600,000 − $515,575) × 1.03 = $86,958. Also shown are the results of a last-minute cut in the price of ready-mix concrete and an increase in the delivered price of metal doors. When the procedure just described is followed, entries under "changes" must include all applicable costs with the exception of markup and bond.

6.33 THE UNIT-PRICE BID

In a manner similar to that for a lump-sum bid all costs associated with a project being bid as unit prices are accumulated and summarized on a final recap sheet. Figure 6.5 illustrates a typical recap sheet for a unit-price bid. Summary sheets similar to Figure 6.3 are compiled for each bid item. Each summary sheet lists the work necessary to accomplish the total quantity of that particular bid item and may include several different categories of work; for example, suppose that the bid item is reinforced concrete in place, per cubic yard. The summary sheet for that bid item would compile the total costs of labor, equipment, forms, reinforcing steel, inserts, aggregate, and portland cement (unless cement is itself a bid item) necessary to accomplish all of the reinforced concrete work. On the recap sheet costs of labor, equipment, and material are entered from the summary sheets for each bid item. Subcontract bids are also entered on the recap sheet when appropriate, although subcontracting is not generally practiced nearly so extensively on engineering construction (bid as unit prices) as on building construction (bid as a lump sum).

In Figure 6.5, the total direct cost of the entire quantity of each bid item is obtained as the sum of its labor, equipment, material, and subcontract costs. The sum of all such bid-item direct costs gives the estimated total direct cost of the entire project ($1,022,405). To this are added the job overhead, sales tax, markup, and bond, giving the total bid price ($1,226,600). Dividing the total project bid price by the total direct project cost gives a factor of 1.200. By multiplying the total direct cost of each bid item by this factor, the total bid amount for that work item is obtained. Dividing the total bid amount of each work item by the quantity gives the unit price for that bid item.

6.34 COST OF CONTRACT BOND

Almost every construction contract, except some of a cost-plus nature, requires that a contract bond be provided by the contractor to the owner as a guarantee against any default, failure, or malfunction on the part of the contractor during the construction period. The various aspects and characteristics of contract bonds are discussed more fully in Chapter 8. For the present we are concerned more with the cost of their premiums than with their nature.

The contract documents may require a performance bond only or both a performance and a payment bond. Many different combinations are used. For example, the contract documents may require a performance bond in the amount of 100 percent of the contract price and no payment bond. On the other hand, a performance bond of 50 percent and a payment bond of 50 percent are sometimes required. Many of the professional societies recommend a 100 percent performance bond and a 100 percent payment bond. Federal projects generally require a 100 percent performance bond and a sliding-scale payment bond. Generally speaking, however, the contract amount, not the total face value of the bonds, determines the premium that the contractor must pay. The explanation for this is that the risk depends upon the nature and size of the contract rather than upon the bond penalty. Consequently, the bond premium is the same for any of the preceding combinations of performance or performance and payment bonds. Special rules apply when low-percentage performance bonds or payment bonds only are required.

The premium that the contractor must pay for the required contract bonds is based upon the project completion time, the class of construction, the total contract amount, and any deviations from regular bureau rates that may apply. These matters are discussed in Section 8.7. Figure 6.4 illustrates the addition of the bond premium as the last step in arriving at the lump-sum bid. The amount of $22,736 is obtained by using the rates shown in Table 8.2 for Class B construction (buildings). The first $100,000 is assessed at $10.00 per $1,000 or at a rate of 1 percent. Everything in excess of $100,000 and less than $2,500,000 is charged at the rate of 0.65 percent, and everything over $2,500,000 and less than $5,000,000 has 0.525 percent applied to it. The sum of these is $22,617. To this total is added 0.525 percent of $22,617 or $119 because the bond premium is based on the total contract amount, including the cost of the bond. The bond premium rates given in Table 8.2 apply for a construction time of up to 24 months or 731 days. For longer periods, the premium is increased by 1 percent per whole month.

6.35 ESTIMATING BY COMPUTER

The preceding sections have been devoted to a discussion of the underlying principles of construction estimating. Not by statement, but by implication, the procedures presented were based on manual methods. It must be pointed out, however, that electronic computers are being utilized increasingly in conjunction with both the quantity survey and pricing phases of estimating. This does not mean that drawings and specifications are fed into one end of a machine and the finished proposal is printed out at the other. The estimator must still tabulate quantities and dimensions from the drawings and make the decisions concerning construction procedures, equipment, sequence of operations, and prices to be used.

Computer estimating starts with the estimator making the usual compilation of work dimensions from the drawings. When these data have been obtained, the computer can be programmed to generate material and labor costs for use in compiling the final estimate. This requires that not only the necessary material, labor, and equipment unit costs be stored in the computer's memory but also a computer program that will carry out the necessary computations and print out the information in the desired format. Usually the computer is programmed to produce summary sheets, priced and totaled, similar to the one illustrated in Figure 6.3.

Whether to acquire a computer or to rent computer time from a commercial data processing center presents the contractor with a very real problem. The question is principally one of economics and can be answered only by a detailed analysis of the contractor's mode of operation. Nevertheless, the computer is rapidly becoming an almost indispensable tool for management control. Electronic equipment is now widely used for bookkeeping, payrolls, cost accounting, cost reports, financial status reports, CPM schedules, and weekly project status reports and is beginning to assume an important role in the estimating process. Application of the computer to such a broad range of activities can make its acquisition economical for the contractor whose business is of substantial size.

6.36 THE PROPOSAL

A proposal is a written offer, tendered by the contractor to the owner, which stipulates the price for which the contractor agrees to perform the work described by the contract documents. A proposal is also a promise by the bidder that, upon its acceptance by the owner, he will enter into a contract with the owner for the amount of his bid. Thus, timely acceptance of a proposal by the owner is automatically binding upon the bidder.

A prepared proposal form is included with the contract documents and must be used by the contractor to present his bid. The prepared proposal form is both desirable and necessary so that all bids will be presented and evaluated on the same basis. It assists contractors in avoiding omissions and makes the comparison and analysis of the figures an easier matter for the owner and the architect-engineer.

A typical example of a lump-sum proposal is shown in Appendix F. The usual basis of contract award, assuming that all bidders are considered to be qualified, is the base bid plus or minus any alternates accepted by the owner.

Appendix G illustrates the usual nature of a unit-price bid form. It is to be noted that each bid item in Appendix G is accompanied by an estimate made by the architect-engineer of the quantity of that work item which is to be done. These estimated quantities are multiplied by the respective quoted unit prices, and the results are added. This sum represents an approximate total project cost and is the basis for the contract award. In cases of error in multiplication or addition by the contractor in preparing the proposal form, it is usual for the unit prices to control and the corrected total sum to govern.

6.37 UNBALANCED BID

On a unit-price project, a balanced bid is one in which each bid item includes its own direct cost plus its pro rata share of the project overhead, taxes, markup, and bond. For a variety of reasons, a contractor may occasionally raise the prices on certain bid items and decrease the prices on others proportionately so that the bid for the total job remains unaffected. This is called an "unbalanced" bid. It is common practice, for example, for a contractor to increase certain unit prices for items of work that are accomplished early in the course of construction operations and reduce proportionately prices for certain bid items that follow later. This process serves the purpose of making the early progress payments to the contractor of such disproportionate size that a minimum of his own capital is required to finance his early operations. Such extra early payment is of considerable assistance in helping the contractor to recover his heavy moving-in and other initial costs that are involved before the actual start of construction. Unbalancing is unnecessary when a suitable pay item covering the start-up costs is provided.

Unbalanced unit-price quotations may be submitted for other reasons. When the contractor detects what he believes to be a substantial error in the quantities listed in the proposal form, some unbalancing of unit costs is likely to be necessary in order that fixed costs such as equipment and overhead will be properly distributed over the true quantities of work. Also, for profit motives, the contractor may increase his unit prices on items that he believes will substantially exceed the estimated quantities and lower his unit costs commensurately on other items. When submitting an unbalanced bid, the contractor must be willing to assume the risk of having his proposal declared unacceptable by the contracting authority.

To illustrate some of the elements of unbalanced bidding, let us consider a numerical example. In order to understand the rationale behind unbalancing, two characteristics of a unit-price contract must be kept in mind. First, the low bid is determined on the basis of total cost, using the engineer's quantity estimates and the unit prices bid by the contractor. Consequently, the raising of some prices and the corresponding reduction of others is done in such a way that the total amount of the bid remains unchanged. Second, the contractor is paid on the basis of his quoted unit prices and the quantities of work actually done.

Suppose, for illustration, that we consider two bid items, one of which the contractor believes to be substantially in error. The engineer's estimate for ordinary excavation is 150,000 cubic yards, but the contractor's take-off indicates that the actual amount will be about 200,000 cubic yards. He decides to unbalance his bid as follows:

Bid Item	Engineer's Estimates	Straight Bid		Unbalanced Bid	
		Unit	Total	Unit	Total
Ordinary excavation	150,000 c.y.	$1.00	$150,000	$1.50	$225,000
Selected excavation	100,000 c.y.	$3.10	$310,000	$2.35	$235,000
			$460,000		$460,000

Let us assume that ordinary excavation actually turns out to be 200,000 cubic yards and selected excavation to be 100,000 cubic yards. Payment made on the basis of actual quantities of work done could vary as follows between a straight bid and the unbalanced bid that the contractor decided to use:

Bid Item	Actual Quantities	Straight Bid		Unbalanced Bid	
		Unit	Total	Unit	Total
Ordinary excavation	200,000 c.y.	$1.00	$200,000	$1.50	$300,000
Selected excavation	100,000 c.y.	$3.10	$310,000	$2.35	$235,000
			$510,000		$535,000

As can be seen, the contractor's use of unbalanced bidding resulted in his receiving an increased payment of $25,000.

6.38 ALTERNATES

Proposal forms frequently request price quotations for alternative methods, materials, or units of construction. These are called "alternate proposals" and may be additive or deductive to the base bid. Appendix F illustrates the use of alternate proposals. Such quotations must be complete within themselves and include all direct costs, taxes, overhead, markup, and bond. Alternates can be of special importance to the owner as a means of ensuring a bid within limited financing or providing him with an opportunity to make the most judicious selection of a material or process.

The award of lump-sum contracts is based upon the total of the base bid and any alternates accepted by the owner. When there are several alternates, it may be possible for the owner to juggle his acceptance of them so that a preferred contractor receives the contract. To combat this possibility, it is usual for the bidding documents to state the order of acceptance of additive and of deductive alternates.

6.39 BID SECURITY

With few exceptions, the proposal must be accompanied by some form of security as a guarantee that the contractor, upon being declared the successful bidder, will enter into a contract with the owner for the amount of his bid and will provide contract bonds as required. A bid bond is generally used for the purpose of bid security, although a certified check, cashier's check, or other form of collateral may sometimes be preferred. When a contractor becomes the successful bidder, the owner retains his security until such time as the contract is signed and satisfactory contract bonds are provided.

Bid bonds, which are provided by the contractor's surety for an annual service charge of $5.00, have the advantage of not immobilizing appreciable sums of the contractor's money. Bid bonds may be executed on the usual form of the surety, or the contract documents may include a specific form of bid bond that the contractor is required to use. On public works, the bid bond must be of such form as to satisfy statutory requirements. A form used by the Hartford Accident and Indemnity Company, reproduced in Figure 6.6, illustrates the usual style and content of a bid bond. The format and wording of bid bonds, as well as of contract bonds, which are discussed in Chapter 8, are substantially the same for all surety companies.

The minimum bid security required by the instructions to bidders may be stated as a given percentage of the maximum possible contract amount, including alternates, or as a designated lump sum. Bid security in the amount of 5 or 10 percent of the maximum bid price is a common requirement, although larger percentages are also used. Legal requirements must be followed on public work. Because bid bonds are prepared in advance of the bidding and before the proposal amount is accurately known, the contractor must arrive at some advance rough estimate of project cost for the use of his bonding company. If a fixed-sum bid bond is to be written, the amount of which is to be at least a given percentage of the maximum possible contract amount, the preliminary estimate of cost must be made conservatively high to ensure that sufficient bid security is available.

Should the contractor refuse or be unable to enter into a contract or to provide contract bonds as promised, the bid security may be proceeded against by the owner as reimbursement for the resulting damages. When a bid bond is involved, the surety must pay to the owner the difference between the low bid and the price that the owner must pay to the next lowest responsible bidder, up to the face amount of the bid bond. The form used by the federal government imposes the condition that, if the contract is refused or if contract bonds are not provided, the

SURETY DEPARTMENT   BOND NO.

HARTFORD ACCIDENT AND INDEMNITY COMPANY
690 Asylum Avenue
Hartford, Connecticut 06115

(A Stock Company)

BID BOND

Know All Men By These Presents,
That we,

as Principal,

hereinafter called the Principal, and the HARTFORD ACCIDENT AND INDEMNITY COMPANY, a corporation created and existing under the laws of the State of Connecticut, whose principal office is in Hartford, Connecticut, as Surety, hereinafter called the Surety, are held and firmly bound unto

as Obligee, hereinafter called the Obligee,

in the sum of

Dollars ($),

for the payment of which sum, well and truly to be made, the said Principal and the said Surety bind ourselves, our heirs, executors, administrators, successors and assigns, jointly and severally, firmly by these presents.

Whereas, the Principal has submitted a bid for

Now, Therefore, if the Obligee shall accept the bid of the Principal and the Principal shall enter into a contract with the Obligee in accordance with the terms of such bid, and give such bond or bonds as may be specified in the bidding or contract documents with good and sufficient surety for the faithful performance of such contract and for the prompt payment of labor and material furnished in the prosecution thereof, or in the event of the failure of the Principal to enter such contract and give such bond or bonds, if the Principal shall pay to the Obligee the difference not to exceed the penalty hereof between the amount specified in said bid and such larger amount for which the Obligee may in good faith contract with another party to perform the work covered by said bid, then this obligation shall be null and void, otherwise to remain in full force and effect.

Signed and sealed this...................................day of...A. D. 19.......

Witness...   ....(SEAL)
(If Individual)   (Principal)

By..(SEAL)
(Title)

Attest...   ....(SEAL)
(If Corporation)

....(SEAL)

HARTFORD ACCIDENT AND INDEMNITY COMPANY

Attest...   By..(SEAL)
(Title)

(Approved by The American Institute of Architects,
A. I. A. Document No. A-310, Sept. 1963 Edition)

Form S-3266-2   Printed in U. S. A.   5-'64

Figure 6.6 Bid bond. Reproduced by permission of the Hartford Accident and Indemnity Company, Hartford, Conn.

surety shall pay to the government the difference between the bid in question and the next highest acceptable bid with no limitation on the amount. Regardless of the exact provisions, however, the contractor bears the final liability for the payment of any such damages to an owner. When he signs the formal application for the bid bond, the contractor agrees to indemnify the surety company from all claims that may be made against it under the bond.

Upon deciding to bid a project, the contractor should immediately inform his surety company, particularly if the project is unusually large or different, or if the contractor is already burdened with a near-capacity volume of work. When the surety writes the bid bond, it is obligated to provide the necessary contract bonds should the contractor become the successful bidder. For this reason, considerable investigation by the surety may be required before the bid bond can be written. This matter is discussed more fully in Section 8.10.

6.40   SUBMISSION OF PROPOSAL

It is the responsibility of the contractor to deliver his bid to the proper place at the proper time. The completed proposal form, together with the bid security and other necessary supplementary information, is sealed in an envelope that is addressed as directed by the instructions for bidders and clearly labeled as a proposal for the project being bid. Bids may be submitted at any time previous to the deadline scheduled for their acceptance. If feasible, it is usual practice for the contractor or his representative to deliver the sealed bid shortly before opening time. However, proposals may also be dispatched by letter, telegraph, or messenger service.

The contractor sometimes bids under circumstances that prevent his proposals from being delivered personally. A typical example would be a Western contractor's bidding a project for which proposals are being accepted in the East. Under such circumstances the contractor is faced with the problem of conforming with all bid technicalities, getting his proposal delivered on time, yet taking advantage of last-minute quotations and price changes. Instructions to bidders usually state that all bids must be presented on the requisite proposal form but that telegraphic modifications are acceptable, provided written confirmation is subsequently submitted. It is common practice in such cases for the estimating department to rough-out a conservatively high bid price and mail in the correspondingly filled-out proposal form several days in advance of the bid opening. The bid security and other supplementary information are also included. This proposal submission is followed by a subsequent telegraphic modification that reduces the original figure to the desired final bid amount.

Public contract policy dictates that all proposals shall be opened publicly and read aloud. All bid formalities are noted for each bidder as the proposals are read. Private owners are under no compulsion to open the bids in public and occasionally conduct a closed opening. This procedure is viewed with considerable distrust by the bidding contractors, however.

After the bids have been opened and read, the contractor is expected to communicate the results of the bidding to his surety company. This information is incorporated into the surety's permanent file on the contractor and constitutes an important part of his record of performance.

6.41 COMPLIMENTARY BIDDING

Complimentary bidding refers to the submission of a proposal the amount of which the contractor did not estimate himself but obtained from another contractor. Complimentary bids may be used for a variety of reasons. For example, there are times when every contractor finds it impossible or undesirable to bid a project when asked to do so by an architect-engineer. In order to keep the goodwill of this architect-engineer, the contractor may obtain a complimentary figure from one of his fellow contractors who is bidding the job. Complimentary proposals may also be submitted to obtain the refund of plan deposits or to please an owner-client, as well as for other legitimate reasons.

The contractor furnishing the complimentary figure makes it safely larger than his own bid but sufficiently close to appear a bona fide proposal. It is obvious that the using of complimentary bids smacks of collusion, even when none is intended or involved. Contractors who provide or use complimentary bids must be particularly careful in this regard, especially on publicly financed projects.

6.42 BID ETHICS

Upon being designated the successful bidder, the general contractor should feel obligated to award his subcontracts to the firms whose bids he used in making up his estimate. Unfortunately, this is not always done. The low-bidding general contractor may try to obtain new and lower subbids than those he had at the time that he bid the job. He may even make the amounts of his low subbids known to competing subcontractors in the hope that they will submit even lower prices. This practice, known as "bid shopping," enables the general contractor to increase his profit at the expense of the subcontractors, who must rely upon his good faith to award them the work when their original bids are low. Although perhaps not actually illegal, this procedure can scarcely be considered a desirable business practice. Obviously, contractors can also "shop" for lower material prices.

Bid shopping on publicly financed projects has come in for a great deal of criticism, and considerable effort has been expended to minimize or eliminate this practice. Several of the states have passed legislation that imposes regulations on the bidding of state-financed projects; for example, heating, ventilating and air conditioning, plumbing, and electrical work on state-financed projects must be awarded as separate contracts and not as a portion of the overall prime contract in some states. Another procedure requires each general contractor bidding on a public building project to name his principal subcontractors at the time he submits his bid to the owner. Bills providing for similar requirements on the bidding of federal construction have been introduced in Congress, and certain federal agencies, by administrative regulation, have specified the use of these procedures.

Efforts of the construction trade associations to eliminate unsavory bidding and procurement practices have gone far in making these unethical procedures the exception rather than the rule. The Associated General Contractors of America promulgates a Code of Ethical Conduct, a portion of which pertains to the general contractor and his relations with subcontractors and material suppliers. The following quotation is from Section 3, "Rules of Ethical Practice," and is reproduced by permission of the Associated General Contractors of America.

"The operations of the contractor are made possible through the functioning of those agencies which furnish him with service or products, and in contracting with them he is rightfully obligated by the same principles of honor and fair dealing that he desires should govern the actions toward himself of architects, engineers, and client owners.

Ethical conduct with respect to subcontractors and those who supply materials requires that:
1. Proposals should not be invited from anyone who is known to be unqualified to perform the proposed work or to render the proper service.
2. The figures of one competitor shall not be made known to another before the award of the subcontract, nor should they be used by the contractor to secure a lower proposal from another bidder.
3. The contract should preferably be awarded to the lowest bidder if he is qualified to perform the contract, but if the award is made to another bidder, it should be at the amount of the latter's bid.
4. In no case should the low bidder be led to believe that a lower bid than his has been received.
5. When the contractor has been paid by a client owner for work or material, he should make payment promptly, and in just proportion, to subcontractors and others."

6.43 BID DEPOSITORIES

The problems associated with the submission of subcontract bids (and certain material and equipment prices) were mentioned in Section 6.25. The last-minute placing and changing of price quotations results in a mad scramble as the general contractor attempts to gather his figures together and compute his final bid. The process is particularly difficult when there are several alternates or bid items. Serious errors may be made as a result of the haste with which the final figures must be compiled. The use of bid depositories is one means of circumventing some of the problems associated with the bids of subcontractors and material suppliers. Bid depositories can also reduce bid shopping.

Although there are about as many types of bid depository as there are groups using them, all depositories are designed to accomplish a central purpose. A bid depository is a facility created by a group of contractors or a trade association and operated by an independent agency, such as a bank, to collect bids from subcontractors and material suppliers and convey them to the general contractors. The quotations from subcontractors and material dealers must be submitted to the depository before an announced deadline, four hours before the time of bid opening being a common requirement. After the deadline these price quotations are conveyed by the depository to the bidding general contractors for their use in compiling their final cost figures.

Bid depositories are not a new idea and have had a long and sometimes stormy history. Few depositories have experienced unqualified success. It is axiomatic that to be workable the depository must have the wholehearted support of a large majority of the members of the industry within the area served. Some depositories have been found to be in illegal restraint of trade and in violation of antitrust laws. If depositories engage only in the unrestricted collection and distribution of bids, it seems improbable that such difficulties will be encountered. Restrictions on the acceptance of subcontract bids not processed through the depository and on the submission of bids from subcontractors not members of the depository have led to serious legal difficulties.

6.44 PROPOSAL IRREGULARITIES

The instructions to bidders set forth specific requirements for the submission of the proposal. Any deviation from these provisions constitutes a bidding irregularity that could possibly result in the proposal being rejected, even though a saving clause is usually present that allows the owner to waive minor technicalities. The following check list can assist the estimating department in avoiding most of the commonly occurring bidding informalities:

1. Date the proposal with the day of the bid opening.
2. Fill in all blanks of the proposal form.
3. Make no interlineations or qualifications if prohibited by the instructions to bidders.
4. Properly countersign all erasures and corrections.
5. Make sure that signatures agree exactly with names as typed.
6. Check that the bid is signed by the proprietor, partner, or duly authorized agent.
7. Be sure that the individual signing for a corporation is so authorized by proper action of the corporation, this action having been entered into the minutes as a matter of formal record.
8. Attach corporate seal, if applicable.
9. Get signatures of witnesses, if required.
10. Have proposal notarized, if required.
11. Enter contractor's license number, if required.
12. Acknowledge receipt of changes in drawings.
13. Acknowledge receipt of addenda.
14. Submit required number of copies of proposal.
15. Check multiplications and additions on unit-price proposal.

16. Check to see that unit prices are on basis of correct unit, for example, per square yard rather than per square foot.
17. Quote a price for all items indicated, including all bid items and alternates.
18. Enter prices both in writing and in figures, where required.
19. When modifying unit-price proposals, revise total as well as item costs.
20. Submit all supplementary information required, such as experience record, list of equipment, proposed plan of operations, and list of subcontractors.
21. Check face value of bid security against that required by the contract documents.
22. Post mailed bids in ample time to ensure their receipt before the time of opening.
23. Follow up a telegraphic bid or modification with a written confirmation. Check for clarity.

6.45 ACCEPTANCE PERIOD

Either the instructions to bidders or the proposal form contains a provision that gives the owner a stated period of time after the opening of bids to make acceptance. Thirty days is common, although other periods of time are sometimes specified. During this waiting period, the subcontractors and material dealers are presumably obligated to the general contractor to stand by their price quotations just as the prime contractor is obligated to the owner.

Contractors are sometimes requested by the owner to grant an extension of the acceptance time. The contractor is generally willing to oblige, but sometimes in his eagerness to get the job he will agree to such an extension without giving the matter sufficient consideration. Such action means that the completion date of the project will be set back by a length of time equal to the extension of the acceptance period. Therefore, raises in labor wages that may occur during the construction period will be in force for the additional time. Also, the extension means that the entering of material orders will be delayed with the ever-present possibility of price advances. Another important aspect of this matter is that a subcontractor or supplier, having submitted what he considers to be an excessively low price, may not be willing to stand by his price quotation past the original acceptance period.

All of these factors represent potential elements of additional cost that the contractor may have to assume should he too hastily grant an owner additional acceptance time. When increased costs are anticipated and the contractor does not wish to absorb them, he should quote the required additional amount to the owner in exchange for extending the acceptance period.

6.46 WITHDRAWAL OF BID

Generally speaking, after the deadline for receipt of proposals a general contractor cannot alter his bid or withdraw it without forfeiture of his bid security.

The courts have long held that the lowest bidder cannot unreasonably refuse to comply with his bid without penalty.

If the contractor has made a substantial error in the compilation of his bid, the courts have consistently refused to allow him to correct his bid but have usually permitted him to withdraw it without penalty provided that certain conditions are met. Generally, withdrawal is permitted if:

1. The mistake is of such grave consequences that to enforce the contract as offered would be unconscionable.
2. The mistake relates to a material feature of the contract.
3. The mistake has not come about because of the violation of a positive legal duty or from culpable negligence.
4. The other party is put in status quo to the extent that he suffers no serious prejudice except the loss of his bargain.

When the error in computing was excusable and the owner's attention was drawn to the mistake before acceptance of the bid, the courts have almost unanimously permitted withdrawal of the bid and the return of the contractor's bid security.

The refusal of a subcontractor to honor his bid can be an entirely different matter. If the low-bidding general contractor used a subbid in good faith in preparing his proposal, the courts have usually awarded him damages when the subcontractor refused to honor his bid, regardless of the reason. The courts have stated that either a general contractor or a subcontractor may rescind a bid made in error only if it can be shown that the party making the mistake was in the exercise of ordinary diligence, and also that the rescission can be made without serious loss to the other party. Where the low-bidding general contractor based his proposal on a subcontract bid that was substantially lower than any other submitted, the withdrawal of the low subbid would cause him substantial loss. On this basis, the courts usually require the subcontractor to honor his bid or pay damages to the general contractor.

6.47 REJECTION OF PROPOSALS

The contract documents reserve the right for the owner to reject any or all bids. Rejection may be based upon irregularities in the bidding procedure, suspected collusion, flagrant unbalancing of bid unit costs, or unexpectedly high proposals. The lowest proposal sometimes far exceeds the available funds, and the project must then be abandoned or revamped. Public contracts are subject to statutory regulations in this regard.

In the event that the owner wishes to reduce the project cost by a minor amount, he is likely to negotiate a final contract with the low-bidding contractor. If major savings are required, it is usual that all proposals are rejected. After redesign or other corrective procedure the project is readvertised and new bids are taken.

6.48 STATE PREFERENCE STATUTES

Several states have enacted statutes pertaining to the award of state-financed construction projects that give preference to bidding contractors domiciled in that state. These statutes typically provide that construction contracts for state public works shall be awarded to the lowest responsible resident bidder if his bid is not more than 5 percent above that of the lowest responsible nonresident bidder.

CONSTRUCTION CONTRACTS

7.1 AWARDING THE CONTRACT

After the opening of the bid proposals the owner and his architect-engineer must determine the successful bidder, often called the "lowest responsible bidder." In the absence of bidding discrepancies, and if all of the bidders are judged to be qualified and responsible, the successful bidder is determined on the basis of lowest total project cost. Responsibility of the low bidder is established on the basis of his reputation and experience record. Default by the contractor on a previous contract, proof of dishonesty, past difficulties in completion of projects on time, and litigation associated with earlier contracts may be considered as grounds for disqualification on the basis of irresponsibility. In this regard, the Bureau of Contract Information, Inc., Washington, D. C., accumulates, compiles, and makes available information concerning the record of responsibility and contract performance of general contractors in the United States. This nonprofit organization is supported by the surety companies and is dedicated to the improvement of the construction industry through constraint of contract awards to irresponsible and unqualified contractors.

Upon selection of a contractor, the owner advises him in writing that his proposal has been accepted. This acceptance is conveyed by the issuance of a "notice of award," which is forwarded to the contractor together with information concerning arrangements for the signing of the contract. This notice, usually in letter form, sets forth the conditions pertaining to the award.

7.2 LETTER OF INTENT

Occasionally, the owner may wish the contractor to start construction operations before the formalities associated with the signing of the contract can be completed.

However, the contractor must proceed with caution in placing material orders, issuing subcontracts, or otherwise obligating himself before he has an executed and signed contract in his possession. In such urgency, it is common practice for the owner to authorize the start of work by a "letter of intent." This letter is prepared for the signatures of both parties and states their intent of entering into a suitable construction contract at a later date. When signed, the letter is binding on both parties and furnishes the contractor with sufficient authority to proceed with construction in the interim before the contract is formally executed. Normally, the letter provides that suitable compensation shall be made to the contractor should the formal contract not be forthcoming.

7.3 THE CONTRACT DOCUMENTS

Fundamentally, there is no reason why a contract cannot arise out of the proposal, which is an offer, and the notice of award, which is an acceptance. Although this may sometimes be done, it is universal practice in construction for the contract to be formalized by a written contract document. The basic purpose of a contract document is to define exactly and explicitly the rights and obligations of each party thereto. The complex nature of construction dictates a form of contract that is relatively lengthy, sacrificing brevity in order to describe precisely the legal, financial, and technical provisions. Construction contracts are substantially different from the usual commercial variety. The commodity concerned is not a standard one but a structure that is unique in its nature and whose realization involves considerable time, cost, and hazard. Construction contracts involving public or government bodies are regulated by statute in form and procedure.

Actually, the usual construction contract consists of a number of different documents. Although practice in this regard varies somewhat, the essential documents that go to make up the contract may be listed as follows:

1. General conditions
2. Special conditions
3. Technical specifications
4. Drawings
5. Addenda
6. Agreement

In essence, the advertisement, instructions to bidders, and proposal are preliminary to the contract. Nevertheless, these three documents are commonly included in the contract by reference. In addition, the contract bond is sometimes considered to be one of the contract documents. Collectively, all of the foregoing documents constitute the construction contract, and they are construed together for purposes of contract interpretation.

7.4 THE AGREEMENT

The agreement is a document specifically designed to formalize the construction contract. It acts as a single instrument that brings together the contract segments by reference and functions for the formal execution of the contract. It serves the purpose of presenting a condensation of the contract elements, stating the work to be done and the price to be paid for it, and providing suitable spaces for the signatures and seals of the parties. The agreement usually contains a few clauses that are closely akin to the special conditions and serve to amplify them. To illustrate, it is common for the agreement to contain clauses that designate the completion time of the project, liquidated damages, and particulars concerning payments to the contractor, and that list the contract documents. However, practice varies in this regard, with such clauses appearing sometimes in the special conditions, other times in the agreement, and perhaps in both.

The agreement can be a standard form, or it may be specially prepared for the purpose. Appendix H illustrates the use of *Document A101* of the American Institute of Architects, which is a popular choice for building construction contracts. *Document A101* is designed for use with the AIA "General Conditions of the Contract for Construction," *Document A201,* as contained in Appendix C. Appendix I reproduces AIA *Document A111,* a form of agreement between the contractor and owner that is widely used for cost-plus-fee contracts. A standard agreement form recommended for engineering construction projects has been prepared jointly by the American Society of Civil Engineers and the Associated General Contractors of America. Municipal construction contracts can use a standard form devised by the American Public Works Association together with the Associated General Contractors of America. Each of these two forms must be used in conjunction with its own particular set of general conditions.

Before affixing his signature to a contract involving private financing the contractor should make some investigation of the financial integrity of the owner. This applies particularly to projects of a speculative or promotional nature. On public contracts statutory requirements must have been observed by the responsible public officials for a valid contract to exist. In most jurisdictions the omission of the required procedural steps can leave the contractor without any remedy to obtain payment for work that he has performed under what he assumed to be a binding contract. If a government body enters into a contract without complying with the statutory requirements pertaining to the bidding and awarding of public construction contracts, the contract is considered beyond the power of the public agency and may be declared void.

7.5 TYPES OF CONSTRUCTION CONTRACTS

Although there are many different types of construction contracts, they may be grouped together into two large divisions. One division constitutes those contracts for which the contractor is selected on the basis of competitive bidding. Almost all public construction contracts, as well as a large proportion of private work, are in this category. Competitive-bid contracts are customarily prepared on a fixed-price basis and consist of two types. The unit-price contract is drawn on the basis of estimated quantities of specified work items and a unit price for each item. In the lump-sum contract, the second of the two types, the contract amount is a fixed sum that covers all aspects of the work described by the contract documents.

The second major division of construction contracts consists of those that result from direct owner-contractor negotiation. Negotiated contracts can be on any mutually agreeable basis: lump sum, unit price, or cost-plus-fee. Most negotiated contracts are on a cost-plus-fee basis where the owner reimburses the contractor for all construction costs and compensates him for his services. The provisos regarding compensation of the contractor constitute the major source of difference between the various types of negotiated contract. The contractor's fee may be designated as a fixed percentage of the cost of the work, a sliding scale percentage of the cost of the work, a fixed fee, a fixed fee with a guaranteed top price, a fixed fee with bonus, or a fixed fee with an arrangement for sharing any cost saving.

Prime contractors of federal construction projects are required by the Truth in Negotiation Act (Public Law 87-653) to submit certified cost or pricing data before the award of any negotiated contract expected to exceed $100,000 and before the negotiation of any contract modification expected to exceed $100,000. Corresponding requirements apply to a subcontractor at any tier for which the prime contractor and each higher tier subcontractor have been required to furnish certified data. The law and federal procurement regulations require that contractors furnish cost and pricing information which they certify to be accurate, complete, and current. Also required is a contract provision that provides for price reduction if the costs are found to have been inflated by inaccurate, incomplete, or outdated cost data.

7.6 THE LUMP-SUM CONTRACT

The lump-sum contract is one in which the contractor agrees to carry out a stipulated job of work in exchange for a fixed sum of money. The satisfactory completion of the work for the stated number of dollars remains the obligation of the contractor, regardless of the difficulties and troubles he may experience in the course of his construction activities. This type of contract is popular from the owner's viewpoint for the obvious reason that he knows the total cost of his project in advance. Its use is limited, however, to construction programs that can be accurately and completely described at the time of bidding. If the work is of such a nature that it is not accurately determinable in advance of field operations, the lump-sum type of contract is not suitable.

7.7 THE UNIT-PRICE CONTRACT

This type of contract is based on estimated quantities of certain well-defined items of work and costs per unit amount of each of these work items. The estimated quantities are compiled by the architect-engineer and the unit costs are those bid by the contractor for carrying out the stipulated work in accordance with the contract documents. The total sum of money paid to the contractor for each work item remains an indeterminable factor until completion of the contract, because payment is made only on the basis of units of work actually done and measured in the field. Therefore, the exact ultimate cost of the construction is not known to the owner until completion of the project. In addition, the owner must support, either directly or through the architect-engineer, a field force for the checking of true quantities of work.

Such contracts offer the advantages of open competition on projects involving quantities of work that cannot be accurately forecast at the time of bidding. An example might be the driving of piles or the excavating of foundations. A price per linear foot of pile or cubic yard of excavation allows reasonable variation to be made in the driven length of the individual piles or the quantity of excavation on account of subterranean conditions that cannot be determined precisely before actual construction operations. However, drawings and specifications must be available for bidding that are complete enough for the contractor to assess the overall magnitude of the project and the general nature and complexity of the work.

7.8 COST-PLUS CONTRACTS

Contracts of the cost-plus variety are usually used when the work is to be conducted in accordance with terms negotiated between the owner and the contractor. Contracts are negotiated between the two parties for a number of reasons. The owner may want a particular contractor to do the work. The nature of the construction may be such that it is impossible or impracticable to prepare complete drawings and specifications before operations are begun. Unusual speed of construction may be a pressing requirement. Perhaps many major changes in the work may become necessary during the construction program that will be particularly troublesome under a competitive type of contract.

When negotiating contracts of the cost-plus type, the contractor and the owner should pay particular attention to four important considerations:

1. A definite and mutually agreeable subcontract-letting procedure should be arranged. Competitive lump-sum or unit-price subcontracts are generally to be preferred by both parties when they are feasible. If the nature of the work is such that competitive subbids cannot be compiled, provisions must be made for the negotiation of cost-plus-fixed-fee or other form of cost-plus subcontracts.
2. There must be a clearly understood agreement concerning the determination and payment of the contractor's fee. Fees may be determined in many different ways, the most important of these being discussed in subsequent sections. Involved here is not only the amount of the fee but also the method by which it will be paid to the contractor during the life of the contract. A statement concerning any variation of fee with major changes in the work should be included.
3. A common understanding regarding the accounting methods to be followed is essential. Many controversies can be avoided by working out in advance

the details of record keeping and purchasing, and the reimbursement procedure.
4. A list of job costs to be reimbursable to the contractor should be set forth. Articles 9 and 10 of Appendix I present typical lists of reimbursable and nonreimbursable items.

7.9 SPECIAL REIMBURSABLE COSTS

With respect to reimbursable costs, two categories of expense are particularly troublesome and merit special attention. One of these is the contractor's office overhead. Involved are the costs associated with the preparation of payrolls, purchasing, record keeping, engineering, preparation of working drawings, and similar office functions that are necessary elements of a construction project. If the job is of reasonably large extent, the contractor can establish a project field office that performs all of the necessary office functions directly on the site. All expenses, including salaries, incurred by the project office are directly assignable to the job and are considered to be legitimate costs for reimbursement. When the project is smaller, office functions usually are carried out in the contractor's main office, and items of office overhead directly assignable to a specific project are difficult to establish. It is usual practice under such circumstances to eliminate office overhead altogether as a reimbursed cost and to increase the contractor's fee by a reasonable amount to provide for it.

The second troublesome category of reimbursed expense is that associated with construction equipment. When the equipment is owned by the contractor it is usual that he be reimbursed on the basis of the actual cost of the equipment with no allowance for profit—that is, at rates equal to his ownership expense plus operating costs. In addition, it is usual for the contract to provide that his equipment shall be placed in as good condition as when delivered to the job, minus ordinary wear and tear. The cost of such repairs and overhaul constitute reimbursable cost items under the contract.

In the event that equipment is to be required that the contractor does not own, provision must be made for its purchase by the owner or for rental from a third party. When the project is large or when the equipment has a limited useful life it is common practice for the contractor to purchase the equipment for the owner on a reimbursement basis. At the end of the project whatever salvage or resale value the equipment might have reverts to the owner. When rental of equipment from third parties is involved, it is best to be as explicit as possible concerning item requirements and rental rates to be paid.

7.10 COST-PLUS-PERCENTAGE-OF-COST CONTRACT

From the contractor's point of view, one of the most advantageous ways of determining his fee in a negotiated contract is as a percentage of the cost of construction. This type of contract is particularly well fitted to cover work whose scope and characteristics can be only poorly defined at the outset of operations. Work may be involved of such an emergency nature that time is not available for the advance preparation of contract documents and for the usual bidding routine. Wars and other periods of extreme urgency afford instances of this type. On the other hand, the work entailed may be such that no one can ascertain what difficulties will be encountered or even of what order of magnitude the eventual cost may be. Cleanup and repair of damage such as that resulting from fire, storm, and flood afford many examples of situations where the cost-plus-percentage contract is suitable. Remodeling, expansion of facilities where services must be maintained, underpinning, and certain classes of demolition work also are occasionally done under this form of construction contract.

The generally poor favor with which this form of contract is now viewed has been occasioned by contractor abuses in the past. This once-popular means of carrying out construction has been all but eliminated except for the unusual jobs mentioned here. The fringe element of contractors who neglected to practice strict economy in the interests of their owner-clients and who refused to be satisfied with a reasonable profit has very effectively "killed the goose that laid the golden egg."

7.11 COST-PLUS-FIXED-FEE CONTRACT

A popular type of cost-plus contract is one in which the contractor's fee is established as a fixed sum of money. When this scheme is utilized, the work must be of such a nature that it can be fairly well defined and a reasonably good estimate of cost approximated at the time of the negotiations. The contractor computes the amount of his fee on the basis of the size of the project, estimated time of construction, nature and complexity of the work, hazards involved, location of the project, equipment and manpower requirements, and similar considerations.

Under this arrangement, the contractor's fee is fixed and does not fluctuate with the actual cost of the project. Hence it is to the advantage of the contractor to prosecute the work in as diligent a manner as possible. Failure to do so will cause additional office overhead expense to be incurred for which he is not reimbursed. Expeditious handling of construction operations will minimize time and cost, two factors that contribute directly to overhead. Speed is also desirable from the viewpoint of freeing men and equipment for other contracts.

7.12 BONUS AND PENALTY PROVISIONS

Many innovations have been devised concerning the determination of the contractor's fee. Some of these schemes are designed to provide the contractor with added incentive to keep the cost of the work and the time of construction to a minimum. Some are positive in character, rewarding the contractor for any savings, whereas others are punitive, penalizing him for any overage. One aspect common to these variants is the presence of a target estimate that the contractor has compiled on the basis of the drawings, specifications, and other available information. Bonus or penalty arrangements are tied to this target figure. Hence, this type of cost-plus contract must of necessity be applied to work of a fairly definite nature for which drawings and specifications are sufficiently developed to enable a reasonably accurate cost to be determined.

As an incentive for the contractor to minimize costs, a bonus clause can be written according to which he shall receive, in addition to a base fee, a stated percentage of the amount by which the total actual cost is less than the target estimate. A figure of 25 to 50 percent is common for the contractor's share of the savings. When time is essential to the owner, a provision can be included stating that the contractor shall receive, in addition to a base fee, a fixed sum of money for each day of beneficial occupancy realized before the originally proposed completion date. This provision is sometimes extended to assess the contractor the same amount as liquidated damages for each day that completion is delayed beyond the estimated date.

7.13 GUARANTEED MAXIMUM COST

An objection of many owners to the cost-plus type of contract is that the cost of the project is not accurately known until after completion of the construction. One answer to this criticism has been the cost-plus-fixed-fee contract with a guaranteed maximum. Under this form of contract, the contractor guarantees that he will construct the project in full accordance with the drawings and specifications and that the cost to the owner will not exceed some total maximum or "upset" price. In return for his services, the contractor receives a fixed fee. If the cost of the work exceeds the assured maximum, the contractor pays for the excess. In this way, a ceiling price is established, which the owner is assured will not be exceeded.

The determination by the contractor of the upset cost must be based upon careful estimates made from complete drawings and specifications. Such a contract establishes an ironclad maximum cost above which the contractor will not be reimbursed. Any overage is his own direct responsibility. An incentive for the contractor to keep costs below the guaranteed maximum is sometimes provided by a bonus clause stating that the contractor and the owner will share any savings.

7.14 SLIDING-SCALE FEE

A form of cost-plus contract that acts in the nature of a compromise between the percentage-of-cost fee and the fixed fee is one in which the fee is established in accordance with a sliding-scale arrangement. Either of two general schemes may be followed. The fee may be determined as a percentage of cost, with the percentage increasing as the cost falls below the target estimate and the percentage decreasing as the cost rises above the target figure. A second scheme is the setting of a lump-sum base fee with provision for (1) increasing it for costs below the target estimate and (2) decreasing it for costs above the estimate. Under either arrangement, a minimum fee or percentage is stipulated that is subject to no further decrease regardless of the final cost of the work.

An example of a sliding-scale fee arrangement will help to clarify the preceding discussion.

$$Fee = R\ (2T - A)$$

where T = target cost,
A = actual cost, and
R = base fee rate.

To illustrate, suppose that the target estimate, T, of a project is $100,000 and the contractor's fee is to be $10,000 if the actual cost, A, of the project turns out to be $100,000. On this basis, the base fee rate, R, is 10 percent. Now consider three cases:

A = $ 80,000   Fee = 0.1($200,000 − $80,000) = $12,000
                  Actual fee rate = 15%
A = $100,000   Fee = 0.1($200,000 − $100,000) = $10,000
                  Actual fee rate = 10%
A = $120,000   Fee = 0.1($200,000 − $120,000) = $8,000
                  Actual fee rate = 6.7%

7.15 DESIGN-CONSTRUCTION CONTRACT

In a considerable volume of construction the same firm handles both the design and the field construction. Such a project is called a "turn-key" or "package" job. This practice is standard in much of Europe and Latin America. In the United States, it is more the exception than the rule, although a substantial portion of residential and industrial construction is carried out under this type of arrangement.

The combined type of contract can be drawn up on the basis of any of the several schemes previously discussed. Both design and construction can be included in one contract with the owner on a fixed-sum or cost-plus basis. The fixed-price arrangement is widely used in residential construction. A cost-plus contract calling for planning, design, drawings, specifications, and construction services is common practice in industrial construction. A different method that is occasionally used is to have separate contracts for the design services and the field construction.

7.16 MANAGEMENT CONTRACTS

A management contract is one whereby a contractor is engaged to manage construction work on behalf of the owner. By using this arrangement, the owner can engage the services of a selected contracting concern that possesses a high degree of administrative ability and construction expertise. Because details of such contracts vary, the following discussion presents only typical provisions.

In return for his fee, the contractor exercises general control over the construction and does the purchasing, disbursing, expediting, letting of subcontracts, keeping of records, hiring of labor, engineering, and supervision of construction. With contracts of this type, all the work is likely to be subcontracted, although the contractor may choose to carry out certain portions of the construction with his own forces. The management form of contract may include architectural and engineering services as well as field construction.

In the pure management contract the contractor is made the agent of the owner. All actions of the contractor, such as purchasing, subcontracting, and employment of labor, are carried out in the name of the owner. Under the agency stipulation, the owner assumes full responsibility for the actions of the contractor.

Another type of management contract is that in which the usual independent contractor status is maintained, although the contractor is engaged in a managerial capacity only. Usually the contractor does not carry out any of the construction operations with his own forces except for general supervision. He selects and supervises the subcontractors, probably provides certain basic items of construction equipment, and coordinates the entire construction process. His actions are taken in his own name and on his own responsibility. Disbursements by the contractor are made from funds usually advanced by the owner for this purpose. The contractor remains responsible for the work until its completion and acceptance by the owner.

7.17 CONTRACT CLAUSES

Construction contracts contain many nontechnical provisions that pertain to the conduct of the work. These contract clauses constitute the general conditions (Appendixes C and D), special conditions (Appendix E), and provisions of the agreement (Appendixes H and I).

These clauses are devised predominantly for the protection of the owner and must be carefully examined and studied by the contractor so that he thoroughly understands the obligations he is to assume. As a general legal principle, contract clauses prevail when conflict exists between them and the technical specifications. When standard document forms are involved, such as those of The American Institute of Architects, the American Railway Engineering Association, the federal government, the American Society of Civil Engineers, or the Associated General Contractors of America, there is no need for the contractor to concern himself with ferreting out "weasel" clauses and "loaded" provisions. These standard contract clauses have well-established records of service and have become familiar to the industry. Many of them have received legal interpretation by the courts.

The contract clauses of many construction contracts are not of the standard variety, however, but have been specially prepared by the architect-engineer. These sometimes impose burdensome, one-sided obligations on the contractor, who must single out such documents for more than the usual hurried scanning. Obviously, the time for a careful reading of all contract articles is before the project is bid rather than after the contract is signed. After execution of the contract, the contractor is bound by all of its provisions. A person entering into a contract is presumed to understand what it says. Each party to a contract must read it carefully, and failure to do so will not excuse ignorance of its contents.

The contractor must recognize that he is not a lawyer and hence is not competent to appraise the legal implications of contract clauses. Should he have reason to question any legal aspect of a contract document, he should seek the assistance of his attorney. Failure to do so has resulted in serious complications that could have been avoided had competent legal advice been obtained.

During the bidding period, the contractor must evaluate each clause with regard to its possible or probable contribution to the cost of construction. Upon becoming the successful bidder, he must again examine the contract but with a different purpose in mind. Many provisions require specific action on the part of the contractor during the life of the contract.

It is beyond the scope of this book to attempt a complete discussion of the meanings, implications, and legal record of all contract clauses. Nevertheless, the most important aspects of the principal contract provisions are discussed under appropriate topic headings. The following sections consider contract clauses of special significance that have not been treated elsewhere.

7.18 PROGRESS PAYMENTS

It is customary that contracts of more than very limited duration require the owner to make periodic progress payments or cost reimbursements to the contractor. With competitive-bid contracts, progress payments by the owner are usually made on a monthly basis, although other payment periods are sometimes used. The amount paid is based upon the value of work put into place during the preceding period. Under lump-sum contracts, the degree of completion is usually expressed as a percentage (see Section 10.22). The quantities of work done on unit-price contracts are determined by the field measurement of work put into place. Materials stored on site are customarily taken into account, as well as any prefabrication or preassembly work that the contractor may have done at some location other than the job site. It is to be noted that partial payments in no way constitute an acceptance of the partially completed work by the owner and are only part payments of the total contract amount.

A certain percentage of each progress payment is usually retained by the owner for his protection. A retainage of 10 percent is typical, although other percentages are also used. In some cases, retainage is withheld only during the first half of the project with subsequent progress payments being made in full. The retainage is kept by the owner until final certification by the architect-engineer and acceptance by the owner, after which final and complete payment is made to the contractor.

Cost-plus contracts usually provide for the contractor to submit payment vouchers to the owner at specified intervals during the life of the contract. A common contract provision is weekly reimbursement of payrolls and monthly reimbursement of all other costs, including a pro rata share of the contractor's fee. It is not uncommon under this type of contract for the owner to pay all vouchers in full without deducting any percentage as retainage. In a procedure somewhat analogous to retainage on cost-plus projects, the owner makes full reimbursement to the contractor up to some designated percentage (80 percent is sometimes used) of the total estimated project cost. Further payments are then withheld until some specified amount of money has been set aside. This reserve is retained by the owner until final payment is made.

7.19 ACCEPTANCE AND FINAL PAYMENT

Acceptance of the project by the owner is based upon a final inspection of the completed work and the correction by the contractor of detected deficiencies. The owner conveys his acceptance to the contractor in writing, and final payment, including retainage, follows. When the prime contractor has unsatisfied claims against the owner, he must be careful that his acceptance of the final payment does not act as a release of all claims under the contract. If such is the case, he may have to refuse final payment if he intends to press for collection of additional claims.

A legal question that frequently arises concerns the degree of contract performance required of the contractor. The modern tendency is to look to the spirit and not the letter of the contract. The vital question is not whether the contractor has complied in an exact and literal way with the precise terms of the contract but whether he has done so substantially. "Substantial performance" may be defined as accomplishment by the contractor of all things essential to fulfillment of the purpose of the contract, although there may be inconsequential deviations from certain terms. This is a recent principle, peculiar to construction contracts generally, and has been evolved by the courts to mitigate the severity of the rule of exact performance. A contractor who has in good faith endeavored to perform all that is required of him by the terms of his contract and has in fact substantially done this is ordinarily entitled to recover the contract price less proper deductions for minor omissions, deviations, and defects chargeable to him. In evaluating substantial performance, consideration must be given to the contractor's intentions, the amount of work performed, and the benefit received by the owner.

Certainly, the "substantial performance" concept does not confer on the contractor any right to deviate freely from his contractual undertaking or to substitute materials or procedures that he may consider equivalent to those actually called for by the contract. Only where defects are purely unintentional and not so extensive as to prevent the owner from receiving almost what he bargained for does the principle come into play.

7.20 WARRANTY PERIOD

Generally speaking, acceptance of the work by the owner and his payment for it constitutes a waiver of his rights for damages on account of defects in the structure if no claim is made within a "reasonable time." Many construction contracts obligate the contractor to make good all defects brought to his attention by the owner during some warranty period after completion, 1 year being a commonly specified time of guarantee although periods of up to 5 years are sometimes required on certain categories of work such as utility construction. The contractor is required, upon notice, to make good at his own expense defects developing during this period. In most cases, the prescribed warranty period fixes the "reasonable time" and releases the contractor from further responsibility after its expiration. Warranty periods required by the contract are normally covered by the performance bond, and they do not operate to defer final payment.

An exception to the "reasonable time" concept occurs when a defect caused by the contractor's inadequate performance is latent in nature and could not have been detected by the owner during ordinary usage and maintenance of the structure. In such a case, the owner has a right of action against the contractor with no time limit unless there is an applicable statute of limitations.

A contractor's warranty does not imply, however, that he is liable for the sufficiency of the plans and specifications. A contractor is required to construct in accordance with the contract documents, and when he does so, he cannot be held to guarantee that the work performed will be free from defects or that the completed job will accomplish the purpose intended. He is responsible only for improper workmanship, inferior materials, or other faults resulting from his failure to perform.

7.21 CONTRACT TIME

Most construction contracts are explicit regarding construction time, designating either a completion date or a specific number of calendar days within which the work must be finished. The term "calendar days" includes Saturdays, Sundays, and holidays and is used rather than "working days" to eliminate possible controversy concerning weather, overtime, multiple shifts, weekends, and holidays. When the contract contains a specific completion requirement, time is declared to be "of the essence" of the contract and the completion date becomes a vital part of the agreement. Failure of the contractor to complete his obligations within the time specified can make him liable to the owner for damages caused by the delay.

When the contract time is stated to be a given number of calendar days, the date on which the time begins is an important matter. Construction contracts usually state that the time shall begin on the date that the contract is signed or on the date that the contractor receives a formal "notice to proceed" (Section 7.34) from the owner.

If the construction contract is silent regarding contract time, the contractor is expected to perform his work within a "reasonable time." This also applies when the contract requires project completion "at the earliest possible date," "as soon as possible," or "without delay." As one might expect, such imprecise statements regarding contract time can be troublesome. What constitutes a reasonable time is subject to wide differences of opinion and may have to be decided by the courts in case of dispute.

7.22 LIQUIDATED DAMAGES

Many projects are of such a nature that the owner will incur hardship, expense, or loss of revenue should the contractor fail to complete the work within the time specified by the contract. Failure to complete on time is a breach of contract and makes the contractor liable to the owner for damages. The amount of such damages may be determined by agreement or by a suit in a court of law. Damages of this sort are difficult to determine exactly, and in construction contracts it is common practice to provide that the contractor shall pay to the owner a fixed sum of money for each calendar day of delay in completion.

This assessment against the contractor, known as "liquidated damages," is used in lieu of a determination of the actual damages suffered. Liquidated damages, when provided for by contract, are enforceable at law provided that they are a reasonable measure of the actual damages suffered. The effect of a clause for liquidated damages is to substitute the amount stipulated for the actual damages that would be caused by late completion and thereby prevent a controversy between the parties as to the amount of damages. The owner deducts any liquidated damages from the sum due the contractor at the time of final payment. Typical values of liquidated damages appearing in construction contracts vary from $50 to $1,000 per calendar day, although much higher values are occasionally stipulated.

It is to be emphasized that the courts have enforced liquidated damage provisions in contracts only when they reasonably represented the actual damages suffered by the owner. When it has been established that the amount was excessive and unreasonable, the courts have ruled that such payment by the contractor to the owner constituted a penalty and was not enforceable, at least not without revision. It may be noted that architect-engineers are careful when writing such provisions to state that the sum named is in the nature of liquidated damages and not a penalty. Article 5b of Appendix E illustrates this point.

7.23 EXTENSIONS OF TIME

Reference has been made to the fact that the time allowed for completion of construction is a very important contract provision. However, during the life of a contract, there are often occurrences that cause delay or that add to the period of time necessary to construct the project. Many of these occurrences justify an extension of contract time for the contractor. Because of the importance of time in construction contracts, it is usual for such extensions of time to be formalized by a signed instrument, called a change order, that constitutes a legal and binding change to the contract.

The addition of extra work to the contract is a common justification for an extension of time. In this case, the additional contract time made necessary by the broadened scope of the work is negotiated at the same time that the cost of the extra work is determined. Delay of the project caused by the owner or his representative is another frequent cause of contact time extensions.

Many other circumstances can contribute to late project completion. Contracts often list specific causes of delay deemed to be excusable and beyond the contractor's control. Certain causes are essentially of an undisputed nature, provided that the contractor is not directly at fault and has exercised due care and reasonable foresight. These causes include flood, earthquake, fire, epidemic, war, riots, hurricanes, tornadoes, and similar disasters. Other legitimate but less spectacular causes may or may not be included; some contracts are unduly severe in this regard. Strikes, freight embargoes, acts of the government, accidents, and unreasonable delays in receiving ordered materials or equipment usually constitute acceptable reasons for an extension of contract time.

As a general rule, claims for extra time are not considered when based on delays caused by conditions that existed at the time of bidding and about which the contractor might be reasonably expected to have had full knowledge. Also, delays caused by failure of the contractor to anticipate the requirements of the work in regard to materials, labor, or equipment do not constitute reasons for a claim for extra time. Normally, inclement weather does not justify time extensions unless it can be established that such weather could not have been reasonably anticipated during the season and in the location of its occurrence.

Whenever a delay in construction is encountered over which the contractor has no control, he must bring the condition to the attention of the owner and/or architect-engineer in writing within a designated period of time after the start of the delay. Seven to ten days is the time period commonly specified in construction contracts. This communication should present specific facts concerning times, dates, and places and include necessary supporting data about the cause of delay. Failure by the contractor to submit a timely written request with justification may seriously jeopardize his chances of obtaining an extension of time.

7.24 CHANGES

A construction contract almost always gives the owner the right to delete work from the project or add extra work to it after the contract has been signed and during the construction period. How such a change is handled depends largely upon the type of contract involved and its provisions.

Cost-plus contracts of the fixed-fee type should include some provision for adjustment of the contractor's fee when changes in the scope of the work are involved. When the change is relatively minor and is directly related to the contract, the fee can be changed in the same proportion that the anticipated amount of the change bears to the target estimate of the original work. If the change is substantial and involves additional work of a totally different character, however, a supplemental agreement should be entered into by the parties, which makes provision for its own separate and individual fee.

When unit-price contracts are involved, changes in the work are automatically provided for unless the additional work involves classifications that were not included in the original contract or unless the changes are so extensive that the contractor or owner is authorized by the contract to request adjustments in the unit prices affected. Under lump-sum contracts, changes can be negotiated as fixed-sum modifications of the original contract amount, or extra work can be done on the basis of direct cost plus a percentage for overhead and profit.

Construction contracts provide that the contractor shall not proceed with extra work until it has been authorized in writing by the owner or his authorized representative. To proceed without written authorization may make it impossible for the contractor to obtain payment from the owner for the additional work. In many instances an item of work is of such a nature that the contractor considers it to be an addition to the contract and the owner does not. This can become a sticky situation for the contractor, particularly if the work must be done for the project to progress on schedule. He should notify the owner in writing that he considers the work to be extra to the contract and quote the most accurate probable cost that he can. If the owner refuses to consider the work as extra and directs the contractor to proceed, it probably is better for the contractor to go ahead with the work than to risk commission of breach of contract. In such an event, the contractor should advise the owner in writing that he is proceeding under protest with the work in dispute and that he intends to press his claim for payment. Separate and detailed records of all costs involved must be kept by the contractor to substantiate his claim.

7.25 CHANGED CONDITIONS

A changed condition refers to some physical aspect of the project or its site that proves to differ materially from that indicated by the contract documents or that is of an unusual nature and differs materially from the conditions ordinarily encountered. The most common instances are subsurface soil and water conditions.

The construction cost and time of many projects depend heavily on local conditions at the site, conditions that cannot be determined exactly in advance. This applies particularly to underground work, where the nature of the subsoil and ground water has great influence upon costs. At the time of bidding, the owner and his architect-engineer must make full disclosure of all information available concerning the proposed project and its site. The contractor uses the information as he sees fit and is responsible for his interpretation of it.

Who pays for the "unexpected" depends upon the wording of the contract. Some contracts state that borings and other site data provided by the owner are not warranted to be correct and that the owner assumes no responsibility. Such contracts usually further provide that the contractor will be responsible for conditions encountered at the site which differ from those indicated on the bidding documents. Needless to say, such contract wording places the risk on the contractor unless known information was deliberately withheld from him or he was supplied with erroneous information that he was reasonably entitled to accept as being correct.

Other contracts provide for an adjustment of the contract amount if actual subsurface or other physical conditions at the site are found to differ materially from those indicated on the plans and specifications or from those inherent in the type of work involved. This proviso is a "changed conditions" clause, the objective of which is to provide for unexpected physical conditions that come to light during the course of construction. When such a contract clause is present, the responsibility for unexpected conditions is placed on the owner. Documents of The American Institute of Architects and the federal government contain such provisions.

It must be noted that, regardless of the contract wording, if changed conditions are found at the site and if the contractor intends to claim additional cost or time, he must promptly notify the owner in writing and he must also keep detailed and separate cost records of the additional work involved. Failure to do so may make it impossible for him to collect.

7.26 SUSPENSION, DELAY, OR INTERRUPTION OF WORK

This section deals with owner-caused delay or interruption of unchanged work, that is, postponement of work items whose quantities or natures have not been changed from those shown by the contract documents. Additional time made necessary by changes (Section 7.24) or changed conditions (Section 7.25) is negotiated when the change order is processed. There are, however, many instances in which work physically unaffected by changes is delayed by some act of the owner or by his failure to act. Examples are delays in making the site available, failure to deliver owner-supplied equipment, or suspension of the work because of financial or legal difficulties. Additionally, work that is unchanged can be prolonged because of changes made in another phase of the project.

Such delays are of concern to the contractor for two reasons. First, when the overall completion of the project is affected, suitable extensions of contract time must be negotiated. As a usual rule, contracts provide for extensions of time caused by owner delay.

The second and more difficult problem for contractors involves the "consequential damages" or "impact costs" that can result from project delay. Examples of impact costs are standby costs of workmen, supervisors, and equipment; startup and stopping costs such as those incurred in moving equipment on and off the project; and overhead costs. It sometimes happens that work is delayed until the winter months, resulting in greatly increased costs, or until higher wage rates go into effect or bargains and discounts have been lost.

Construction contracts seldom provide directly for such consequential costs. Public contracts, in particular, frequently disclaim all responsibility for damages caused by owner delay. General experience has been that, in the presence of such contract language, the only recourse for the contractor is to claim breach of contract and take his case to the courts. Contractors have received favorable judgments in situations where the delay was for an unreasonable period of time, the delay was not caused or contributed to by the contractor, and the consequential costs were a direct result of the delay.

7.27 CHANGE ORDERS

When additions, deductions, or changes in the work are made by the owner, a supplement to the contract between the owner and the prime contractor is prepared that can be on the basis of a lump sum, unit prices, or a cost-plus arrangement. This supplement, called a "change order," is consummated by a written instrument that describes the modification to be made, the change in the contract amount, and any authorized extension of contract time. The change-order form identifies the change being made as a modification to the original construction contract and bears the acceptance signatures of both the owner and the prime contractor. It is usual that change orders also be signed by the architect-engineer. Many architect-engineer firms have developed their own individual change-order forms, an example of which is shown in Figure 7.1. The American Institute of Architects has prepared a form that is in wide usage for this purpose on building construction.

A change order, as a modification of the contract, means that the parties have entered into a new contract. It is presumed that a contract modification has taken into account all prior negotiations and understandings leading up to its signing and also that the terms of each change order reflect proper consideration of these negotiations.

7.28 VALUE ENGINEERING

Construction contracts with public agencies sometimes include what are called "value engineering incentive clauses." Value engineering applies after the contract is awarded and is concerned with the elimination or modification of any contract provision that adds cost to a project but is not necessary to the structure's required performance, safety, appearance, or maintenance. A clause of this type provides an opportunity for the contractor to suggest changes in the plans or specifications and to share in the resulting savings. These changes may involve substitutions of materials, modifications of design, reduction in quantities, or procedures other than those set forth and required by the contract documents. Value engineering is designed to take advantage of the contractor's special knowledge and to cut the cost of a project to the lowest level without compromising its function or sacrificing quality or reliability. In short, the contractor is encouraged to develop and submit to the owner cost-reducing proposals leading to changes in the plans or specifications. If the owner accepts them, a change order is processed and the savings are usually shared equally by the owner and the contractor.

It is to be noted that value engineering refers to making a change in the

JONES AND SMITH
ARCHITECT–ENGINEERS
PORTLAND, OHIO

CONTRACT CHANGE ORDER

Project: Municipal Airport Terminal Building   Change Order No. ___1___

For: City of Portland, Ohio   Date: July 30, 19 _____

To: The Blank Construction Co., Inc.
1938 Cranbrook Lane
Portland, Ohio

Revised Contract Amount

Previous contract amount $3,602,138.00
Amount of this order
(decrease) (increase)   5,240.00
Revised Contract Amount $3,607,378.00

An (increase) (decrease) (no change) of _____ days in the contract time is hereby authorized.

This order covers the contract modification hereunder described:

Providing and installing folding partitions and ornamental
screens as shown and described by Supplemental Drawing X-1
attached hereto. This change includes all grounds, nailer
blocks, and other provisions required for the satisfactory
installation of said partitions and screens.

The work covered by this order shall be performed under the same terms and conditions as included in the original construction contract.

Changes Approved   Jones and Smith, Architect–Engineers

_____   by_____
      (Owner)

by_____

_____
      (Contractor)

by_____

Figure 7.1   Contract change order.

drawings, specifications, or other contract provision and requires the approval of the owner. Savings that can be realized without a contract change properly belong to the contractor.

7.29 RIGHTS AND RESPONSIBILITIES OF THE OWNER

Under a typical construction contract, the architect-engineer acts for the owner during the day-to-day construction operations. The architect-engineer advises and consults with the owner, and all of the owner's communications with the contractor are normally made through the architect-engineer. Consequently, the owner seldom has much direct contact with the contractor during the construction process. Nevertheless, the contract between owner and contractor typically makes special provision for certain owner rights and responsibilities; for example, construction contracts usually make the owner responsible for furnishing property surveys that describe the project site, securing and paying for necessary easements, providing certain insurance, and making periodic payments to the contractor.

The owner, as a contracting party, has several rights especially reserved for him. He is normally authorized to award other contracts in connection with different portions of the project, to require contract bonds from the contractor, to approve the surety proposed, to retain a specified portion of the contractor's periodic payments, to make changes in the work, to carry out portions of the work himself in case of contractor default or neglect, to withhold payments to the contractor for adequate reason, and to terminate the contract for cause.

It is important to note, however, in any discussion of owner rights that he cannot intrude on the direction and control of the work. By the terms of the usual construction contract the contractor is known as an "independent contractor." Even though the owner enjoys certain rights with respect to the conduct of the work, he cannot issue direct instructions as to method or procedure, unreasonably interfere with construction operations, or otherwise unduly assume the functions of directing and controlling the work. By so doing, the owner can relieve the contractor from many of the latter's rightful legal and contractual responsibilities. If the owner oversteps his rights, he may not only assume responsibility for the accomplished work but also become liable for negligent acts committed by the contractor in the course of construction operations.

7.30 DUTIES AND AUTHORITY OF THE ARCHITECT-ENGINEER

Construction contracts impose many duties and bestow considerable authority on the architect-engineer. All construction operations are conducted under his surveillance, and he generally oversees the progress of the work. It is his direct responsibility to see that the workmanship and the materials fulfill the requirements of the drawings and specifications. In order to ensure this fulfillment, he or his designated representative exercises the right of job inspection. The architect-engineer approves all materials and project equipment. In addition, he may exercise the privilege of approving the contractor's general program of field procedure and even the construction equipment that the contractor proposes to use. Should the work be lagging behind schedule, the architect-engineer may reasonably instruct the contractor to speed up his activities.

The foregoing paragraph does not mean that the architect-engineer will assume responsibility for the contractor's methods merely because he retains the privilege of approval. The rights of the architect-engineer are essentially concerned with verifying that the contractor is proceeding in accordance with the contract documents. It should, however, be pointed out that the architect-engineer cannot unreasonably interfere with the conduct of the work or dictate the contractor's procedures. Here again, if the direction and control of the construction are taken out of the hands of the contractor, he is effectively relieved of many of his legal obligations under the contract.

The contract documents authorize the architect-engineer to interpret the requirements of the contract. The usual stipulation is that "the decision of the architect-engineer shall be final and binding on both parties." Actually, the jurisdiction of the architect-engineer is restricted to the settlement of questions of fact, such as what quantity and quality of materials are required or whether the work performed meets contract requirements. The answers to questions of fact require the professional knowledge and skill of the architect-engineer, and it is proper that he should make such decisions. In the absence of fraud, bad faith, or gross mistake, the decision of the architect-engineer may, in fact, be considered as final provided the subject matter falls within the proper scope of his authority. Most public contracts, however, provide for appeals to higher authority from decisions made by the architect-engineer or the contracting officer. Practically every federal agency has some form of contract appeals board.

With respect to disputed questions of law, however, the architect-engineer has no jurisdiction. He cannot deny the right of a citizen to due process of law, and the contractor has the right to submit a dispute concerning a legal aspect of the contract to arbitration or to the courts. Whether a particular matter is one of fact or one of legal construction can depend upon the language of the contract. Matters pertaining to time of completion, liquidated damages, and claims for extra work usually involve points of law.

7.31 RIGHTS AND RESPONSIBILITIES OF THE CONTRACTOR

As one might expect from a document prepared especially for the owner, the contractor has few rights and many obligations under the contract. His major responsibility, of course, is to construct the project in conformance with the contract documents. Despite all the troubles, delays, adversities, accidents, and mischances that may occur, the contractor is expected to "deliver the goods" and finish the work in the prescribed manner. Although some casualties are considered as justification for allowing him more construction time, nothing serves to relieve him from his obligations under the contract. Barring contract provisions to the contrary, the contractor is free to process the work in any way that he pleases so long as the requirements of the contract documents are met.

The contractor is expected to give his personal attention to the conduct of the work, and either he or his representative must be on the job site at all times during working hours. The contractor is required to conform with the laws and ordinances concerning job safety, licensing, employment of labor, sanitation, insurance, codes, and other aspects of the work. He is responsible for the payment of patent royalties and for the defense of suits brought against the owner for patent infringement.

The contractor is responsible also for his interpretation of the contract documents and guarantees materials and workmanship, as put into place both by his own forces and those of his subcontractors, as being in accordance with these documents. Although the contractor has no direct responsibility for the adequacy of the plans and specifications, he can incur a contingent liability for proceeding with faulty work whose defects should be manifest to one in his position. Should an instance occur in which the contractor is directed to do something he feels is not proper and is not in accordance with good construction practice, he should protect himself by writing a letter of protest to the owner and the architect-engineer, stating his position before proceeding with the matter in dispute.

Insurance coverage is an important contractual responsibility of the contractor, both as to type of insurance and policy limits. The contractor is required to provide insurance not only for his own direct and contingent liability, but frequently also for the owner's protection. He is expected to exercise every reasonable safeguard for the protection of persons and property in, on, and adjacent to the construction site.

7.32 ARBITRATION

Customarily, when a controversy arises between the contractor and the owner or the architect-engineer concerning the work, the matter is referred to the architect-engineer for settlement. However, as has been pointed out previously, the architect-engineer can make binding decisions only on such questions of fact as qualities of materials, standards of workmanship, and interpretations of technical aspects of the drawings and specifications. Disputes concerning alleged breach of contract, interpretations of contract clauses, claims for extra work, liquidated damages, and other matters of law can be settled only by the courts or through a process of arbitration. Arbitration is the reference of a dispute to one or more impartial persons for final and binding determination.

Court action can impose delay, expense, and inconvenience on both the contractor and the owner. For this reason, most construction contracts provide for the arbitration of disputes. Actually, no contract clause is necessary for arbitration because any dispute can be arbitrated at any time by mutual consent of the parties. Arbitration implies a common consent by the disputants to have their differences settled. It offers the advantages of a settlement that is prompt, private, and economical. At the same time, arbitration is an orderly proceeding governed by rules of procedure and standards of conduct. Arbitration is not a replacement for the law but rather is an adjunct to it.

Contract clauses that provide for arbitration are essentially phrased so that the parties to the contract agree to submit to arbitration any future disputes that may arise during the course of construction operations. However, agreements to arbitrate are enforceable only in about one half of the states. In the other states, either party can refuse to submit to arbitration even though he may have promised to do so by terms of the contract. However, such cases of refusal are rare.

Most construction contracts provide that the arbitration shall be conducted under the *Construction Industry Arbitration Rules* as administered by the American Arbitration Association, a nationwide organization that administers arbitration cases in all industries. The association neither gives legal advice nor arbitrates disputes, but does provide assistance in obtaining arbitrators, furnishing rules of procedure, and giving other help. In exchange for its assistance, the association charges a nominal fee.

Whether or not conducted strictly under the rules of the American Arbitration Association, the general arbitration procedure is well established. The party wishing to arbitrate first makes a written demand upon the other side, stating the subject of the dispute and requesting that the matter be submitted to arbitration. A board of arbitration, usually three persons, is then selected. This can be done by the parties involved, each of whom selects a person, with these two people choosing the third member of the board. When rules of the American Arbitration Association are being followed, the association appoints the arbitrators from a list approved by the two disputing parties. Arbitrators are picked not only for their impartiality and disinterest in the subject at arbitration but also for their experience in and knowledge of the construction field. No arbitrator should have any family, business, or financial relationship with either party to the controversy. A point to be stressed is that the arbitrator's authority to hear and decide exists only by virtue of the agreement of the parties. He is endowed with only such authority as they confer upon him.

After the board has been selected, a hearing is conducted during which each side is free to call witnesses and to present such evidence as it wishes and the arbitrators consider admissible. Each party can be represented by counsel and is entitled to question the other party and his witnesses. Arbitration is a less formal process than litigation in a court of law. The parties, having elected to resolve their controversy by arbitration rather than in a lawsuit, have themselves agreed not to be bound by strict rules of evidence. The principal legal requirement is that a fair and full hearing for both sides be held.

After the hearing has been terminated, an award is made within a reasonable period of time. A written copy of the findings and award signed by the arbitrators is sent to each of the parties. It is usual practice that the arbitrators stipulate how the fees and costs shall be apportioned between the parties. Once the disputants have submitted to arbitration and an award is handed down, the parties are bound to it and the award is enforceable at law. No appeal can be taken against the arbitrators' findings, although an avenue of appeal is open if a party thinks that the award was not within the submission or that there was bias, misconduct, or prejudice on the part of the board. Reversal of awards on such grounds is seldom requested and almost never found justified. Courts give every reasonable presumption in favor of the award and of the arbitrators' proceedings. The burden rests on the party attacking the award to produce evidence sufficient to invalidate it.

7.33 TERMINATION OF THE CONTRACT

Construction contracts may be ended in a variety of ways, full and satisfactory performance by both parties being the usual manner of contract termination. However, there are other means of bringing a contract to an end that are of interest and importance.

Breach of contract by either party is occasionally a cause for contract discharge. Failing to make prescribed payments to the contractor or causing unreasonable delay of the project are probably the most common breaches by the owner. In such circumstances the contractor is entitled to damages caused by the owner's failure to carry out his responsibilities under the contract.

Default or failure to perform under the contract are the usual breaches committed by contractors. Nonperformance, faulty performance, failure to show reasonable progress, failure to meet his financial obligations—these are examples of material default by the contractor that convey to the owner a right of action against the contractor. When the owner terminates the contract for contractor breach, the owner is entitled to take possession of all materials and job equipment and to make reasonable arrangements for completion of the work. It is interesting to note that, when failure to complete the job within the contract time is the breach involved, the owner probably will not be awarded liquidated damages if he terminates the contract and does not allow the contractor to finish the job late when the latter is making a genuine effort to complete the work. The record is not completely clear on this point, however.

A third way in which a contract can be terminated is by mutual agreement of both parties. This is not a common procedure in the construction industry, although there have been instances. For example, it sometimes happens that the contractor faces unanticipated contingencies such as financial reverses, labor troubles, or loss of key personnel that make his proper performance under the contract a matter of considerable doubt. Under such circumstances, it may happen that both the owner and the contractor agree to terminate the contract and to engage another contractor. When little or no work has yet been done, termination of the contract by mutual consent can sometimes be attractive to both parties.

Construction contracts, particularly those publicly financed, normally provide that the owner can terminate the contract at any time it may be in his interest to do so by giving the contractor written notice to this effect. Where such a provision is present, the contractor has agreed to termination at the prerogative of the owner. However, in such an event, the contractor is entitled to payment for all work done up to that time, including a reasonable profit, plus such expenses as may be incurred by him in canceling his orders and demobilizing the work.

If the owner terminates the contract capriciously, he may become liable for the full amount of the contractor's anticipated profit plus costs.

A contract may be rescinded because of impossibility of performance under circumstances beyond the control of either party. For instance, unexpected site conditions may be found that make it impossible to carry out the construction described by the contract. Operation of law may render the contract impossible of fulfillment. Bankruptcy of either party can result in abrogation of the contract. Public construction projects are sometimes halted by taxpayers' suits, court orders, and other legal directives.

7.34 NOTICE TO PROCEED

The beginning of the contract time is generally established by a written "notice to proceed," which the owner dispatches to the contractor. The date of its receipt is normally considered to mark the formal start of operations. This notice, in the form of a letter advising the contractor that he may enter the site immediately, directs him to start work forthwith. If by some chance the owner does not yet have clear title to the property, the notice will relieve the contractor of liability caused by his construction operations. Contracts usually require that the contractor shall commence operations within ten days after receipt of the notice to proceed.

7.35 SUBCONTRACTS

A subcontract is an agreement between a prime contractor and a subcontractor under which the subcontractor agrees to perform a certain specialized part of the work at the site. A subcontract does not establish any contractual relationship between the subcontractor and owner, and neither is liable to the other in contract. A subcontract binds only the parties to the agreement: the prime contractor and the subcontractor. Nevertheless, construction contracts frequently stipulate that all subcontractors shall be approved by the owner or architect-engineer. The bidding documents may require that a list of subcontractors be submitted with the proposal or that a similar list be submitted for approval by the low-bidding prime contractor after the owner has accepted his proposal. (See Subparagraph 5.2.1 of Appendix C.)

It is to be noted that the right to disqualify subcontractors injects the architect-engineer into the contractor's proprietary field. There is some doubt that a valid distinction exists between the responsibility of the general contractor and of the architect-engineer if a contract document bestows on one party the authority to intrude into an area of responsibility of the other. There is some legal opinion that his exercise of a contract provision that permits subcontractor disqualification may place the architect-engineer in the position of sharing responsibility for that portion of the work.

If approval of subcontractors is required, it must be obtained before the general contractor enters into agreements with his subcontractors. Actually, the disapproval of a subcontractor is not a common occurrence. This is particularly true on public projects in which refusal to approve a subcontractor may result in litigation and is usually difficult to sustain. Nevertheless, there have been cases in which the owner refused to accept a subcontractor with whom the prime contractor had already signed an agreement. In such cases the prime contractor can be subject to suit for breach of contract by the subcontractor.

Although informal letters of proposal and acceptance may suffice for subcontracted work of small consequence, the prime contractor should formalize his subcontracts with a written instrument that sets forth in detail the rights and responsibilities of each party to the contract. A well-prepared subcontract document will eliminate many potential disputes concerning the conduct of subcontracted work. The prime contractor may use a standard subcontract form such as the one prepared by The American Institute of Architects, or he may develop his own special form to suit his particular requirements. The Associated General Contractors of America, together with several national specialty contractor associations, has prepared a subcontract form that is recommended as a guide and is presented in Appendix J. Subcontract forms must be prepared with extreme care and with the advice of an experienced lawyer. The Associated General Contractors of America publishes a pamphlet entitled *A Suggested Guide and Check List for Subcontracts,* which contains valuable subcontract information.

Change orders (discussed in Section 7.27) to construction contracts often involve modifications to subcontracted work. When this is the case, the general contractor and the subcontractor must execute a suitable change order to the subcontract affected. The prime contractor normally uses a standard form for this purpose, similar to that shown in Figure 7.1.

7.36 SUBCONTRACT PROVISIONS

Subcontracts are similar in many respects, both in form and in content, to the prime construction contract. Two parties contract for a specific job of work that is to be performed in accordance with a designated set of contract documents. All of the documents of the general construction contract are made a part of the subcontract by reference, as illustrated by Article I of Appendix J. Consequently, all of the provisions in the general contract, including changes in the work, minimum wage rates, warranty period, compliance with applicable laws, approval of shop drawings, and retainage, extend to the subcontractors.

In addition to the provisions of the general construction contract, there are many relationships peculiar to the conduct of the subcontracted work itself for which provision must be made. These provisions, which are in the nature of general conditions to the subcontract, are made a part of the written subcontract form. Appendix J illustrates the kinds of contract articles typically included in construction subcontracts. Payment to the subcontractor can be established as a lump sum, as unit prices, or on a cost-plus basis. A length of time, usually in calendar days, or a completion date is generally stipulated within which the subcontractor is required to complete his work.

7.37 PURCHASE ORDERS

A purchase order is a written document that defines and prescribes the conditions pertaining to a purchase of materials. When a purchase order is signed by both the buyer (contractor) and the seller (material dealer), it becomes a purchase contract between the parties. Contracts for the sale of materials may, like other contracts, contain conditions. Purchase-order forms used in the construction industry normally include certain clauses or terms pertaining to the materials being ordered and their delivery.

Normally, a purchase order is prepared by the contractor on a form that he has devised to meet his own needs. Any terms and conditions included are, therefore, directed primarily toward protecting the interests of the contractor and ensuring that the materials and their delivery conform to the requirements of the construction contract and the contractor. It is not unusual, however, that a vendor will sell materials only on the basis of his own terms and conditions. Under such circumstances, the contractor must sign a purchase-order form prepared by the seller. By so doing, the contractor accepts all terms and conditions of the resulting purchase contract.

Regardless of whose form is used, the terms and conditions of a purchase order are important and worthy of close study. They define the rights and obligations of each party and can be of great significance to the contractor in the event of a default or dispute.

8

CONTRACT BONDS

8.1 SURETY BONDS IN CONSTRUCTION

The use of contract bonds in the construction industry is but one of many applications of surety bonds in business and commerce. A surety, in law, is a party that assumes legal liability for the debt, default, or failure in duty of another. A surety bond is the written document that describes the conditions and obligations pertaining to such an agreement. Surety bonds act in the nature of an extension of credit by the surety, not in the sense of a financial loan but as an endorsement.

By the terms of a contract bond, the surety agrees to indemnify the owner, called the "obligee," against any default of the contractor, called the "principal." Contract bonds guarantee that the work will be completed in accordance with the contract documents and that all construction costs will be paid. When the contractor properly discharges his obligations and after any warranty period covered by the bond expires, the bond agreement is discharged and is no longer of any force or effect. If the contractor defaults, the surety must complete the contract and pay all costs up to the face amount of the bond. The bond can be invoked by the owner only if the contractor is in breach of contract.

8.2 DOUBLE FORM OF CONTRACT BOND

Under his contract with the owner, the contractor accepts two principal responsibilities: to perform the objective of the contract and to pay all costs associated with the work. Both of these obligations can be included within one bond instrument, but it is now standard practice for construction contracts to require two separate contract bonds, one bond covering performance of the contract and the other guaranteeing payment for labor and materials.

Under the single type of bond, there is a potential conflict of interest between the owner and persons furnishing labor and materials. Because the owner has priority, the face value of the bond can be used up in satisfying his claims. Thus, in many instances the single bond form has afforded little or no protection for material dealers, workmen, and subcontractors. In addition, there have been serious problems as to the priority of rights of the persons covered. The double form of bond covers separately the interest of the owner and of subcontractors, material suppliers, and workmen. The premium cost of the bond protection is not increased by furnishing two separate bonds.

A contract bond form is a simple document that makes no attempt to describe in detail the specific liabilities of the surety. The bond guarantees the contract in all of its provisions, and the obligations of the bond are identical with the provisions of the contract.

Private owners customarily accept the usual bond forms used by the surety companies, these forms being standardized nationally and approved by professional groups such as The American Institute of Architects. These forms can also be used for public construction projects provided that statutes do not control the express conditions and form of such bonds. However, most public jurisdictions must use statutory bonds, that is, bond forms that conform with a governing statute. Because the laws that govern the form and content of bonds differ somewhat from one jurisdiction to another, bond forms for public contracts are not standardized nationally. Nevertheless, certain public agencies that have substantial building programs have developed standard bond forms that reflect the legal requirements pertaining to their own situation. The federal government and many states and municipalities use standardized bond forms. When the owner either desires or requires the use of a specific bond form, it is usual that the blank forms be included with the bidding documents.

8.3 PERFORMANCE BONDS

The owner is entitled to receive what he contracted for or its equivalent. A performance bond acts primarily for the protection of the owner and guarantees that the contract will be performed and that the owner will receive his structure built in substantial accordance with the terms of the contract. This bond customarily covers any warranty period that may be required by the contract, the usual bond premium including one year of such coverage.

Figure 8.1 reproduces the performance bond form of the Hartford Accident and Indemnity Company and illustrates the provisions of a typical standard form. The standard form used by the federal government provides that the bond shall apply to all contract modifications and that the life of the bond must include all extensions of time and any guarantee period required.

BOND NO.............................

HARTFORD ACCIDENT AND INDEMNITY COMPANY
Hartford, Connecticut

PERFORMANCE BOND

(NOTE: THIS BOND IS ISSUED SIMULTANEOUSLY WITH PAYMENT BOND ON PAGE 2, IN FAVOR OF THE OWNER CONDITIONED FOR THE PAYMENT OF LABOR AND MATERIAL.)

KNOW ALL MEN BY THESE PRESENTS:

That..
(Here insert the name and address, or legal title, of the Contractor)

as Principal, hereinafter called Contractor, and the HARTFORD ACCIDENT AND INDEMNITY COMPANY, a corporation organized and existing under the laws of the State of Connecticut, with its principal office in the City of Hartford, Connecticut, as Surety, hereinafter called Surety, are held and firmly bound unto..................................

....
(Here insert the name and address, or legal title, of the Owner)

as Obligee, hereinafter called Owner, in the amount of..

....Dollars ($..............................),

for the payment whereof Contractor and Surety bind themselves, their heirs, executors, administrators, successors, and assigns, jointly and severally, firmly by these presents.

Whereas, Contractor has by written agreement dated...
entered into a contract with Owner for..

....

in accordance with drawings and specifications prepared by..
(Here insert full name, title and address)

....

which contract is by reference made a part hereof, and is hereinafter referred to as the CONTRACT.

Now, Therefore, the condition of this obligation is such that, if Contractor shall promptly and faithfully perform said CONTRACT, then this obligation shall be null and void; otherwise it shall remain in full force and effect.

The Surety hereby waives notice of any alteration or extension of time made by the Owner.

Whenever Contractor shall be, and declared by Owner to be in default under the CONTRACT, the Owner having performed Owner's obligations thereunder, the Surety may promptly remedy the default, or shall promptly

(1) Complete the CONTRACT in accordance with its terms and conditions, or

(2) Obtain a bid or bids for submission to Owner for completing the CONTRACT in accordance with its terms and conditions, and upon determination by Owner and Surety of the lowest responsible bidder, arrange for a contract between such bidder and Owner, and make available as work progresses (even though there should be a default or a succession of defaults under the contract or contracts of completion arranged under this paragraph) sufficient funds to pay the cost of completion less the balance of the contract price; but not exceeding, including other costs and damages for which the Surety may be liable hereunder, the amount set forth in the first paragraph hereof. The term "balance of the contract price," as used in this paragraph, shall mean the total amount payable by Owner to Contractor under the CONTRACT and any amendments thereto, less the amount properly paid by Owner to Contractor.

Any suit under this bond must be instituted before the expiration of two (2) years from the date on which final payment under the CONTRACT falls due.

No right of action shall accrue on this bond to or for the use of any person or corporation other than the Owner named herein or the heirs, executors, administrators or successors of Owner.

Signed and sealed this   day of   A. D. 19

Witness...   ....(Seal)
(If Individual)   (Principal)

Attest..   ....(Seal)
(If Corporation)   (Title)

                                                                      ....(Seal)

HARTFORD ACCIDENT AND INDEMNITY COMPANY

Attest...   By..(Seal)
                                                                                                        (Title)

Form S-3213-2 Page 1.   Printed in U. S. A. 9-'64
(A. I. A. Form — Document No. A-311, Sept., 1963 Edition
Approved by The American Institute of Architects)

Figure 8.1 Performance bond. Reproduced by permission of the Hartford Accident and Indemnity Company, Hartford, Conn.

8.4 PAYMENT BONDS

A payment bond acts primarily for the protection of third parties to the contract and guarantees payment for labor and materials used or supplied in the performance of the construction. Figure 8.2 presents the form of labor and material bond used by the Hartford Accident and Indemnity Company. This bond, typical of those employed by corporate sureties for privately financed projects, provides the following:

1. The claimant must have had a direct contract with the general contractor or a subcontractor.
2. Labor and material include water, gas, power, light, heat, oil, gasoline, telephone, and rental of equipment directly applicable to the contract.
3. Written notice must be given by claimant, other than one having a direct contract with the general contractor, to any two of these: general contractor, owner, or surety, within 90 days after claimant performed his last work or furnished the last of the materials.
4. The owner is exempted from any liabilities in connection with such claims.
5. Claims must be filed in the appropriate court.
6. No claims shall be commenced after the expiration of 1 year following the date on which the general contractor stopped work, barring a statute to the contrary.

The form of payment bond used on a public project is commonly prescribed by law. Because statutes do not give workers, material dealers, or subcontractors a lien on public work for their services and products, the payment bond may be the only protection these parties have for payment. Whether or not specific instances of labor, material, or sub-subcontractors are protected by such payment bonds depends on the language of the related statute. It must be stressed that in the case of a statutory bond the right to recover on it is limited by the conditions of the statute to the same extent as though the provisions of the statute were fully incorporated into the bond instrument. Claims against the bond must be filed in accordance with the requirements of the applicable statute.

The standard payment bond form used by the federal government is written to comply with the provisions of the Miller Act (Section 8.5). This bond protects laborers, material men, and subcontractors who perform work or supply materials for the project, but the extent of this protection depends on how far removed the unpaid parties are from the defaulting general contractor.

8.5 THE MILLER ACT

The Miller Act prescribes the requirements of performance and of payment bonds used in conjunction with federal construction projects. Enacted in 1935, this statute provides that on all federal construction contracts of more than $2000 the contractor shall furnish a performance bond for the protection of the United States and a payment bond for the protection of persons supplying labor and materials in the prosecution of the work.

BOND NO.......................................

HARTFORD ACCIDENT AND INDEMNITY COMPANY
Hartford, Connecticut

LABOR AND MATERIAL PAYMENT BOND

(NOTE: THIS BOND IS ISSUED SIMULTANEOUSLY WITH PERFORMANCE BOND ON PAGE 1, IN FAVOR OF THE OWNER CONDITIONED FOR THE FULL AND FAITHFUL PERFORMANCE OF THE CONTRACT.)

KNOW ALL MEN BY THESE PRESENTS:

That..,
(Here insert the name and address, or legal title, of the Contractor)

as Principal, hereinafter called Principal, and the HARTFORD ACCIDENT AND INDEMNITY COMPANY, a corporation organized and existing under the laws of the State of Connecticut, with its principal office in the City of Hartford, Connecticut, as Surety, hereinafter called Surety, are held and firmly bound unto...

....,
(Here insert the name and address, or legal title, of the Owner)

as Obligee, hereinafter called Owner, for the use and benefit of claimants as hereinbelow defined, in the amount of

....Dollars ($.....................................),
(Here insert a sum equal to at least one-half of the contract price)

for the payment whereof Principal and Surety bind themselves, their heirs, executors, administrators, successors, and assigns, jointly and severally, firmly by these presents.

Whereas, Principal has by written agreement dated..
entered into a contract with Owner for...

....

in accordance with drawings and specifications prepared by...

....,
(Here insert full name, title and address)

which contract is by reference made a part hereof, and is hereinafter referred to as the CONTRACT.

Now, therefore, the condition of this obligation is such that if the Principal shall promptly make payment to all claimants as hereinafter defined, for all labor and material used or reasonably required for use in the performance of the CONTRACT, then this obligation shall be void; otherwise it shall remain in full force and effect, subject, however, to the following conditions:

1. A claimant is defined as one having a direct contract with the Principal or with a sub-contractor of the Principal for labor, material, or both, used or reasonably required for use in the performance of the contract, labor and material being construed to include that part of water, gas, power, light, heat, oil, gasoline, telephone service or rental of equipment directly applicable to the CONTRACT.

2. The above named Principal and Surety hereby jointly and severally agree with the Owner that every claimant as herein defined, who has not been paid in full before the expiration of a period of ninety (90) days after the date on which the last of such claimant's work or labor was done or performed, or materials were furnished by such claimant, may sue on this bond for the use of such claimant, prosecute the suit to final judgment for such sum or sums as may be justly due claimant, and have execution thereon. The Owner shall not be liable for the payment of any costs or expenses of any such suit.

3. No suit or action shall be commenced hereunder by any claimant,

   (a) Unless claimant, other than one having a direct contract with the Principal, shall have given written notice to any two of the following: The Principal, the Owner, or the Surety above named, within ninety (90) days after such claimant did or performed the last of the work or labor, or furnished the last of the materials for which said claim is made, stating with substantial accuracy the amount claimed and the name of the party to whom the materials were furnished, or for whom the work or labor was done or performed. Such notice shall be served by mailing the same by registered mail or certified mail, postage prepaid, in an envelope addressed to the Principal, Owner or Surety, at any place where an office is regularly maintained for the transaction of business, or served in any manner in which legal process may be served in the state in which the aforesaid project is located, save that such service need not be made by a public officer.

   (b) After the expiration of one (1) year following the date on which Principal ceased work on said CONTRACT, it being understood, however, that if any limitation embodied in this bond is prohibited by any law controlling the construction hereof, such limitation shall be deemed to be amended so as to be equal to the minimum period of limitation permitted by such law.

   (c) Other than in a state court of competent jurisdiction in and for the county or other political subdivision of the state in which the project, or any part thereof, is situated, or in the United States District Court for the district in which the project, or any part thereof, is situated, and not elsewhere.

4. The amount of this bond shall be reduced by and to the extent of any payment or payments made in good faith hereunder, inclusive of the payment by Surety of mechanics' liens which may be filed of record against said improvement, whether or not claim for the amount of such lien be presented under and against this bond.

Signed and sealed this   day of   A. D. 19

Witness..   ....(Seal)
(If Individual)   (Principal)

Attest..   ....(Seal)
(If Corporation)   (Title)

....(Seal)

HARTFORD ACCIDENT AND INDEMNITY COMPANY

Attest..   By...(Seal)
(Title)

Form S-3213-2 Page 2.   Printed in U. S. A.   9-'64
(A. I. A. Form — Document No. A-311, Sept., 1963 Edition
Approved by The American Institute of Architects)

Figure 8.2   Labor and material payment bond. Reproduced by permission of the Hartford Accident and Indemnity Company, Hartford, Conn.

The Act provides that the performance bond be written in such amount that, in the opinion of the contracting officer, the interests of the United States are adequately protected. Under issued regulations of the Comptroller General, federal agencies customarily require a performance bond in the amount of 100 percent of the contract amount. Payment bond amounts are established in accordance with the following sliding scale: 50 percent if the contract is $1,000,000 or less; 40 percent if the contract is more than $1,000,000 and not in excess of $5,000,000; and a fixed sum of $2,500,000 if the contract price is above $5,000,000.

The Miller Act gives workers, subcontractors, and material men the right to sue on the prime contractor's payment bond if payment is not received in full within 90 days after the date on which the last of the labor was done or the last of the materials was furnished. The law further provides that any person having a direct contractual relationship with a subcontractor but no contractual relationship with the prime contractor shall have a right of action upon the prime contractor's payment bond provided that the claimant gives written notice to the prime contractor within a 90-day period; otherwise he has no right of action on the payment bond. There is no requirement for notice in the case of an individual who deals directly with the prime contractor.

Suit must be brought within 1 year after the last of the labor was performed or the last of the materials was delivered. Suits authorized by law are brought in the name of the United States, for the use of the party suing, in the appropriate district court. Suit is brought and prosecuted by the unpaid party's own attorney. The courts have held that the Miller Act protects persons who supply labor or materials directly to the prime contractor or to a subcontractor having a direct contractual relationship with the prime contractor. The statute does not protect all persons who perform or supply services of labor or material used on the project. For example, third-tier subcontractors who deal only with a sub-subcontractor have been denied recovery under the Miller Act.

Several of the states have enacted "little Miller Acts." These statutes apply to projects financed by these states and establish contract bond requirements similar to those imposed by the Miller Act.

8.6 CONTRACT CHANGES

Construction contracts typically give the owner the right to make changes in the work. Because the contract is before the bond and the bond guarantees the contract, it is commonly assumed that extension of the contract bond to include changes in the contract is provided for automatically. However, the construction contract is between the owner and the contractor, and in the event of changes the surety is put in the position of being obligated by the terms of a contract to which it is not a party. Common law does not allow two contracting parties to bind a third without his consent. It is possible, therefore, that a change in the contract may discharge the surety from its obligation unless approval of the change by the surety is obtained. Of course, the terms of the bond itself may stipulate otherwise.

Most construction contracts provide that changes or modifications to the contract do not release the surety under any bond previously provided. Many standard bond forms, including those of the federal government, stipulate that the surety waives notice of all extensions or modifications to the contract. Notwithstanding such wordings, however, the legal record is not entirely clear on this matter, and the courts have released the surety from its obligation when extensive and material modifications were made to the contract without its consent. For this reason, owners frequently require submission of written consent of surety with contract change orders.

8.7 BOND PREMIUMS

For the purpose of computing bond premiums, construction contracts are divided into four classifications: A-1, A, B, and Miscellaneous. Table 8.1 contains a representative listing of these contract classifications.

Table 8.2 presents the regular bureau premium rates used in conjunction with lump-sum or unit-price contracts where performance or performance and payment bonds are required. These rates include a warranty period of 1 year if required by the construction contract. If a longer warranty period is required, an additional premium charge is made. The rates shown in Table 8.2 apply to the total contract amount and include all subcontracted work. Special rates apply when only payment bonds or when bonds totaling 20 percent or less of the contract price are involved.

The premium information given in Table 8.2 is not complete and is subject to change without notice. Only the regular bureau rates are listed. In many instances downward revisions of these rates are used, these being called "deviations" or "deviated rates." For example, contractors who have an established record of successful operation and whose financial resources meet certain standards may qualify for lower premium rates. Certain classes of work such as air-conditioning systems, railroads, and privately owned public utilities can be subject to deviated premium rates. Such deviations are in a constant state of flux and may vary from state to state

When the work can reasonably be assigned to more than one classification, the classification requiring the higher premium rate controls. Neither the classification of the contract nor the premium rate can be altered by segmenting the work or by parties other than the contractor furnishing the materials. All separate contracts are assigned the same classification as the general contract. Bond premiums for cost-plus contracts are subject to some variation from the rates of competitive contracts as contained in Table 8.2. Premium rates for cost-plus contracts with guaranteed maximum amounts are the same as for competitive contracts. Cost-plus-percentage-fee contracts have a premium of $6 per $1,000 of cost to the owner, excluding contractor's fee. Cost-plus-fixed-fee contracts are assessed a premium of $3 per $1,000 of cost to the owner, excluding the contractor's fee. Such contracts in excess of $2,500,000 use 30 percent of the basic rates for competitive contracts as given in Table 8.2.

The premiums for contract bonds are payable in advance, and the bonds are

TABLE 8.1   Construction Contract Classifications for Surety
Bond Premium Rates

Classification			
A-1	A	B	Miscellaneous Contracts
Doors	Airfield grading	Air conditioning	Ash removal
Fire alarms	Airfield surfacing	Airport hangers	Automatic sprinkler
Floodlights	Airfield runways	Aqueducts	systems
Floors, wood and	Ceilings, metal or	Breakwaters	Bridges
composition	acoustical tile	Buildings, erection	Buildings,
Gas tanks	Ducts, underground	and repair	prefabricated
Guard rails	Elevators	Canals	Culverts
Iron work,	Glazing	Dams	Demolition
ornamental	Golf courses	Dikes	Draying
Lock gates	Greenhouses	Ditches	Dredging
Machinery	Landscaping	Docks	Garbage removal
Metal windows	Levees	Electrical work	Grade eliminations
Parking meters	Millwork	Excavation	Hauling
Pipelines, oil or gas	Murals	Filling stations	Highways
Police alarms	Painting	Foundations	Maintenance
Radio towers	Parking areas	Gas mains	Overpasses
Refrigerating plants	Piping, high-pressure	Gas piping	Roads
Signal systems,	Playgrounds	Grain elevators	Shipbuilding
railroad	Revetments	Gunite contracts	Shoring
Signs	Roadbeds, railroad	Heating and	Sidewalks, curb and
Stack rooms	Roofing	ventilating	gutter
Stand pipes	Sandblasting	Incinerators	Street paving
Steel shutters	Stone, furnishing	Jetties	Structural iron and
Street lighting	Storage tanks, metal	Locks	steel
Tanks, gas	Tennis courts	Masonry	Test borings
Thermostat equip-	Transmission lines	Piers	Timber cutting
ment	Waterproofing	Piling	Underpasses
Towers, water	Wind tunnels	Pipelines, water	Viaducts
Track laying		Plants, power	
Traffic control		Plants, sewage-	
systems		disposal	
Weatherstripping		Plastering	
Window cleaning		Plumbing	
		Seawalls	
		Sewers	
		Spillways	
		Stone setting	
		Subways	
		Terminals	
		Tile	
		Tunnels	
		Waterworks	
		Wells	
		Wharves	

TABLE 8.2   Regular Bureau Rates for Performance or Performance and Payment Bonds. Lump-Sum or Unit-Price Contracts.

Contract Price	Premium Rate per $1,000 of Contract Price for First 24 Months * (Subject to change without notice)		
	Class A-1† (All)	Class A‡ (All)	Class B (All)
First $ 100,000	$5.00	$7.50	$10.00
Next 2,400,000	5.00	5.00	6.50
Next 2,500,000	3.84	4.00	5.25
Next 2,500,000	3.67	3.90	5.00
Over 7,500,000	3.34	3.60	4.70

* For construction time in excess of 24 months or 731 calendar days, increase basic premium by 1 percent per whole month.

† For Class A-1 contracts under $2.5 million, annual renewal premium beyond 24 months is $2.50 per $1,000 of uncompleted contract.

‡ For Class A contracts under $2.5 million, annual renewal premium beyond 24 months is $3.75 per $1,000 of uncompleted contract.

delivered to the owner at the time the contract is signed. This premium payment is subject to adjustment based on the final contract amount, including all contract changes.

8.8 THE SURETY

Almost all contractors utilize the services of a corporate surety, one of whose specialties is the writing of contract bonds for contractors. These concerns are subject to public regulation in the same manner as are insurance companies. They operate under charters and file their schedules of premium rates with designated public authorities. Because the true worth of the bond is no greater than the surety's ability to pay, the owner reserves the right to approve the surety company and the form of bond. The federal government requires that all corporate sureties proposed for use on government projects be approved by the U. S. Treasury Department.

Occasionally, on private work, the contract documents require that the contract bonds be obtained from a particular company. This requirement usually means that the contractor must do business with an unfamiliar surety company. In this situation, obtaining the bond may turn out to be a lengthy process, requiring the submission of financial reports, lists of jobs in progress, experience record, and other data of voluminous proportions that may be required to establish the contractor's record and financial standing. The professional associations of contractors, architects, and civil engineers oppose the practice of having the surety designated by the owner and support a policy of leaving the contractor free to obtain surety bonds from a company of his choice. However, the private owner is at liberty to follow whatever practice he wishes in this regard, and the contractor must comply with his instructions or not bid.

On large contracts, a single surety may seek protection for itself by enlisting other sureties to underwrite a portion of the contract. This is very much like reinsurance. The original surety remains completely responsible for guaranteeing the proper performance of the contract. If the bond is invoked, it is up to the original surety company to get its underwriting sureties to stand behind it in the completion of the contract.

In some instances the owner will require that the contract bonds be provided by co-sureties, which means that two or more sureties split up the total contract obligation among them. On very large contracts, this practice spreads the risk over the participating co-sureties and correspondingly reduces the magnitude of the risk to which any one of them is exposed. This procedure also affords the owner a measurable degree of protection against possible financial default by a surety. Occasionally, it is necessary to have co-sureties on large federal contracts because of limits established by the U.S. Treasury Department on the maximum amounts of single contract bonds that a single surety is authorized to execute.

8.9 INDEMNITY OF SURETY

A contract bond is not insurance for the contractor and does not function for his protection. Under the bond, the surety idemnifies the owner against default by the contractor. However, the contractor in turn must indemnify the surety against any claim that may be brought against it because of the contractor's failure to perform in the prescribed manner. Legal fees incurred by the surety by reason of claims under the bond are recoverable from the principal. In order to receive a bid bond or contract bond, the contractor must first sign a formal application form. This form is lengthy and contains a great deal of "fine print." The net result, however, is that the contractor agrees to indemnify the surety and hold it harmless from expenses of every nature that the surety may sustain by reason of invocation of the bond.

When the application is signed by an individual contractor or a partnership, each principal is obligated to the entire extent of his personal fortune. If a corporation makes application, only the corporation assets are pledged. However, under circumstances in which the corporate assets are already fully obligated under existing contracts, some or all of the corporate officers, who are probably also the principal stockholders, often submit their personal contracts of indemnity to the surety in order to increase the firm's bonding capacity.

8.10 INVESTIGATION BY SURETY

Before a surety will furnish a contractor with a bid bond or contract bond, a thorough program of investigation is carried out in order to establish the past record and current commitments of the contractor. The experience, financial standing, equipment, integrity, personal habits, and professional ability of the contractor and his key personnel are carefully examined. His financial statements, both for the current period and for some years past, are subject to study and analysis. His bank credit is verified together with his relations with his sources of credit and supply. Once a contractor has firmly established relations with a bonding company, his maximum bonding capacity becomes reasonably well established, and future investigations by the surety underwriter are concerned with keeping the contractor's records current and investigating the individual bond requests as they are submitted. If the contractor's work load is well below his limit, and contracts of the usual variety are proposed, the application is generally approved without delay. However, when the maximum bonding capacity is to be approached, or when a completely new type of construction is proposed, approval of the bond application may require a considerably longer period of time.

When the contractor makes application for a bond for a new project, he will find that his surety is interested in many aspects of the work he proposes to do. The following presents the usual and most important subjects of investigation:

1. The total amount of uncompleted work that the contractor presently has on hand, of both the bonded and the unbonded variety. This work must, of necessity, include that which has not yet been awarded. The obvious point of concern here is to prevent the contractor from becoming overextended in regard to working capital, equipment, and organization.

2. The adequacy of working capital and the availability of credit. The contractor can assist his own cause by keeping his banker fully informed as to his activities and supplied with an up-to-date financial statement. This phase of investigation can often protect the contractor against taking on a project that is too big for him to handle.

3. The amount of money that the contractor "left on the table," that is, the spread between the low bid and the next highest. Competitive conditions in the construction industry are such that a spread of more than 5 or 6 percent between the two lowest bidders is generally the cause of some concern. The surety wishes to ensure that the contractor's estimating and bidding procedures are sound.

4. The largest contract amount of similar work that the contractor has successfully completed. Inexperience in a new field of construction has contributed a long list of contractor failures. The surety would like the contractor to stay with the kind of work in which he is most experienced. If he wishes to change to another type, the surety will urge that the first steps be small ones until the contractor acquires the necessary experience. If the contractor is not properly equipped for the new work, he must demonstrate to the surety how he proposes to solve his equipment problems.

5. The terms of payment to the contractor as provided for by the contract clauses. Questions of how often the contractor is to receive progress payments, the amount of retainage, and the nature of the job warranties influence the surety's appraisal of the contractor's financial ability to do the work.

6. The amount of work subcontracted and the qualifications of the subcon-

tractors. The surety's concern here is that the prospective subcontractors possess the necessary organization, experience, and financial resources to carry out their end of the work.

8.11. BONDING CAPACITY

A useful concept widely used by the construction industry is "bonding capacity." This term has no precise definition but refers to the maximum value of uncompleted work that the surety will allow the contractor to undertake at any one time. This total is based upon the surety's considered appraisal of the contractor's abilities and resources, and it is obvious, therefore, that the maximum uncompleted work volume of a given contractor is an individual matter. Nevertheless, it is a common rule of thumb that a contractor can carry between $15.00 and $20.00 of uncompleted work for each dollar of net working capital, or $10.00 of uncompleted work for each dollar of net worth. Net working capital and net worth are discussed in Chapter 10.

The difference between a contractor's maximum work capacity and his current total of uncompleted work, both bonded and unbonded, is a measure of the additional work for which his surety will bond him. There are, of course, other factors involved, such as the type of new work being considered and the size of the project. In computing the current value of a contractor's uncompleted work, the surety may decide to take into account at least part of the value of the subcontracts that are bonded.

8.12 DEFAULT BY THE CONTRACTOR

Should the contractor default, the surety is required to perform in accordance with the terms of the bond up to a maximum amount that is the face value of the bond. How the surety company elects to complete the contract is a matter for it to decide. There are several alternative courses of action, but the most common is for the original contractor to finish the job with the financial help of the surety. The surety may decide, however, to put the remaining work out for competitive bids and select a new contractor to take over, or a new contractor may be engaged on a cost-plus basis. The surety may even send in a project supervisor and finish the job itself by force account.

Contract bonds can offer the contractor a genuine advantage when his ability to proceed has been temporarily curtailed by legal or financial difficulties. If the financial condition of the contractor is basically sound, the surety may choose to help him get back on his feet and into business again. It may elect to advance the contractor credit in sufficient amount for him to proceed with his work. If claims have tied up his capital, the surety may furnish bonds to discharge these claims, thereby enabling the contractor to proceed on his own.

When the contractor defaults and the surety undertakes to complete the work, the surety becomes entitled to all of the remedies that the owner has against the contractor under the contract. In addition, the surety is entitled to receive from the owner all moneys yet due the contractor, including retainage, up to the total expense incurred by the surety.

8.13 SUBCONTRACT BONDS

The general contractor, to protect himself against default by subcontractors, frequently requires certain or all of them to provide performance and payment bonds. In this instance, the subcontractor is the principal and the prime contractor is the obligee. General contractors have found, to their dismay, that not every bond form and not every surety company provide them with the kind of financial protection desired. It is for this reason that many prime contractors require the use of their own subcontract bond forms. Otherwise, the contractor must reserve the right to approve the surety and bond form proposed for use. Figure 8.3 is a widely used form of subcontract performance bond, and Figure 8.4 is a form of subcontract payment bond.

A factor of major importance to be emphasized at this point is that the bond serves in no way to replace honesty, integrity, and competence on the part of the subcontractor. Bond or no bond, an inferior subcontractor spells trouble. Although the bond will afford the general contractor some measure of protection against financial loss directly attributable to a particular subcontract, it does not and cannot cover expenses caused by work stoppages, delays, and disruptions of the overall construction program that inevitably result from subcontractor default.

8.14 WARRANTIES AND SURETY BONDS

A warranty is a certification, express or implied, that a certain aspect of a contract is, in fact, as it was declared or promised to be. Previously mentioned is the usual warranty period after the completion of construction, during which time the general contractor guarantees that the project is free from defects caused by his failure to perform. Manufacturers' or applicators' warranties are also sometimes required to guarantee the performance requirements of machinery, operating equipment, processes, or materials. A written instrument is not necessarily required in conjunction with a warranty, although specifications sometimes stipulate that a written warranty be delivered to the owner.

The true value of a warranty is, quite obviously, determined by the integrity of the firm standing behind it. In the event of breach of warranty, the warrantor becomes liable for damages. Whether damages can actually be collected may, of course, be an entirely different matter. In order to ensure proper compliance with a warranty, a surety bond, called a "maintenance bond," is sometimes required. Already mentioned is the fact that the performance bond customarily includes the required project warranty period. Another common example of a

Bond No.

THE EMPLOYERS' GROUP OF INSURANCE COMPANIES

(NAME OF INSURANCE COMPANY)

BOSTON, MASSACHUSETTS

SUBCONTRACT PERFORMANCE BOND FORM A

KNOW ALL MEN BY THESE PRESENTS: That_____

_____ as Principal,

(Here insert the name and address, or legal title, of the Subcontractor)

hereinafter called Principal, and_____

(Name, corporate state and home office city of Surety)

_____ as Surety, hereinafter called Surety,

are held and firmly bound unto_____

(Here insert the name and address, or legal title, of the General Contractor)

_____as Obligee, hereinafter called Obligee,

in the amount of_____

_____ Dollars ($_____),

for the payment whereof Principal and Surety bind themselves, their heirs, executors, administrators, successors and assigns, jointly and severally, firmly by these presents.

WHEREAS, Principal has by written agreement dated _____

entered into a subcontract with Obligee for _____

_____

in accordance with drawings and specifications prepared by_____

(Here insert full name and title)

_____, which subcontract is by reference made a part hereof, and is hereinafter referred to as the subcontract.

NOW, THEREFORE, THE CONDITION OF THIS OBLIGATION is such that, if Principal shall promptly and faithfully perform said subcontract, then this obligation shall be null and void; otherwise it shall remain in full force and effect.

Whenever Principal shall be, and be declared by Obligee to be in default under the subcontract, the Obligee having performed Obligee's obligations thereunder:

   (1) Surety may promptly remedy the default subject to the provisions of paragraph 3 herein, or;

   (2) Obligee after reasonable notice to Surety may, or Surety upon demand of Obligee may arrange for the performance of Principal's obligation under the subcontract subject to the provisions of paragraph 3 herein;

   (3) The balance of the subcontract price, as defined below, shall be credited against the reasonable cost of completing performance of the subcontract. If completed by the Obligee, and the reasonable cost exceeds the balance of the subcontract price, the Surety shall pay to the Obligee such excess, but in no event shall the aggregate liability of the Surety exceed the amount of this bond. If the Surety arranges completion or remedies the default, that portion of the balance of the subcontract price as may be required to complete the subcontract or remedy the default and to reimburse the Surety for its outlays shall be paid to the Surety at the times and in the manner as said sums would have been payable to Principal had there been no default under the subcontract. The term "balance of the subcontract price," as used in this paragraph, shall mean the total amount payable by Obligee to Principal under the subcontract and any amendments thereto, less the amounts heretofore properly paid by Obligee under the subcontract.

Any suit under this bond must be instituted before the expiration of two years from date on which final payment under the subcontract falls due.

No right of action shall accrue on this bond to or for the use of any person or corporation other than the Obligee named herein or the heirs, executors, administrators or successors of the Obligee.

Signed and sealed this_____ day of _____ A. D., 19____.

In the presence of:

_____(Seal)

Principal

_____(Seal)

Surety

Subcontract Performance Bond Form A.
Revised to August, 1956.
SB 5716 (1) Printed in U.S.A.

by _____

Attorney-in-fact

Figure 8.3 Subcontract performance bond. Reproduced by permission of the Surety Association of America.

Bond No.

THE EMPLOYERS' GROUP OF INSURANCE COMPANIES

(NAME OF INSURANCE COMPANY)

BOSTON, MASSACHUSETTS

SUBCONTRACT LABOR AND MATERIAL PAYMENT BOND

KNOW ALL MEN BY THESE PRESENTS: That_____

_____ as Principal,

(Here insert the name and address, or legal title, of the Subcontractor)

hereinafter called Principal, and _____

(Name, corporate state and home office city of Surety)

_____ as Surety, hereinafter called Surety,

are held and firmly bound unto _____

(Here insert the name and address, or legal title, of the General Contractor)

_____ as Obligee, hereinafter called Obligee,

for the use and benefit of claimants as hereinbelow defined, in the amount of_____

_____ Dollars ($_____),

for the payment whereof Principal and Surety bind themselves, their heirs, executors, administrators, successors and assigns, jointly and severally, firmly by these presents.
WHEREAS, Principal has by written agreement dated _____
entered into a subcontract with Obligee for _____

_____

in accordance with drawings and specifications prepared by _____

_____

(Here insert full name and title)

which subcontract is by reference made a part hereof, and is hereafter referred to as the subcontract.
NOW, THEREFORE, THE CONDITION OF THIS OBLIGATION is such that if the Principal shall promptly make payment to all claimants as hereinafter defined, for all labor and material used or reasonably required for use in the performance of the subcontract, then this obligation shall be void; otherwise it shall remain in full force and effect, subject, however, to the following conditions:

(1) A claimant is defined as one having a direct contract with the Principal for labor, material, or both, used or reasonably required for use in the performance of the contract, labor and material being construed to include that part of water, gas, power, light, heat, oil, gasoline, telephone service or rental of equipment directly applicable to the subcontract.

(2) The above-named Principal and Surety hereby jointly and severally agree with the Obligee that every claimant as herein defined, who has not been paid in full before the expiration of a period of ninety (90) days after the date on which the last of such claimant's work or labor was done or performed, or materials were furnished by such claimant, may sue on this bond for the use of such claimant, prosecute the suit to final judgment for such sum or sums as may be justly due claimant, and have execution thereon. The Obligee shall not be liable for the payment of any costs or expenses of any such suit.

(3) No suit or action shall be commenced hereunder by any claimant,
   (a) After the expiration of one (1) year following the date on which Principal ceased work on said subcontract it being understood, however, that if any limitation embodied in this bond is prohibited by any law controlling the construction hereof such limitation shall be deemed to be amended so as to be equal to the minimum period of limitation permitted by such law.
   (b) Other than in a state court of competent jurisdiction in and for the county or other political subdivision of the state in which the project, or any part thereof, is situated, or in the United States District Court for the district in which the project, or any part thereof, is situated, and not elsewhere.

(4) The amount of this bond shall be reduced by and to the extent of any payment or payments made in good faith hereunder.

Signed and sealed this_____ day of _____ A. D., 19____.

In the presence of:

_____ (Seal)
Principal

_____ (Seal)
Surety

by _____
Attorney-in-fact

Subcontract Labor and Material Payment Bond.
This bond is issued simultaneously with another bond in favor of the general contractor conditioned for the full and faithful performance of the contract.
Revised to March, 1960.
SB 5716 (2)   Printed in U.S.A.

Figure 8.4 Subcontract labor and material payment bond. Reproduced by permission of the Surety Association of America.

maintenance bond is a roof bond, by the terms of which a surety guarantees the roof against defects of workmanship or materials for some specified period of time.

8.15 MISCELLANEOUS SURETY BONDS

In addition to proposal, performance, payment, subcontract, and maintenance bonds, the general contractor occasionally finds it necessary or desirable to furnish or accept several other forms of surety bonds. The most important of these are the following.

Bonds to Discharge Liens or Claims. Persons who have not received payment for labor or materials supplied to a construction project are entitled to file a mechanic's lien (see Section 10.26) against the property of a private owner or against moneys due and payable to the general contractor in the case of a public contract. Other claims can also be filed. Such actions can freeze capital needed by the contractor to conduct his operations.

A surety bond in an amount fixed by an order of the court can be used to discharge a mechanic's lien. When claims for personal or property damage are involved, the bond amount is generally decided upon by the owner. In any case, the bond functions as a financial guarantee to the owner and releases money he has withheld from the contractor.

Bonds to Indemnify Owner Against Liens. The contractor may be called upon to post a bond in advance that indemnifies the owner against any impairment of title or other damage he may suffer by reason of liens or claims filed on his property. In this situation, bond is required before any such liens are filed, rather than being used to discharge liens after they are filed in the way described in the previous paragraph.

Bonds to Protect Owners of Rented Equipment and Leased Property. In his construction operations, the contractor may find it desirable to rent or lease equipment, parking lots, access roads, storage installations, and similar facilities. The owner of such property often requires the contractor to post a bond that guarantees proper maintenance and payment of rental charges, and indemnifies the owner against loss, damage, or excessive wear of his property.

Judicial or Court Bonds. When the contractor is the plaintiff in a legal action, he sometimes is required to furnish security for court costs, possible judgments, and similar financial eventualities. Such security is often provided in the form of judicial or court bonds. This legal requirement is commonly applied when the contractor institutes legal proceedings in states or jurisdictions other than his own.

License Bond. Also known as a permit bond, this is a bond required by state law or municipal ordinance as a condition precedent to the granting of a contractor's license. License bonds guarantee compliance with statutes or ordinances and make provision for payment to the obligee in the event that the licensee violates his legal or financial obligations. This topic has been discussed previously in Section 2.14.

Termite Bond. This form of bond is given by manufacturers or applicators of substances intended to prevent the damage caused by termites.

Subdivision Bond. This bond, given by the developer to a public body, guarantees construction of all necessary improvements and utilities.

Self-Insurers' Workmen's Compensation Bond. This bond, given by a self-insured contractor to the state, guarantees payment of all statutory benefits to injured employees.

Union Wage Bond. This bond, given by a contractor to a union, guarantees that the contractor will pay union wages and will make proper payment of fringe benefits required by union contract.

9

CONSTRUCTION INSURANCE

9.1 RISKS

Construction work by nature is hazardous, and accidents are frequent and often severe. The annual toll of deaths, personal injuries, and property damage in the construction industry is extremely high. The potential severity of accidents and the frequency with which they occur require that the contractor protect himself with a variety of complex and expensive insurance coverages. Without adequate insurance protection, the contractor would be continuously faced with the momentary possibility of serious or even ruinous financial loss.

As has been discussed previously in this book, construction projects usually have in force several simultaneous contractual arrangements: between owner and architect-engineer, between owner and general contractor, and between the general contractor and his several subcontractors. Construed as a whole, these contracts can establish a complicated structure of responsibilities for damages arising out of the construction operations. Liability for accidents can devolve on the owner or architect-engineer, as well as on the prime contractor and subcontractors whose equipment and employees are doing the actual work. Construction contracts typically require the contractor to assume the owner's legal liability for construction accidents or to provide insurance for the owner's direct protection. Consequently, a contractor's insurance program normally includes coverages to protect other persons than himself and to protect him from liabilities not legally his own.

9.2 THE INSURANCE POLICY

An insurance policy is a conditional contract under which the insurer promises, for a consideration, to assume financial responsibility for a specified loss or liability.

The policy itself is a legal document containing many provisions pertaining to the loss against which it affords protection. Fundamentally, the law of insurance is identical with the law of contracts. However, because of its intimate association with public welfare, the insurance field is closely controlled and strictly regulated by statutes. Insurance companies are regulated as to their organizational structure, financial affairs, and business methods. In most states, insurance policies must conform to statutory requirements as to form and content.

A loss suffered by a contractor as a result of his own deliberate action cannot be recovered by the contractor under an insurance policy. However, negligence or oversight on the part of the contractor will not generally invalidate the insurance contract.

The contractor must pay a premium as the consideration for the insurance company's promise of protection against the designated loss. This premium is payable in advance before the policy becomes of force and effect. In the event of a loss covered by an insurance policy, the contractor cannot recover more than his loss, that is, he cannot make a profit at the expense of the insurance company.

Insurance companies can be organized as stock companies or as mutual companies. The stock companies are organized in a manner similar to that of a bank, and ownership is vested in stockholders. The owner of an insurance policy has no ownership in the company and assumes no risk for assessments if the insurance company becomes bankrupt. A mutual company is so organized that the policy owners assume some risk if the company becomes bankrupt. In the event of high loss incidence, mutual insurance companies are empowered to levy assessments, in addition to the normal premium payment, against their policyholders. These assessments are enforceable at law and can be substantial in size. On the other hand, profits realized by mutual companies are usually disbursed as a dividend to the policyholders at the time of renewal of the policy.

9.3 CONTRACT REQUIREMENTS

Because the owner can be made responsible for certain liabilities arising out of the construction operations, it is standard practice for construction contracts to require that appropriate insurance be provided for the owner's protection. In some cases, the contract documents stipulate that the owner himself shall provide certain of these insurance coverages. Article 11 of Appendix C makes the owner responsible for obtaining his own liability insurance and for providing fire, extended coverage, vandalism, and malicious mischief insurance on the project.

Construction contracts frequently make the contractor responsible for obtaining all of the insurance stipulated, including the coverages just mentioned as well as workmen's compensation insurance, contractor's public liability and property damage insurance, contractor's contingent liability insurance, and contractual liability insurance. Each of these insurance types will be discussed subsequently in this chapter. There are, of course, many examples of special insurance being required by contract when the construction involves unusual risks or conditions. When the contract delegates to the contractor specific responsibility for obtaining certain insurance, it is customary that he be required to submit insurance certificates to the owner or the architect-engineer as proof that the coverage stipulated has, in fact, been provided.

Construction contract documents frequently require the contractor to "hold the owner harmless" by accepting any liability that the owner may incur because of operations performed under the contract. This matter will be discussed more fully in Section 9.22. When the contractor signs a contract that contains such a provision, he has accepted someone else's legal liability—that of the owner. The contract may or may not be explicit in requiring the contractor to provide an appropriate contractural liability policy. Even in the absence of such a requirement the contractor must purchase a suitable policy for his own protection.

9.4 LEGAL REQUIREMENTS

Certain kinds of insurance are required by law, and the contractor must provide them whether or not they are called for by the contract. Workmen's compensation; motor vehicle; unemployment; and old-age, survivor's, and disability insurance (OASDI) are examples of coverages required by statute. It can be argued that unemployment and social security payments made by the contractor are more in the nature of a tax than of insurance premiums in the usual sense. Nevertheless, both unemployment and social security are treated as forms of insurance for the purposes of discussion in this chapter.

The law makes the independent contractor liable for damages caused by his acts of omission or commission. In addition, the prime contractor has a contingent liability for the actions of his subcontractors. Therefore, whether or not the law is specific concerning certain types of insurance, the contractor as a practical fact must procure several different categories of liability insurance to protect himself from his legal responsibility for damages caused by his own construction operations as well as those of his subcontractors.

9.5 ANALYSIS OF INSURABLE RISKS

Aside from coverages required by law and the construction contract, it is the contractor's prerogative to decide what insurance he shall carry. Such elective coverages pertain principally to the contractor's own property or to property for which he is responsible. It is not economically possible for the contractor to carry all of the insurance coverages available to him. If he purchased insurance protection against every risk that is insurable, the cost of the resulting premiums would impose an impossible financial burden on his business. The extent and magnitude of a contractor's insurance program should be decided only after careful study and consideration. If a risk is insurable, the cost of the premiums must be balanced against the possible loss if the coverage is not taken. There are, of course, risks that are not insurable, and associated losses must be regarded simply as business expenses.

At times, careful planning and meticulous construction procedures can minimize a risk at less cost than the premium of a covering insurance policy. Thus, the contractor may choose to assume a calculated risk rather than to pay a high insurance premium. A common example of assuming such a risk involves construction that is to be erected immediately adjacent to an existing structure. If the nature of the new construction is such that the existing structure may be endangered by settlement or collapse, the contractor has two courses of action open to him. As one alternative, he can include in his estimate the premium for a collapse policy. Such protection is high in cost and is generally available only with substantial deductible amounts. Instead, the contractor can assume the risk himself without insurance protection, choosing to rely on his skill and on extraordinary precautions in construction procedures to get the job done without mishap. Many analogous cases can be cited with respect to pile driving, blasting, water damage, and others.

9.6 CONSTRUCTION INSURANCE CHECK LIST

Insurance coverages are complex, and each new construction contract presents its own problems. The contractor should select a competent insurance broker who is experienced in construction work and familiar with contractors' insurance problems. Without competent advice, the contractor is quite liable either to incur the needless expense of overlapping protection or to expose himself to the danger of vital gaps in his insurance coverage. The contractor can often reduce his insurance costs by keeping his broker advised in detail as to the nature and conduct of his construction operations.

In the long list of possible construction insurance coverages, not every policy is applicable to any one construction project. The following check list is not represented as being complete but does contain the insurance coverages of major interest to the construction industry.

A. Project and Property Insurance.
   1. Builder's risk fire insurance. This insurance provides protection for projects under construction against direct loss by fire or lightning.
      a. Extended coverage endorsement. This covers property against all direct loss caused by windstorm, hail, explosion, riot, civil commotion, aircraft, vehicles, and smoke.
      b. Vandalism and malicious mischief insurance. Protection of this type may be obtained by endorsement to the builder's risk policy.
      c. Water damage insurance. This can be purchased as an endorsement to the builder's risk policy; it does not include damage caused by sprinkler leakage.
      d. Sprinkler leakage insurance. Protection against all direct loss to a building project as a result of leakage, freezing, or breaking of sprinkler installations may be obtained as an endorsement to the builder's risk policy.
      e. Earthquake insurance. This coverage may be provided by an endorse-

ment to the builder's risk policy in some states. Elsewhere, a separate policy must be issued.

2. Fire insurance on contractor's own buildings. This coverage affords protection for offices, sheds, warehouses, and stored contents. Endorsements for extended coverage and for vandalism and malicious mischief are also available.

3. Contractor's equipment insurance. This type of policy, often termed a floater, insures a contractor's construction equipment regardless of its location.

4. Bridge insurance. This insurance is of the inland marine type and is often termed the "bridge builder's risk policy." It affords protection during construction against damage that may be caused by fire, lightning, flood, ice, collision, explosion, riot, vandalism, wind, tornado, and earthquake.

5. Motor truck cargo policy. This insurance covers loss by named hazards to materials or equipment carried on the contractor's own trucks.

6. Steam boiler and machinery insurance. A contractor or owner may purchase this form of insurance when the boiler equipment of a building under construction is used to heat the structure for plastering, floor laying, or other purposes. This policy covers any injury or damage that may occur to or be caused by the boiler during its usage by the contractor.

7. Burglary, robbery, and theft insurance. This form of insurance protects the contractor against the loss of money or negotiable securities through burglary, theft, robbery, destruction, disappearance, or wrongful abstraction.

8. Fidelity insurance. This policy affords the contractor protection against loss caused by dishonesty of his own employees.

9. Dishonesty, destruction, and disappearance policy. Items 7 and 8 above, together with forgery insurance, can be grouped together in a single dishonesty, destruction, and disappearance policy.

10. Valuable papers destruction insurance. This policy protects the contractor against the loss, damage, or destruction of valuable papers such as books, records, maps, drawings, abstracts, deeds, mortgages, contracts, and documents. It does not cover loss by misplacement, unexplained disappearance, wear and tear, deterioration, vermin, or war.

11. Installation floater policy. Insurance of this type provides protection for property of various kinds such as project equipment and machinery (heating and air-conditioning systems, for example) from the time that it leaves the place of shipment until it is installed on the project and tested. Coverage terminates when the insured's interest in the property ceases, when the property is accepted, or when it is taken over by the owner.

12. Consequential loss or damage insurance. This insurance covers loss caused by the shutdown of public utility service resulting from fire or windstorm. Contractors who depend on uninterrupted power service or the service of a material supply plant and who might be penalized for failure to complete contracts on time because of such failure may purchase this form of protection.

B. Liability Insurance.

1. Employer's liability insurance. This insurance is customarily written in

combination with workmen's compensation insurance. It affords the contractor broad coverage for personal injury or death of an employee in the course of his employment, but outside of and distinct from any claims under workmen's compensation laws.

2. Contractor's public liability and property damage insurance. This insurance protects the contractor from his legal liability for injuries to persons not in his employ and for damage to the property of others, which property is not in the contractor's care, custody, or control, when such injuries or damage arise out of the operations of the contractor.

3. Contractor's protective public and property damage liability insurance. This protects the contractor against his liability imposed by law arising out of acts or omissions of his subcontractors.

4. Contractual liability insurance. This form of insurance is required when one party to a contract, by terms of that contract, assumes certain legal liabilities of the other party. The usual forms of liability insurance do not afford this coverage.

5. Owner's protective liability insurance. This insurance protects the owner from his contingent liability for damages arising from the operations of the contractor or his subcontractors.

6. Completed operations liability insurance. This form of insurance protects the contractor from damage claims stemming from his alleged faulty performance on projects since completed and handed over to the owner. The usual forms of liability insurance provide protection only while the contractor is performing his work and not after it has been completed and accepted by the owner.

C. Employee Insurance.

1. Workmen's compensation insurance. This insurance provides all benefits required by law to employees killed or injured in the course of their employment.

2. Old-age, survivor's, and disability insurance. This all-federal insurance system operated by the United States government provides old-age benefits to an insured worker and his family, survivor's benefits to his family when the worker dies, and disability benefits.

3. Unemployment insurance. This federal-state insurance plan provides workers with a weekly income during periods of unemployment between jobs.

4. Disability insurance. This insurance, required by some states, provides benefits to employees for disabilities caused by nonoccupational accidents and disease.

D. Motor Vehicle Insurance.

Various forms of insurance are available in connection with the ownership and use of automobiles and trucks. Liability coverages protect the contractor against third-party claims of bodily injury or property damage involving the contractor's vehicles or nonowned vehicles that are used in his interest. Collision insurance, together with comprehensive fire and theft coverage, indemnifies the contractor for damage to his own vehicles.

E. Business, Accident, and Life Insurance.
   1. Business interruption insurance. This insurance is designed to reimburse the owner for losses suffered because of an interruption of his business.
   2. Sole proprietorship insurance. A policy of this type provides cash to assist heirs in continuing or disposing of the business without sacrifice in the event of death of the owner.
   3. Accident insurance on partners or key men.
   4. Life insurance on partners or key men. This insurance reimburses the business for financial loss resulting from the death of a key man in the business. It also builds up a sinking fund to be available on his retirement.
   5. Group life insurance. Contractors often purchase life insurance for their employees. This affords protection for each participant at a low group cost, the premium for which may be paid wholly or partly by the contractor. Additional amounts can often be purchased by the employees at their own expense.
   6. Group hospitalization insurance. Such insurance covers hospitalization and surgical expenses incurred by covered employees. Policies are often written to include the families of the employees. A portion of the premium may be paid by the employer and the balance by the individuals insured.

9.7 BUILDER'S RISK FIRE INSURANCE

The basic builder's risk policy protects building projects against direct loss caused by fire and lightning. This insurance is effected and maintained to 100 percent of the insurable value of the project, including all subcontracted work. Such insurance ordinarily covers the cost of facilities and materials connected or adjacent to the structure insured, including temporary structures, materials, equipment, and supplies of all kinds incident to the construction of the structure and, when not otherwise covered by insurance, construction machinery, tools, and equipment owned by the contractor or similar property of others for which he is legally liable. All property is protected that is a part of or contained in the structure, in temporary structures, or on vehicles, or is stored on the premises adjacent to the project.

Builder's risk policies typically provide that the coverage ceases when the project is allowed to remain vacant for more than 60 days. Protection under the policy may also be jeopardized if the contractor permits early occupancy by the owner, unless a suitable endorsement is obtained from the insurance company. As a general rule, any specifications, drawings, records, or documents kept in the building are excluded as well as any loss to foundations. It is customary to deduct the cost of labor and materials associated with land preparation, excavation, underground utilities, and foundations below the lowest basement floor when computing the insurable value of the structure.

Premium rates for builder's risk insurance vary considerably with the type of construction and the availability of fire-fighting facilities. The availability of fire protection is described as "protected" or "unprotected," depending upon the distance between the job site and the nearest fire stations and plugs. Premium rates are higher for unprotected areas and for the more combustible classes of construction.

9.8 BUILDER'S RISK FORMS

There are two principal forms of builder's risk insurance in general usage. The coverage of the two forms is the same, the difference being in the method of premium payment. One type of builder's risk insurance is the reporting form, which establishes the insurable value of the structure, and hence the face value of the policy, in accordance with periodic progress reports submitted to the insurance company by the contractor. This form requires the contractor to make a monthly report of the insurable value of the work in place, including all materials stored on the site. The premium for this form of policy is paid in monthly installments, the amount of each installment being computed on the basis of the last progress report. The premium, therefore, is initially low but increases progressively each month as the job advances toward completion.

The form of builder's risk insurance most commonly used is the completed value type. This policy is written for the full amount of the project value, which is the contract price less the cost of the foundations and other excluded work. The coverage must be written by the time the foundations are completed, and the premium is payable as a lump sum in advance. This form requires no monthly report. Because the full value of the completed project is protected from the start of construction, a premium of only 55 percent of the regular fire rate is paid.

9.9 CHOICE OF BUILDER'S RISK FORM

In general, the insured is free to choose the form of builder's risk insurance he desires. One advantage of the reporting form is that considerable time may be required for excavating, driving of piling, construction of footings, and similar work exempted from the insurable value. The 55 percent factor used in computing the rates for the completed value form is intended to reflect approximately a straight-line increase in insurable value from zero at the start to full value at completion of the structure. Under the reporting form the values are reported monthly and follow more closely the actual curve of values as they are added to the structure. For this reason the final cost of the reporting form may be less, particularly for a large project, if the insurable value increases slowly for a considerable period of time and later rises rather abruptly. An important consideration with the reporting form is keeping the reports accurate and up to date. Should a report be undervalued or overlooked, the insured stands the risk of assuming a part of the loss if a severe fire occurs.

As a general rule, the completed value form of builder's risk insurance is somewhat cheaper for short-term jobs. In addition, it does not require the monthly progress reports. However, the preparation of these reports does not usually involve any real amount of additional time or expense because the essential information is already available from the monthly project pay requests.

9.10 ENDORSEMENTS TO BUILDER'S RISK

There are, of course, many possible causes of physical loss or damage to a construction project besides fire and lightning. Other significant risks can be insured against by purchasing various endorsements to the basic builder's risk policy. The purchase of the extended coverage endorsement is standard practice, this endorsement providing protection against damage or loss caused by windstorm, hail, explosion, riot, riot attending a strike, civil commotion, aircraft, vehicles, and smoke. The vandalism and malicious mischief endorsement is also usually obtained. It is to be noted that each endorsement protects against only the hazards named and that each additional endorsement is obtained by the payment of an extra premium. Many other special endorsements to builder's risk are available, including protection against water damage, sprinkler leakage, occupancy by the owner, and earthquake in certain states.

An alternative to the basic builder's risk policy with endorsements is the "all-risk" policy that is usually available and that protects building projects against all physical loss or damage caused by external causes with stipulated exceptions. This policy, for example, will not insure against loss caused by testing of equipment, glass breakage, mysterious disappearance, explosion of steam boilers, inadequate packing or shipping, or damage to trees and shrubbery. Some losses under this policy are subject to deductible amounts.

9.11 PROVIDING OF BUILDER'S RISK INSURANCE BY OWNER

The standard documents of The American Institute of Architects (see Subparagraph 11.3.1 of Appendix C) provide that the owner shall purchase and maintain the builder's risk policy. It is common practice, however, for the general contractor to provide this coverage. The matter of who purchases this insurance is of no great import, although certain types of projects lend themselves well to the provision of fire insurance by the owner. One such example is a project that involves several independent contractors. Another good example is a remodeling job or an addition to an existing building. If the contractor is to provide the fire insurance, there is always considerable uncertainty as to the fire protection for the existing structure. In such circumstances, the contractor usually makes an arrangement with the owner to add the additional coverage to the owner's existing policy, although this matter can become involved from an insurance standpoint. It is much simpler and perhaps cheaper for the owner in such cases to obtain the insurance in the first place.

If the owner does purchase the fire insurance, the contractor must determine that the policy provides the customary construction coverage. For example, he must check that materials and supplies stored on the site but not yet incorporated into the work are included. The contract might not require the owner to obtain the very important endorsements for extended coverage and for vandalism and malicious mischief.

It has been standard practice when the owner provides the project fire insurance that the prime contractor be included as a named insured under the policy. The principal reason is to protect the contractor against possible action by the insurance company under the subrogation clause present in all fire insurance policies. This clause gives the insurance company the right to sue in the insured's name for recovery of losses. Thus, if the contractor's name does not appear as an insured and if his operations cause or contribute to a loss, he may find himself exposed to action by the insurance carrier for recovery of its loss under the policy. If a subcontractor's operations cause or contribute to a fire loss on a construction project, he also may be subject to suit by the fire insurance company unless he is a named insured under the policy.

To avoid the dangers of subrogation, contract documents sometimes include clauses whereby the owner and general contractor and the general contractor and his subcontractors waive all rights against each other for damages caused by fire. Subparagraph 11.3.6 and Clause 5.3.1.5 of Appendix C illustrate such provisions.

9.12 TERMINATION OF BUILDER'S RISK INSURANCE

Builder's risk policies may be canceled on a pro rata basis at any time requested by the policyholder. If the contractor provides this insurance, the time at which he can terminate the policy is an important matter. On the one hand, the premiums are expensive, and the contractor naturally wishes the expenditure to cease at the earliest possible moment. On the other hand, the contractor cannot dispense with this protection until such time as the owner is legally responsible. When the contract has been silent in this regard, the courts have repeatedly found that the contractor remains responsible for the project until the owner has presented a written acceptance.

Sometimes the owner occupies the building, but his formal acceptance of the structure is delayed until the contractor completes some remaining work. Under these circumstances, if the contractor's operations should cause a fire, the loss to the structure would be covered by the builder's risk policy. However, the contractor may incur a liability to the owner for the latter's loss of business while the fire damage is being repaired. To protect himself against this contingency, the contractor may wish to take out business interruption insurance.

9.13 CONTRACTOR'S EQUIPMENT INSURANCE

Construction equipment works in scattered locations, must travel about from job to job, and is constantly exposed to damage or loss. Contractors cover their off-the-road equipment with an inland marine policy designated as an equipment floater policy. This policy is flexible and can be designed to fit the needs of the contractor. It may provide for nationwide coverage, regardless of where the equipment is located, or it may be confined to a given locality. The floater policy can be of a schedule or blanket form. The schedule form insures only equipment that is individually listed, whereas the blanket form automatically covers all equipment. The policy can include equipment that is not owned but is rented, leased, or borrowed, or for which the contractor is otherwise legally responsible.

The basic policy coverages are fire, lightning, and transportation, to which, at the contractor's option, may be added specifically named perils such as upset, landslide, earthquake, theft, collision, tornado, flood, collapse of bridges, explosion, windstorm, and overturn. A broad all-risk form is written with chosen deductibles applicable to loss by theft, collision, or vandalism. The all-risk form provides blanket protection against all physical loss or damage by external means that may occur to the equipment on the job, in transit, or temporarily in the contractor's yard. The cost of this broad form is naturally higher than that for the named risks. Under this form, water-borne equipment, being subject to coverage under a marine policy, is excluded. Also not covered is damage caused by overload to certain classes of equipment.

9.14 FIDELITY INSURANCE

Few contractors realize that annual losses attributable to employee dishonesty have exceeded the national fire losses for the past several years. Fidelity insurance, protecting the employer against losses of this type, is usually available in one of three forms. These may be described as follows:

1. A schedule bond that affords a stated maximum amount of protection for each person or position listed.
2. A blanket position bond that covers all employees up to the full amount of the bond.
3. A commercial blanket bond that includes all employees but under which the insurer's total liability for one loss is limited by the face amount of the bond, regardless of whether more than one employee is involved.

As indicated, the contractor can purchase protection on specific persons or positions such as his bookkeeper and other selected personnel. However, records almost invariably show that it is impossible to designate in advance the man who will be dishonest. On this basis, the blanket position bond is preferable, since it covers all employees. In the event of loss under this policy, the contractor need only certify that it was caused by "employee or employees unknown." Under the schedule form, however, the contractor must have definite proof of the dishonesty of the individual employee involved. When the blanket position bond is used, additional protection can be provided for certain key employees or positions.

9.15 BURGLARY, ROBBERY, AND THEFT INSURANCE

Ordinarily, the contractor pays his workmen with checks and keeps a minimum of cash about his place of business. However, the occasional requirement that construction workers be paid in cash can expose the contractor to the risk of loss by burglary, robbery, or theft. The paymaster robbery policy is the most inexpensive of the coverages against this form of loss. In its basic form, this insurance covers only payroll funds in the custody of the paymaster or other payroll custodian. If large sums of money are involved, the insurance company may require that the custodian of the payroll be accompanied by a guard. The paymaster robbery policy is available in a broad form that provides coverage for destruction or disappearance of the funds by occurrences other than actual holdup. This policy may be extended to cover payrolls unattended or otherwise not in physical custody.

A broad form of policy is also available that provides protection against loss of money or securities regardless of their nature or intended use. Loss by robbery, disappearance, or destruction is covered by this type of insurance. Optional insuring clauses are available covering the outside and the inside of the contractor's premises. Protection can be carried under either or both of these options.

9.16 LIABILITY INSURANCE

Liability is an obligation imposed by law. In the course of construction operations, the contractor may incur liability for damages in any one of the following three ways:

1. Direct responsibility for injury or damage to the person or property of third parties, caused by an act of omission or commission of the contractor himself.
2. Contingent liability, which involves the indirect liability of the general contractor for the acts of parties for which he is responsible, such as subcontractors.
3. Contractual liability, whereby the contractor has assumed the legal liability of an owner, or other party, by the terms of a contract.

Liability insurance is also called "defense coverage" and serves no purpose other than to protect the contractor against claims brought against him by third parties. Insurance of this type pays the costs of the contractor's legal defense as well as paying judgments for which the contractor becomes legally liable, up to the face value of the policy. Liability insurance provides no protection to the contractor for loss of his own property or injury to his own employees, who are covered by a workmen's compensation statute. It is important to note that most forms of liability insurance customarily include subrogation clauses that give the insurance company the right to file suit to recover losses.

9.17 CONTRACTOR'S PUBLIC LIABILITY AND PROPERTY DAMAGE INSURANCE

The basic form of this policy, often called simply "public liability insurance," protects the contractor against his legal liability to third persons for bodily injury and property damage arising out of his own operations. The contractor's buildings and premises, owned or leased, are included as well as his business operations in progress anywhere in the United States. Normally included, also, is an elevator liability clause that covers the insured's legal liability for bodily injury or property damage arising from ownership, maintenance, or use of elevators owned, controlled, or operated by the contractor. The term "elevators," in this context, does not include material hoists.

With respect to a contractor's liability for injury to third parties, the concept of "attractive nuisance" is important. An attractive nuisance is any dangerous condition or thing that naturally attracts children. Generally, if a contractor has on his property or other location anything that may fall within this definition, he must either employ a guard to prevent children trespassing from being injured or he must construct fences to protect them. Courts usually hold that a trespassing adult is not entitled to damages for injury not wilfully inflicted by the contractor. However, the situation is different with respect to children. The courts hold that any contractor who maintains a dangerous appliance or hazardous premises is expected to exercise ordinary care to prevent injuries to children.

9.18 PUBLIC LIABILITY INSURANCE PREMIUMS

Premiums for public liability insurance usually are based on the contractor's audited payroll. Workmen's compensation insurance is likewise based on payrolls, and it is convenient for the same insurance company to write both policies so that one audit of the contractor's payroll records will verify premium payments for both coverages at the same time.

An advantage to be gained by the contractor, if the same insurance company writes both policies, is an improved overall loss experience, which may result in lower insurance premiums. An insurance company usually rates a contractor on the basis of its total insurance business with him, and a loss under one coverage may be counterbalanced by favorable experience on the other policies written by the same insurance carrier. These remarks also illustrate the wisdom of a contractor's continuing to do business with an insurance company with which he has established a considerable background of favorable experience.

The premiums for both public liability and workmen's compensation insurance are adjusted up or down according to the contractor's accident experience record. A contractor whose losses are low enjoys a considerable savings in the costs of these insurance coverages. Insurance companies employ safety engineers who visit the various projects and recommend to the contractor any actions they deem necessary to reduce the accident hazard.

9.19 CONTRACTOR'S PROTECTIVE PUBLIC AND PROPERTY DAMAGE LIABILITY INSURANCE

Often called "contractor's contingent liability insurance," this policy protects the contractor from his contingent liability imposed by law because of injuries to persons or damage to property of others arising out of acts of subcontractors. A claimant alleging damages caused by an act or omission of a subcontractor may sue not only the subcontractor but the prime contractor as well. This situation arises from the fact that the prime contractor exercises general supervision over the work and is responsible for the conduct of construction operations, including those of his subcontractors. This insurance not only covers accidents arising out of operations performed for the contractor by an independent subcontractor, but also protects the contractor from any liability that he may incur because of any supervisory act by him in connection with a subcontractor's work. In addition, any accident that occurs after completion of the project because of the existence of or the hauling away of unused or scrap material is covered. This form of liability insurance excludes workmen covered by workmen's compensation laws and property under the care, custody, or control of the contractor. If a subcontractor further subcontracts portions of his work, he himself will also need this form of protection.

The premiums for contractor's contingent liability insurance are derived from the subcontract amounts and do not generally vary with the work classifications. Insurance companies writing this form of insurance may require that the prime contractor obtain from his subcontractors certificates verifying that they have purchased public liability and property damage insurance to cover their own direct liability.

9.20 COMPREHENSIVE GENERAL LIABILITY INSURANCE

It is usual for contractors to purchase a comprehensive general liability insurance policy that combines the coverages discussed in Sections 9.17 and 9.19. The comprehensive policy can also be made to include other liability coverages, either as optional items or by endorsement. Despite its name, the comprehensive general policy is not all-inclusive in its coverage, and there are many exclusions. The most important of these may be summarized as follows:

1. With minor exception, any liability that the contractor assumes by contract (Section 9.21).
2. Damage to property caused by blasting or explosion.
3. Collapse or structural injury of building or structure.
4. Damage to underground utilities.
5. Damages arising out of completed projects.
6. Damage to property under the care, custody, or control of the contractor.
7. Personal injury.
8. Injury to the contractor's own employees, to whom he is responsible under workmen's compensation statutes.
9. Motor vehicle, watercraft, or aircraft liability of any sort.

Most of these exclusions are discussed in the following sections.

In the wording of liability policies, the differing connotations of "accident" and "occurrence" are to be noted. When policy coverage is worded to include only losses caused by accident, the event causing the loss must be identifiable as to time and place. In other words, the event usually has to be sudden to be covered. Liability policies are now more generally written on an occurrence basis, in which case the policy coverage is broader. Policies written on an occurrence basis cover claims arising from conditions that exist over a period of time. There is no requirement that the incident be sudden, but only that it be unintentional and unexpected.

The use of "accident" or "occurrence" in the policy can be an important matter for the contractor. It certainly is not unusual that a happening causing injury or damage may be indeterminable as to whether it was sudden and unexpected but definitely definable as to time and place or as to whether it was the result of continued injurious exposure.

9.21 CONTRACTUAL LIABILITY INSURANCE

The liability coverages discussed to this point protect the contractor only with respect to his liability as imposed by law. In many instances in construction, however, the contractor, by terms of the construction contract, purchase-order agreements, or other forms of contracts, assumes the legal liabilities of others. This form of liability is called "contractual liability" and refers to the contractor's acceptance by contract of another party's legal responsibility. The other party may be the owner; his agent, the architect-engineer; third-party beneficiaries; or a material dealer.

There is an exclusion in the comprehensive general liability policy to the effect that the policy does not apply to liability assumed under a contract, except a contract defined in the policy. These defined contracts are (1) lease of premises, (2) easement agreements, (3) indemnification of a municipality required by ordinance, (4) sidetrack agreements, and (5) elevator or escalator maintenance agreements. Contractual liability coverages such as purchase-order agreement liability and hold-harmless clauses are obtainable as specific endorsements to the general policy in consideration for additional premium. In addition, blanket contractual liability insurance that automatically covers all contractual liability is often available.

Routine purchase-order agreements can impose serious contractual-liability obligations on the contractor. For example, the purchase orders used by some transit-mix concrete companies contain a clause whereby the contractor agrees to save harmless the concrete dealer from all liability that may arise out of any accident involving the transit-mix trucks or the drivers while on a job site. The contractor, when he signs his acceptance of such a purchase order, assumes a legal responsibility normally belonging to the dealer. In the absence of blanket contractual liability coverage or a specific endorsement of the purchase-order provision, the contractor would be unprotected should an accident occur.

9.22 HOLD-HARMLESS CLAUSES

Any contract in which the general contractor agrees to indemnify and hold harmless the owner (sometimes also his agent, the architect-engineer) contains assumed liability. This provision is called an "indemnification clause," an "indemnity agreement," or, more commonly, a "hold-harmless clause." Such clauses are not covered by the comprehensive policy unless blanket contractual liability coverage is procured or each clause is individually insured by endorsement. For the purpose of rating the hold-harmless agreements, the contractor must usually provide his insurance company with a copy of the portion of the contract under which the hazard is assumed.

Hold-harmless clauses typically require that the contractor indemnify and save harmless the owner, his agents, and his employees from all loss or expense by reason of liability imposed by law upon them for damages because of bodily injury or damage to property arising out of or in consequence of the work. The inclusion of these clauses is a result of the increasing number of third-party suits being filed against owners and architect-engineers for damages arising out of construction operations. The present tendency is for parties injured by construction operations to bring suit against practically everyone associated with the construction. Additionally, the courts show a growing inclination to ascribe liability, in whole or in part, for such damages to the owner or architect-engineer. For example, owners have been made responsible for damages caused by construction accidents in states with "safe place to work" statutes. There have been several cases in which an architect-engineer, being responsible in contract with the owner for job inspection, has been judged to be responsible for the safety of the work and has been made liable for damages when he failed to take corrective measures although he knew or should have known of a dangerous job condition.

Hold-harmless clauses are not uniform in their wording. However, these clauses can be grouped into three main categories:

1. Limited form indemnification. The limited form holds the owner harmless against claims caused by the contractor's own negligence or that of his subcontractors.
2. Intermediate form indemnification. The intermediate form includes not only claims caused by the contractor or his subcontractors but also those in which the owner may be jointly responsible.
3. Broad form indemnification. The broad form indemnifies the owner even when he is solely responsible for a loss.

When broad form hold-harmless clauses are used, contractual liability coverage is expensive and some provisions may not be insurable. The effect is compounded when the general contractor logically requires the same indemnification from his subcontractors. Some courts frown upon the use of broad form indemnification, but such clauses have usually stood up legally. Some states have passed laws that make void and unenforceable certain forms of broad form indemnification clauses in construction contracts.

9.23 THIRD-PARTY BENEFICIARY CLAUSES

Contractual liability insurance policies usually state that the coverage does not apply to any obligation for which the insured may be held liable in an action on a contract by a person not a party to the contract. This is called a "third-party beneficiary" clause. Contracts with public agencies normally require that the contractor be responsible for all damage to property caused by his construction operations. Such clauses often refer specifically to blasting. When the contract wording makes the contractor assume direct liability to third parties, a citizen property owner can assert rights as a third-party beneficiary even though he is not a party to the contract and even though the contractor was not negligent in his operations. This contingency is not covered under usual comprehensive liability policies even when endorsed with the customary contractual liability coverage. Third-party beneficiary coverage can be added for an additional premium, usually on a specific contract basis.

It is of interest to note that special provisions are now being included in some public construction contracts to limit the risk of third-party suits. Called "no third-party liability" clauses, they provide that the contracting parties do not intend to make the public or any member thereof a third-party beneficiary under the contract, or to authorize anyone not a party to the contract to maintain a suit for personal injuries or property damage pursuant to the terms or provisions of the contract. The intent of such a clause is, of course, to remove the construction contract as a vehicle for third-party suits and to ensure that the duties, obligations, and responsibilities of the parties to the contract remain as imposed by law.

9.24 XCU EXCLUSIONS

The XCU exclusions refer to the hazards of X (explosion), C (collapse), and U (underground damage). Exclusion X excludes property damage arising out of blasting or explosion other than the explosion of air or steam vessels, piping under pressure, prime movers, machinery, or power-transmitting equipment. Exclusion C excludes property damage arising out of collapse or structural injury to a building or structure caused by grading, excavating, filling, backfilling, tunneling, pile driving, cofferdam or caisson work, or by the moving, shoring, underpinning, or demolition of a building or structure. Exclusion U excludes property damage to wires, conduits, pipes, mains, sewers, tanks, tunnels, and any appurtenance in connection therewith beneath the surface of the ground or water, such damage being caused by mechanical equipment used for grading, paving, excavating, drilling, filling, backfilling, or pile driving.

All three of the XCU exclusions do not necessarily pertain to every category of work. Different classifications of work are subject to one, two, or all three of the exclusions as indicated by the general comprehensive policy. The XCU exclusions can be waived for an additional premium.

The XCU exclusions delete only property damage from the basic liability policy, not bodily injury liability, and neither aspect of the exclusions applies to the contractor's protective or completed operations insurance. So long as the work associated with excavation, blasting, underpinning, pile driving, and similar operations is subcontracted, the prime contractor is protected by the subcontractor's insurance, assuming that the subcontractor purchases the XCU endorsement with his general liability policy. Should the subcontractor's insurance prove to be inadequate or faulty, the prime contractor is then protected under his contractor's protective policy. If the prime contractor does this type of work with his own forces, he obviously must purchase the necessary special coverage.

9.25 COMPLETED OPERATIONS LIABILITY INSURANCE

The basic comprehensive liability policy covers casualties that occur during construction operations. However, once a project has been completed, the liability insurance applicable to that project is automatically terminated. When the liability insurance ceases is not always clear, although policies typically state that field operations are completed when all work to be performed by or on behalf of the contractor has been finished or when the work has been put to its intended use. In general, therefore, termination of the basic liability coverage depends more on completion of the work than on acceptance by the owner.

Generally speaking, the contractor is not liable for damages suffered by a third party on a project after the work has been completed and occupied by the owner. When there exists a dangerous condition that is known to the owner or discoverable by him with the exercise of ordinary care, and the owner allows this condition to continue, he is substituted for the contractor as the party answerable for damage to a third party. This is true even though the dangerous condition was originally created by the contractor. Nor is the contractor liable if he merely carries out plans, specifications, and directions given to him by another, unless the information is so obviously faulty that no reasonable man in his position would follow it.

Although the owner's knowledge of a defective condition may render him subject to liability, this circumstance does not necessarily render the contractor immune from all responsibility. A contractor who creates a dangerous condition on the property of another may be responsible to third persons injured thereby, even after owner acceptance, if the third persons so injured could reasonably have been expected to come into contact with the dangerous condition and provided that the contractor knew of the hazard and did not exercise reasonable care to warn of the dangers. Also, the rule of owner responsibility does not apply to dangerous conditions of such latent nature that their existence would not be discovered by the owner during the exercise of ordinary care. Consequently, a contractor's responsibility does not end with project completion. Rather his liability for his completed operations continues for the full period of the applicable state statute of limitations and without limit in states without such statutes.

Completed operations liability insurance is written as an optional coverage under the comprehensive general liability policy. When a contractor buys this insurance, he is protected from liability for injury or damage occurring on a completed project any time thereafter during the policy period regardless of the completion date of the project. The date of injury or damage, however, must fall within the policy period.

9.26 CARE, CUSTODY, OR CONTROL

Contractor's public liability insurance normally contains the following exclusions:

1. Property owned, occupied by, or rented to the contractor.
2. Property used by the contractor.
3. Property in the care, custody, or control of the contractor.
4. Property over which the contractor for any reason is exercising physical control.

This restriction can be eased somewhat by the use of a broad form of property damage endorsement that restricts application of the exclusion to a considerable extent. Sometimes, the exclusion can be waived entirely in exchange for an appropriate premium charge.

9.27 PERSONAL INJURY

"Bodily injury," as used in insurance policies, refers to physical injury to the body. "Personal injury" refers to intangible harm, and an endorsement to the general comprehensive policy is available that covers personal injury liability. There are a number of reasons why this type of insurance coverage can be important to the contractor.

Personal injury liability insurance protects the contractor against any responsibility he may have for (1) false arrest, malicious prosecution, willful detention, or imprisonment; (2) libel, slander, or defamation of character; and (3) wrongful eviction, invasion of privacy, or wrongful entry. Such protection might be needed if, for example, the contractor caused the arrest of someone he suspected of theft or damage to his property and was sued for false arrest. It could happen that a contractor's watchman might detain someone in the course of his duties. A personal injury liability policy is normally written subject to the exclusion of the contractor's own employees, but the policy can be made to include them.

9.28 OWNER'S PROTECTIVE LIABILITY INSURANCE

Many construction contracts require the contractor to purchase owner's protective liability insurance. This insurance is made out in the owner's name and covers his contingent liability for personal injury, including death, or property damage that may occur during the construction operations of independent contractors and subcontractors. This policy also pays legal expenses associated with the owner's defense. Despite the fact that the contractor and his subcontractors are directly and legally responsible for their acts, the owner is often made a party to legal actions arising from acts or omissions connected with their construction activities. The owner's protective policy protects him against liability imposed by law arising out of construction operations as well as covering any liability he may incur as a result of his direction or supervisory acts in connection with the work being performed. Sometimes the construction contract specifies that the contractor provide contingent liability for both the owner and the architect-engineer. In this case, the architect-engineer can be named as an additional insured on the owner's protective liability policy for an extra premium.

Although owner's protective liability insurance and hold-harmless contractual liability insurance duplicate coverages to some extent, they are basically separate coverages provided by separate policies. Both types of insurance can be required on the same project.

9.29 MOTOR VEHICLE INSURANCE

The operation of motor vehicles exposes the contractor to two broad categories of risk, insurance for which can be written as separate policies or can be combined into a single policy. One form of risk is loss or damage to the contractor's own vehicles caused by collision, fire, theft, vandalism, and similar hazards. The other form of risk is liability for personal injury to others or damage to the property of others caused in some way by the operation of the contractor's vehicles. Many states have statutory requirements concerning the purchase of liability insurance by owners of motor vehicles.

Motor vehicle insurance is usually written as a single policy that includes bodily injury liability, property damage liability, and various forms of protection for the contractor's own vehicles. If only a few units are involved, collision coverage is usually purchased. However, most contractors with large fleets of vehicles prefer to self-insure the collision exposure because of the high premium costs involved. Collision insurance provides for a specified sum of money to be deductible from each collision loss occurrence. This deductible amount can be made to vary, correspondingly changing the premium rates charged. In view of recent large awards in cases of personal injury and the claim consciousness of the public in general, the contractor must maintain high limits in his auto liability policy. As with other liability coverages, the increased premium costs are not excessive and the loss possibilities are very real.

There are endorsements that the contractor should consider when purchasing his motor vehicle insurance. One is a nonownership endorsement that provides protection when an employee uses his private automobile in going about the contractor's business. Another endorsement provides hired vehicle liability insurance that covers rented units. If the rented vehicles are already covered by automobile liability insurance, it is possible for the contractor to receive a reduction in premiums for his hired vehicles coverage.

9.30 MOTOR VEHICLE AND CONSTRUCTION EQUIPMENT INSURANCE

To avoid dangerous gaps in his insurance and to guard against needless duplication, it is important that the contractor have a clear understanding concerning the respective coverages of his motor vehicle insurance, his comprehensive general liability insurance, and his equipment floater policy. This is particularly true with respect to construction equipment being transported on public thoroughfares and equipment that is self-locomoting and that may be licensed as a motor vehicle. With respect to liability coverage, the comprehensive general liability policy usually covers accidents involving such equipment, whether or not it is licensed as a motor vehicle, if its primary role is assisting construction at a job site or on the contractor's premises. By the same token, the equipment floater usually affords the contractor protection against damage to his equipment regardless of location. However, the dividing lines are not always clear, and the advice of an experienced insurance broker should be sought in this regard.

Many accident possibilities involving motor vehicles and construction equipment represent borderline cases between the respective coverages of the three types of insurance mentioned in the previous paragraph. Because of possible dispute concerning the coverages between policies, it is preferable that the contractor purchase all three types from the same insurance company. There is also a "road construction, maintenance, and special equipment endorsement" to the auto liability policy that contractors often find it desirable to obtain. This endorsement removes a twilight zone involving construction equipment that is being transported or towed by the contractor's vehicles.

9.31 THE PRINCIPLES OF WORKMEN'S COMPENSATION

Before the present era of workmen's compensation acts, an employer was obligated to protect his employees only to the extent of exercising reasonable care. To obtain redress at the common law, an injured employee had to file suit against his employer and prove that the injury was due to the latter's negligence. Available to the employer were the accepted common-law defenses of contributory negligence of the injured employee, assumption of risk by the injured employee, and negligent acts of fellow employees. This trinity of common-law defenses made it difficult for a disabled worker to prove employer responsibility and negligence. The process was a slow, costly, uncertain one at best for the employee.

The social and economic consequences of this problem were instrumental in the development of workmen's compensation laws. Wisconsin enacted the first state workmen's compensation law, which became effective in 1911. Since that time, compensation legislation has been passed by the federal government, every state and territory of the United States, and each dominion of Canada.

The underlying economic principle of workmen's compensation is that the costs associated with the personal injury or death of employees, regardless of fault, is an expense of production and should be borne by the industry. The expense incurred by the employer in providing suitable protection for his employees is considered as another cost of doing business and, as such, is presumably reflected in the selling price of his product. The fundamental objective of the compensation statutes is to ensure that an injured workman receive prompt medical attention and monetary assistance during his convalescence or disability. Such assistance is provided by the employer and involves a minimum of legal formality.

Another basic principle is the strict liability of the employer, regardless of any fault of the injured employee. Contributory negligence of the employee, such as failure to wear a company-provided safety helmet or to conform with posted safety regulations, will not usually affect the employer's liability. As a matter of fact, about the only exceptions to the payment of compensation benefits occur when the worker deliberately inflicts the injury on himself, the injury is sustained in the course of committing a felony or misdemeanor, or the injury is intentionally caused by a third party for reasons not associated with the employment.

Secondary objectives of compensation laws are to free the courts from the tremendous volume of personal injury litigation, to eliminate the expense and time involved in court trials, and to serve as an instigating agent in the development of effective safety programs.

9.32 WORKMEN'S COMPENSATION LAWS

Although all of the various workmen's compensation laws embody the same general principles, they differ considerably in their working details, and no two of them are exactly alike. The contractor must be especially careful to buy proper insurance and conform with the legal requirements of the workmen's compensation laws of each state in which he works. Every law makes certain exclusions to its coverage. For example, most of the acts exclude domestic servants, farm labor, and casual employees. Businesses that employ less than a specified number of employees are exempted in some of the states. Interstate railway workers and maritime employees are not covered by the compensation acts but are protected by separate federal legislation.*

Some compensation laws are designated as compulsory and others as elective. Every employer whose employees are covered by a compulsory law must accept the act and provide for the benefits specified. Failure to comply with the pre-

---

* Contractors who own watercraft, operate wharf facilities, or engage in marine construction sometimes employ workers covered by the Longshoremen's and Harbor Workers' Compensation Act or the Jones Act for Seamen. Workers covered by these federal statutes are not ordinarily protected by workmen's compensation statutes, and workmen's compensation insurance does not apply. Separate insurance must be provided in such cases.

scribed provisions can result in severe penalties, the payment of damages to injured workmen, and possible imprisonment. In areas where the law is elective, employers have the option of either accepting or rejecting it. However, if an employer elects to remain outside the legislation, he risks an injured worker's suit for damages and simultaneously loses the three common-law defenses: assumption of risk, negligence of fellow employees, and contributory negligence. In effect, this means that all the laws are compulsory. In most states, the "presumed acceptance" principle applies, whereby in the absence of specific notice to the contrary, the employer is presumed to have accepted coverage by the act. Workers in excepted or excluded employments may usually be brought within the act through voluntary action by their employer.

All of the states, territories, and the District of Columbia have enacted child labor laws that regulate the conditions under which minors may be employed. All of the compensation laws cover legally employed minors. In some jurisdictions, double compensation or added penalties are provided in cases of injury to illegally employed minors. Minors also enjoy special legal benefit provisions.

9.33 ADMINISTRATION OF WORKMEN'S COMPENSATION LAWS

Workmen's compensation laws are generally administered by commissions or boards created by law. A few states provide for court administration. Statutory provisions relating to administration vary somewhat from state to state, but each of the laws contains certain regulations pertaining to its implementation. Notice to the employer of the injury by the injured workman is required within stipulated time limits, although this requirement is excused for cause. A claim must be filed by the injured workman within a statutory period. Such claims are normally settled by agreement subject to approval of the administrative body.

Review and appeal of the compensation award to the injured worker, as well as regulation of attorney fees, are provided for by the various acts. Requirements vary concerning the keeping of accident records by the employer, but all states require that the employer report injuries to a designated authority. Failure to report in accordance with the applicable statute can result in fines and, in some jurisdictions, even imprisonment. Except for preliminary reports, the contractor's insurance company usually makes the formal reports required by law except in states with monopolistic funds.

An employee who files an application for compensation under a workmen's compensation statute ordinarily forfeits his legal right to sue his employer for damages. When an injured employee chooses to reject the statute and sues an employer who is covered by it, the employer usually retains the three common-law defenses. Conditions for rejection of the statute by an employee are usually so severe as to make the privilege of filing suit outside of the applicable workmen's compensation act virtually inoperative.

Benefits to an injured worker under an act are only those provided by the law and approved by the administrative authority. Should the injured party not be satisfied with the award as specified by law, he can appeal to the court designated by the act. Such appeal must be initiated within a statutory period. In some jurisdictions, the employee can file suit against his employer under the compensation act for alleged failure to provide safety devices.

9.34 WORKMEN'S COMPENSATION BENEFITS

All workmen's compensation laws provide various forms of benefits for the injured worker or, in the event of his death, for his family. These benefits include medical treatment, hospitalization, and income payments for the worker during his disability. Also provided are death benefits for the worker's dependents. Many jurisdictions include special benefits such as a lump-sum payment for disfigurement, rehabilitation services, and extra benefits for minors injured while illegally employed. Practically all statutes now stipulate that medical benefits shall be provided without limitation as to maximum total cost. Most states require a waiting period before a worker can collect benefits, 7 days being typical. However, most states allow a worker who has been off the job for a specified length of time to receive benefits for the waiting period retroactively.

Four classifications of disability are used in conjunction with workmen's compensation benefits. These are (1) temporary total, (2) permanent partial, (3) permanent total, and (4) death. These are more thoroughly discussed in Chapter 15.

The great majority of compensation cases involves temporary-total injury classifications, under which the worker is unable to work temporarily but ultimately recovers fully from his injuries and returns to employment. Income benefits payable during his period of convalescence are determined as a percentage of the worker's average wages. Some states limit the minimum and maximum benefits payable weekly, as well as the number of weeks and the total dollar amount of benefit eligibility.

Permanent-partial disability connotes a permanent injury, although the worker usually is able to return to work. This form of disability is classified either as a schedule injury, meaning the loss of a thumb, eye, leg, or other member of the body; or a nonschedule injury, which is of a more general nature. With schedule injuries, most compensation acts stipulate specific benefits that are payable for a fixed number of weeks, depending upon the nature of the loss sustained by the worker.

A permanent-total disability injury prevents the worker from engaging further in gainful employment. Most of the state workmen's compensation laws provide that specified benefit payments shall be made for life in cases of permanent-total disability. The other statutes limit the benefits as to time, amount, or both.

In the event of the accidental death of a workman, all states provide for the payment of death benefits to his family or other dependents. A few acts provide for payment of benefits to the widow for life or until remarriage, and to children until they reach a prescribed age. Most states place a limitation on the time period or total amount of such payments.

9.35 ADDITIONAL PROVISIONS OF WORKMEN'S COMPENSATION LAWS

Practically every workmen's compensation statute now includes occupational diseases within its coverage. Provisions vary, but compensation benefits are generally the same as for other forms of disability. Many states have provided for extended periods of time during which claims may be filed as a result of certain latent, slowly developing occupational diseases. Some states have special provisions regarding silicosis, asbestosis, radiation disability, and occupational loss of hearing caused by noise.

"Second-injury" funds have been developed to meet problems arising when an employee, previously injured, suffers a second injury that, combined with the first, results in a total disability much more severe than that caused by the second injury alone. Under ordinary circumstances, the employer in whose employ the second injury took place must provide benefits as dictated by the total resulting disability. This condition has made employers understandably reluctant to hire previously injured persons. Most states have now provided that the employer is responsible for payments required by the second injury only. Additional compensation to the injured employee as called for by the combined effects of his injuries comes from "second-injury funds," which were created at the time the second-injury provisions were enacted into law.

9.36 WORKMEN'S COMPENSATION INSURANCE

Every compensation act requires the employer either to obtain suitable insurance or to give satisfactory evidence of his financial ability to carry his own risk by qualifying as a self-insurer. Monopolistic state funds have been established in a few states and the provinces of Canada. Under the laws of these jurisdictions, employers whose operations are covered by the compensation laws are required to insure in the state funds, although in some instances employers can qualify as self-insurers. Other states have competitive state funds, whereby the employer may purchase his compensation insurance from a private insurance carrier or a state fund. In the remaining states private insurance companies provide all workmen's compensation insurance.

Workmen's compensation insurance is unlimited in the policy and will pay the medical costs and provide the benefits required by law. This insurance also provides legal defense for the insured and pays any court awards in jurisdictions where an injured workman can bring suit against his employer under the compensation act.

The contractor must have workmen's compensation insurance in force for each state in which he works. By use of an "all-states" endorsement, certain large insurance companies can provide compensation insurance applicable to all but the monopolistic fund states. Otherwise, separate policies must be purchased for each state.

9.37 WORKMEN'S COMPENSATION INSURANCE RATING SYSTEMS

Both compensation legislation and court interpretations of such laws have adopted a very liberal attitude as to what constitutes an occupational injury or disease. This broadened workmen's compensation coverage, together with sizable increases in benefits, has caused compensation insurance rates to rise very substantially during the past years. Insurance companies, in an effort to minimize claims, have become active participants in the field of construction safety and have established merit systems whereby contractors are rated according to their accident experience. In most states, contractors with good safety records are rewarded by reductions in their compensation rates, and those with poor records are penalized through rate increases.

Insurance companies generally regard large contractors as better risks than small concerns for both public liability insurance and workmen's compensation insurance. This fact may be explained by the larger premiums that the insurer receives from the bigger operator. The insurance company is thereby better able to absorb an occasional heavy loss and still enjoy a profit on the contractor's overall business. The small contractor may also be considered as a poorer risk for other reasons. His accounting methods are frequently rudimentary, and the insurance company finds it expensive to make the periodic audits of his payroll records. Also, the small contractor often employs few if any supervisory personnel, with the result that inadequate and unsafe construction techniques may be used.

9.38 WORKMEN'S COMPENSATION INSURANCE PREMIUMS

Premiums for compensation insurance are computed by multiplying each employee's wages, up to $300 per week in most states, by the rate specified for his work classification. For premium purposes, any overtime work is figured at straight time. Any excess in wages over $300 per week is not subject to assessment. Auditors of the insurance company conduct periodic audits of the contractor's books to verify that sufficient premiums have been paid.

Premium rates for compensation insurance vary considerably from state to state and with the classifications of work involved. Since a higher premium rate is charged for the types of work that entail greater risks of injury, it pays the contractor to show accurately the work classifications that his employees are actually filling. To cite an example, the following represent typical base rates for compensation insurance per $100 of wages for an ironworker:

Steel erection
Doors and sash	$ 2.74
Interior ornamental	2.74
Structural	36.06
Dwelling, two stories	13.38
General	36.06

Should the superintendent or payroll clerk carelessly classify ironworkers as doing "structural" work when they actually are employed in one of the other categories, the contractor could be paying more than thirteen times too much for this portion of his compensation insurance. Another important factor is that, using the foregoing example, if all ironwork is simply designated as "steel erection" without a subclassification, the insurance company will charge all such labor at the $36.06 rate. The insurance company can give the contractor valuable tips on how to set up his payroll records so that no more premium payments are made than are necessary.

Workmen's compensation insurance is also sold on a retrospective basis under which the final premium that the contractor pays is adjusted up or down according to his accident experience. When the retrospective rating plan is used, the contractor pays his regular compensation premium rates during the life of the policy. Some period after expiration of the policy (a year is usual) the insurance carrier evaluates the contractor's losses under the policy. The premium is then adjusted up or down, the contractor receiving a rebate if his loss experience was good and being required to pay additional premium if his loss experience was unfavorable. Compensation insurance sold on a retrospective basis stipulates both a minimum and a maximum premium rate that the contractor must pay under the policy. Several different retrospective plans are available, each plan specifying a different set of minimum and maximum premium rates and providing for different possible ranges of final premium adjustment.

9.39 SELF-INSURANCE

A large majority of the compensation acts allows an employer to act as his own insurer, provided that he can satisfy certain minimum legal requirements as stipulated by the various state insurance departments. Self-insurance is limited in a practical sense to big companies having such a large spread of risks that they can assume their own liability on workmen's compensation to their financial advantage. For complete self-insurance, the contractor must establish his own services of claim adjustment, claim investigation, safety engineering, and others similar to those furnished him by insurance companies. In order to qualify as a self-insurer with state officials, a contractor may be required to furnish a surety bond in an amount fixed by law or the administrative agency.

Self-insurance programs have been devised between employers and insurance companies, whereby the employer is self-insured up to certain maximum amounts, payments in excess of which are guaranteed by excess insurance purchased from the insurance company. Under such plans, the employer deposits a percentage (75 percent, for example) of the usual workmen's compensation insurance premiums in a bank. This establishes a fund for the payment of workmen's compensation benefits. The remainder of the premium (25 percent, in our example) is paid to the insurance company. This payment goes in part to purchase the excess insurance coverage. The remainder of the payment to the insurance company provides the contractor with the usual insurance company services pertaining to claims, inspections, engineering, auditing, accident reports, and medical and legal services.

9.40 EMPLOYER'S LIABILITY INSURANCE

Employer's liability insurance is written in conjunction with workmen's compensation insurance and affords the contractor broad coverage for personal injury or death of an employee arising out of or occurring in conjunction with his employment but not covered by the workmen's compensation policy. Workmen's compensation laws, which provide that an injured employee shall receive specified benefits from the employer or his insurer, concomitantly deny the employee the right to sue his employer at common law for his injury under the act. Because he is compensated for his injury, it is impossible in most jurisdictions for the injured employee to bring suit against his employer directly.

There are instances, however, in which an injury to an employee may fall outside the coverage of workmen's compensation or in which an injured employee may choose not to accept workmen's compensation benefits but to sue the contractor for damages. For example, if the employee is injured through failure of his employer to provide safety appliances or working conditions required by state law, the employee may elect to sue his employer for damages rather than accept the compensation specified by the state workmen's compensation act. The employee may be entitled to recover damages from his employer if he can prove that the latter's negligence caused his injuries while eating lunch or performing other similar acts. The contractor may have a minor operation in another state and inadvertently fail to comply with the technical requirements of the workmen's compensation law in that state. The injured employee may sometimes file suit against another party, such as the owner or a subcontractor. In this event, it is usual for the owner or subcontractor immediately to make the contractor a party to the action. In each of the instances just cited, workmen's compensation insurance provides no direct protection for the contractor. However, his employer's liability insurance will pay the legal costs incurred in his defense as well as any judgment that may be made against him, up to the face amount of the policy.

The standard employer's liability insurance coverage, as provided by the workmen's compensation rate structure, is $25,000 for each accident. The premium for this basic amount is included in the workmen's compensation insurance premiums. However, higher limits can be obtained by the payment of additional premium.

9.41 "WRAP-UP" INSURANCE

In "wrap-up" or "umbrella" insurance the same insurance carrier provides all of the workmen's compensation and employer's liability insurance, as well as comprehensive general liability insurance for every contractor and subcontractor on a construction project. Although the general contractor may elect to use wrap-up insurance, this discussion will assume that the choice is made by the owner, as is ordinarily the case. Wrap-up plans do not usually include the builder's risk insurance, vehicle insurance, and other such coverages but can be arranged to include several endorsements to the comprehensive general liability policy, such as contractual liability and completed operations coverage.

When the single-carrier scheme is used, one of two plans is followed. Under one form, the owner buys and pays for all of the insurance required. The general contractors and the subcontractors bid on the project without including the cost of the insurance in their proposals. When the second plan is used, the owner designates one insurance company from which all contractors and subcontractors must buy the designated insurance coverages at their own expense. Under this form, usually called a "designated carrier" plan, each employer is issued his own workmen's compensation and employer's liability policy and his own comprehensive general liability policy.

The prime attraction of this form of insurance coverage is the reduced cost to the owner, both in the direct cost of the premiums and in the saving of the contractor's and subcontractor's markup on the cost of the premiums when the owner buys and pays for the insurance himself. Lower premium rates are effected through volume purchase from a single carrier. Wrap-up insurance also eliminates much of the administrative detail involved when each contractor and subcontractor on a project buys his own insurance. Under these conditions, layer upon layer of hold-harmless clauses can increase the cost of the public liability insurance. There seems to be little question that on large projects the direct cost of insurance can be reduced through use of the wrap-up insurance concept.

However, there are many drawbacks associated with the wrap-up scheme from the viewpoint of the contractor and his subcontractors. Because any insurance dividends revert to the owner when he buys such insurance, the contractor receives no benefit from his having a good safety record on the project. On the other hand, if his record on that project happens to be poor, his experience rating rises, thus increasing his insurance premiums. Under state rating systems, these higher premium costs will apply to all of his subsequent work, including projects where he buys his insurance himself, until such time as his rating is again adjusted.

Wrap-up plans upset the normal business arrangements that contractors have with their usual brokers and insurance companies. The contractor must deal with a different set of brokers, safety engineers, underwriters, claims people, and auditors for each different insurer. Several payroll audits each year by different insurance companies can seriously disrupt a contractor's normal office routine and add to his administrative costs.

9.42 DISABILITY BENEFIT INSURANCE

Disability benefit laws in some states require most employers to provide insurance protection for their employees for disability arising from accidents or diseases not attributable to their occupation. Disability insurance supplements workmen's compensation by paying a weekly indemnity when an eligible wage earner is disabled by an off-the-job injury or illness. Usually, a waiting period of 7 days must elapse before benefits begin, thus eliminating claims for minor disabilities. All state plans provide for maximum weekly benefits and a maximum number of weeks that benefits are paid.

In some states, nonoccupational disability insurance may be obtained through either a private or a state plan. In others, all disability insurance required by law must be acquired through the state. State-administered plans are supported by payroll taxes levied against both the employer and the employee. Private plans are acceptable, particularly if underwritten by a reputable insurance carrier. Benefits provided by private plans must at least equal those in the state plan, while contributions from the employee must be no greater. The cost of disability insurance usually is shared by employer and employee. Some employers, however, regard these benefits as essential in their employee relations programs and underwrite the entire cost.

In some areas, the contractor's legal obligation for providing disability benefit insurance to his employees can be satisfied by his contributions to union welfare funds that provide disability benefits substantially the equivalent of those required by state law. Protection for nonunion employees and for union members who are not covered by such union welfare funds must be acquired through other sources.

9.43   INSURANCE CLAIMS

Every loss or liability for which the contractor's insurance may be responsible must be brought to the attention of the insurance carrier and perhaps other parties through the medium of a written notice or report. State workmen's compensation statutes require that accident reports be submitted covering all compensable accidents to employees. In the event of accidental injury to a person not an employee, the contractor should, for his own protection, submit a complete report of the matter to the company carrying his public liability insurance. Motor vehicle accidents must usually be reported both to the insurance company and to law enforcement agencies on special forms provided. Fire and extended coverage damage is reported on a proof-of-loss affidavit, although final settlement is usually made on the basis of a detailed schedule of costs.

In order to ensure that claims are properly made and followed up, it is wise for the contractor to designate one man of his organization to assume complete responsibility for matters pertaining to insurance. In addition to the filing of reports and claims, this individual should be familiar with all aspects of the various insurance policies of the contractor and of his subcontractors. He should keep a check list of all coverages, examine all new construction contracts for insurance requirements, make necessary cancellations and renewals, keep a file of subcontractors' insurance certificates, and generally oversee the contractor's insurance program.

9.44   SUBCONTRACTORS' INSURANCE

By the terms of his subcontract forms, the prime contractor normally requires each subcontractor to provide and maintain certain insurance coverages. The insurance carried by his subcontractors is an important matter to the prime contractor. The subcontractors' coverage plays an important role in the total insurance protection of the prime contractor and often either of itself or in conjunction with the latter's own insurance provides direct protection for the prime contractor. In cases where the insurance coverage of a subcontractor proves to be faulty or inadequate, responsibility can devolve to the prime contractor from the subcontractor. In addition, when the subcontractor does not provide insurance coverage required by law, such as workmen's compensation insurance, the general contractor may be made responsible. Subcontract forms normally provide that, if the subcontractor does not procure the insurance required, the prime contractor has the right to obtain such insurance for the subcontractor and to charge the account of the latter with the premium cost involved.

9.45 INSURANCE CERTIFICATES

An insurance certificate is a printed form executed by the insurance company certifying that the insured has in force the insurance designated by the certificate. Such certificates are addressed to the party requiring the evidence of insurance and list the types and amounts of insurance that the insured has purchased. These certificates denote the expiration dates of the policies and contain a statement to the effect that the party in whose favor the certificate is drawn will be informed in the event of cancellation or change of the insurance described.

The general contractor is often required to submit certificates of his insurance to owners and other parties. Construction contracts usually contain the provision that the contractor shall submit suitable insurance certificates to the owner or the architect-engineer at the time the contract is signed or, at least, before field operations are started. Many building departments require proof that certain insurance is in effect before they will issue building permits.

It is standard practice for a general contractor to require suitable and up-to-date insurance certificates from all of his subcontractors. A properly maintained file of such certificates will ensure that each subcontractor provides and maintains the insurance coverages and amounts required by law and subcontract.

9.46 FEDERAL OLD-AGE, SURVIVORS, AND DISABILITY INSURANCE

This program, operated by the federal government through the Social Security Administration, provides three basic types of benefits for the workers covered. Old-age benefits are provided after a wage earner reaches a certain age and retires. Survivor benefits are provided for the dependents of a worker should he die at any age. Disability benefits are made available to a worker who suffers a disability that renders him unable to do any substantial work for which he is qualified by age, experience, and education for a period of 12 calendar months or longer. Since the passage of the original Social Security Act in 1935, benefits have been liberalized and the number of workers covered has been increased substantially.

Employees and employers share the cost of old-age, survivors, and disability insurance by paying special taxes into a fund in the U.S. Treasury, out of which benefits are paid. The employer must contribute for each employee the same amount as he deducts from the employee's pay. The tax rates paid by employer and employee are statutory as is the annual amount of wages subject to the tax. Both the tax rates and taxable earnings have been increased several times by Congressional action.

The Social Security Administration keeps a record of each worker's wages received while in employment covered by the Act. This record is maintained as a separate account for each worker, under his name and an identifying number. Each individual must have his own social security number, which he can obtain from any local social security office. Any worker can check up on his social security account by writing to the Social Security Administration and asking for a statement of his wage credits.

9.47 UNEMPLOYMENT INSURANCE

Unemployment insurance provides weekly benefit payments to a worker whose employment is terminated through no fault of his own. Each state has some form of unemployment compensation law that works in conjunction with the Federal Unemployment Tax Act. Also, each state has established its own law and administrative agency which works in partnership with the Bureau of Employment Security, an agency of the U.S. Department of Labor. Excluded from most state laws are firms employing fewer than four persons; railroad workers; domestic workers; federal, state, and municipal workers; workers in nonprofit educational, religious, or charitable organizations; agricultural workers; casual labor; and those who are self-employed.

Unemployment insurance is intended to provide workers with a weekly income to assist them during periods of unemployment. There is no intent to benefit those who cannot or will not work. Only persons who have been working for a specified period of time on jobs covered by their state unemployment compensation law, who are able and willing to work, and who are unemployed through no fault of their own are eligible to receive benefits.

All employers who come under the provisions of the state unemployment insurance laws must pay taxes based upon their payrolls up to a prescribed amount per calendar year for each employee. To be covered, the employment must consist of at least 1 day in each of 20 different weeks. The employer pays a part of such payroll taxes to the federal government and a larger share to the state in which the employment takes place. The federal law imposes on all covered employment a payroll tax whose rate is variable from year to year, depending upon the financial condition of the national fund. With certain restrictions, the employer can take credit against his federal unemployment tax for his payments to the state fund and for amounts that he is excused from paying to the state because of his favorable claim experience.

The standard unadjusted tax rate of the individual states is 2.7 percent. However, this rate is adjusted up or down for a given employer, depending upon his experience. A separate account is set up by the state for each employer covered. Each account is credited with tax payments made and charged with benefits paid to former employees. The extent to which the tax credits exceed the benefits charged determines by how much the employer's rate is adjusted above or below the basic tax rate. A contractor who finds it possible to offer a maximum of steady employment to his men can enjoy a substantial reduction in his state unemployment tax rate. Conversely, if he has a large turnover his tax rate can be raised. The state tax rate can also vary with the solvency of the state unemployment benefit fund. The tax rate applies to a company's entire work force and can vary from a minimum of less than 1 percent to as much as 4 percent. A few states require that employees also pay state unemployment taxes, but an employer in any of these states can elect to pay his employees' share as well as his own.

When a worker files a claim for benefits, his last employer is sent a notice. If the employer replies that the worker was separated for a reason other than lack of work, the benefits may not be chargeable against his account. In addition, an unemployed worker may disqualify himself from unemployment benefits by voluntarily quitting his last job without good cause, being discharged for misconduct, being directly engaged in a strike or other labor dispute, failing to apply for or to accept an offer of suitable work, and other causes. The amount of unemployment payments a worker can receive varies from state to state. The benefits are usually limited both as to weekly amount and the maximum number of weeks for which they are payable.

10

BUSINESS METHODS

10.1 GENERAL

It is the purpose of this chapter to discuss selected business methods that are of particular importance to the management of a construction firm. Because of the eclectic nature of the chapter, not all of the topics discussed bear a direct relationship to one another and are presented in no particular order.

10.2 RECORDS

One of the important reasons why construction contractors, like other business-men, must keep complete and accurate records is that they are required by law. In addition, the contractor must use up-to-date accounting methods to provide a continuous flow of essential management information. Accounting serves the purpose of helping management to control operations and utilize its working capital to the greatest possible advantage. Financial statements and reports are required for submittal to government agencies, bankers, surety companies, owners, insurance companies, and others. The contractor must know how the records are kept and understand the significance of the figures, not only for his own guidance but also for discussing credit needs with bankers and sureties.

10.3 ACCOUNTING METHODS

Although the details of record keeping vary among firms, there still exists a certain pattern of basic accounting procedure that is common to the construction industry. The main theme of a contractor's accounting system centers around the determination of income and expense from each of his individual construction projects. The original estimate of costs pertaining to each contract serves as a budget for that project. As costs are incurred, they are charged, directly or indirectly, against the job to which they pertain. It is customary that the keeping of a contractor's business accounts be concentrated in his home office. However, on large projects and cost-plus contracts, a set of books is frequently established in the field office in which all record keeping pertaining to the project is done directly on the job site. The controlling accounts of such projects are incorporated into a master set of accounting records maintained in the contractor's central offices.

The basic accounting procedure used by a contractor can be either the cash method or the accrual method. Under the cash method, income is taken into account only when cash is actually received and expense is taken into account only when cash is actually expended. This accounting method is used principally by professional men, small businesses, and nonprofit organizations, and for personal records. The pure cash method is applicable only to very small construction companies and is not often used, although a modified form that follows federal income tax regulations is sometimes utilized. If a construction company does only small jobs for cash, maintains little or no materials inventory, and owns no equipment of consequence, the modified cash method is simple and adequate. However, for most construction companies, the cash method is neither adequate nor economical.

For the majority of construction companies, the accrual method is the only acceptable basic accounting procedure. Under this method, income is taken into account in the fiscal period during which it is earned, regardless of whether or not payment is actually received. Similarly, items of expense are entered as they are incurred, whether actually paid out during the period or not. The straight accrual method is used for the accounting of short-term contracts, that is, construction contracts whose operations are completed within a single accounting period. Technically, contracts of less than twelve months duration are short term. However, current practice often treats a contract that extends into more than one accounting period as long term, even if its duration is less than twelve months.

10.4 ACCOUNTING FOR LONG-TERM CONTRACTS

When long-term competitive contracts are involved, two variations or hybrids of the accrual method are used. These are called the "percentage-of-completion method" and the "completed-contract method." The two methods differ in the manner in which costs and expenses are matched against the revenue to which they are most closely related and in the identification of the period in which the income from the job is taken into account.

Each of these methods has both tax advantages and disadvantages. The contractor will be well advised to seek the assistance of a competent tax accountant when selecting one or the other of these two procedures for use by his company. It is possible and preferable in some circumstances to use one method for certain contracts and the other for other contracts. However, the two methods are mutually exclusive for one specific contract. It should be noted that approval of the Internal Revenue Service may be necessary to change an established income-reporting method.

10.5 PERCENTAGE-OF-COMPLETION METHOD

The percentage-of-completion method recognizes job income as the work advances. Thus, the profit is distributed over the fiscal years during which the construction is under way. This method has the advantage of recognizing income periodically on a current basis rather than irregularly as contracts are completed. It also reflects the status of contracts still in process through the current estimates of costs to complete or of progress toward completion.

The major weakness of this procedure is its dependence on estimates of costs to complete the work, which can be subject to considerable uncertainty. The amount of income to be recognized in a given fiscal year from an uncompleted project can be computed in a variety of ways. One typical procedure is to estimate the percentage of the total anticipated profit earned to date as the ratio that the incurred costs to date bear to the anticipated total cost, with proper allowance for any revised estimates of costs to complete.

It must be observed at this point that the usual monthly pay requests do not constitute an acceptable basis for profit allocation. Generally speaking, there is little relation between amounts billed to owners and realized income on partially completed contracts. In some instances, the contractor's early billings are excessive when compared with the work actually performed. As mentioned in an earlier chapter, such unbalanced payments are common and serve to reimburse the contractor for his move-in and start-up expenses. In other instances, the architect-engineer may purposely keep the contractor's progress payments below the amounts due for the work actually performed. On a practical basis, therefore, billings to the owner do not generally provide a proper measure of partial earnings on either a lump-sum or a unit-price contract. On the other hand, costs ordinarily do.

10.6 COMPLETED-CONTRACT METHOD

The completed-contract accounting method recognizes project income only when a contract is completed, or substantially so. Substantial completion is construed to mean that the remaining costs are not appreciable in amount. During construction operations, periodic payments and costs are accumulated but no profits or income are recorded before the project is substantially completed.

The principal advantage of the completed-contract method is that income is reported after final results are known rather than being based on estimates of ultimate costs that can involve many unforseeable variables. A disadvantage of the method is that it does not reflect current performance for long-term contracts and may result in irregular recognition of income and hence, in some situations, in greater income tax liabilities. Another disadvantage of the completed-contract method is that the year of completion of a project can be subject to considerable uncertainty if the end of the project coincides with the end of the accounting period or if there are disputed claims unsettled at the end of that year. Special problems can also arise with respect to allocation of office overhead expense during years with abnormally few or abnormally small contracts in process.

As a rule, the percentage-of-completion method is preferable if the contractor maintains cost records that are sufficiently dependable for him to estimate with reasonable exactness the costs to complete the project. When the lack of records, changes in the scope of the contract, or hazards inherent in the work make the estimation of completion costs subject to considerable uncertainty, the completed-contract method is usually used.

10.7 LONG-TERM COST-PLUS CONTRACTS

Under a cost-plus form of construction contract, it is usual that the contractor be reimbursed at regular intervals for his expenditures and at the same time be paid a pro rata share of his fee. Accounting procedures for recognizing income under cost-plus contracts parallel those discussed previously for competitive lump-sum or unit-price contracts. It is generally accepted practice to recognize as income current payments on the fee in the fiscal period when they become billable if the contract is written so that the risk of losing the fee is negligible. However, when there is a chance that the fee may be lost or reduced through operation of a penalty clause, as in some target-type contracts, or under a fixed-fee contract with a guaranteed maximum cost, the completed-contract method may be preferable with the entire fee being recognized as income when the contract is completed.

10.8 FINANCIAL AND COST REPORTS

Several summary forms of financial and cost reports are derived from the detailed business records. It is the purpose of such a report to group together significant facts in a way that will enable the person reading it to form an accurate judgment concerning some aspect of the company operation, such as the financial condition of the organization or the profit-loss results of its operations. As would be expected, much use of a company's financial reports is made by the company management itself. These reports are invaluable for the advance planning of operations. They reflect the company's borrowing and bonding capacities and yield much information concerning its policies with respect to purchasing, equipment ownership, and office overhead.

In addition, these financial reports serve many important functions with respect to external agencies. Bankers, surety and insurance companies, equipment dealers, credit-reporting agencies, and clients are all concerned with the contractor's financial status and profit experience. Stockholders, partners, and others with a proprietary interest use the financial reports to obtain information concerning the company's financial condition and the status of their investment. Two financial reports of particular importance are the income statement and the balance sheet.

10.9 THE INCOME STATEMENT*

The income statement is an abstract of the nature and amounts of the company's income and expense for a given period of time. This statement shows the profit or loss as the difference between the income received and the expenses paid out during the period. It is to be emphasized at this point that the income statement reports only the company's profit or loss experience during the reporting period and does not reflect the overall financial condition of the firm.

Figure 10.1 is an income statement of the Blank Construction Company, Inc., for the fiscal year ending December 31, 19——. The following paragraphs, keyed to the lower-case letters in parentheses, as they appear in Figure 10.1, explain the various items.

(a) This statement has been prepared on the basis that the Blank Construction Company, Inc., reports its income on a completed-project basis. Project income is the total contract value of all projects completed during the period covered by the statement. The total is obtained from a supporting schedule that shows the income figures for each completed project.

(b) Project costs include all materials, labor, equipment, subcontracts, job overhead, and other expenses that have been charged to the completed projects. A supporting schedule of job costs lists these expenses for the individual projects. Included with job costs is the office overhead expense that has been allocated to the completed projects. Office overhead is periodically distributed among the various projects in proportion to the costs incurred on them during the period.

(c) Subtracting project costs from project income yields net project income for the statement period.

(d) Other income lists the net income received from other sources.

(e) Total net income before taxes is the amount realized from all operations during the statement period.

(f) This sum represents federal and state income taxes paid or due for the statement period.

(g) Net income after taxes is the amount available for company expansion or for distribution to stockholders.

(h) This sum is the earnings accumulated as of the start of the statement period. A corporation can retain its earnings for business expansion or can distribute them as dividends to the stockholders. Tax laws provide penalties if earnings are retained that are not actually required and are surplus to business needs.

---

* The income statement is also known by other titles such as profit and loss statement, statement of earnings, statement of loss and gain, income sheet, summary of income and expense, profit and loss summary, statement of operating results, and operating statement.

THE BLANK CONSTRUCTION COMPANY, INC.

PORTLAND, OHIO

INCOME STATEMENT

For the Year ended December 31, 19___

ITEM	TOTAL
(a) PROJECT INCOME	$8,859,138.39
(b) Less Project Costs, including office	
overhead expense of $239,757.04	8,705,820.15
(c) Net Project Income	$ 153,318.24
(d) OTHER INCOME:	
Discounts Earned	$ 23,064.93
Equipment Rentals	23,758.93
Miscellaneous	12,882.64
Total Other Income	$ 59,706.50
(e) NET INCOME BEFORE TAXES ON INCOME	$ 213,024.74
(f) FEDERAL AND STATE TAXES ON INCOME	97,616.66
(g) NET INCOME AFTER TAXES ON INCOME	$ 115,408.08
RETAINED EARNINGS:	
(h) Balance, January 1, 19___	$ 75,507.24
(i) Dividends Paid	6,260.00
Total	$ 69,247.24
(j) BALANCE, December 31, 19___	$ 184,655.32

Figure 10.1   Income statement.

(i) Dividends paid represents distribution of earnings made to stockholders in the form of dividends on common stock during the statement period.

(j) The balance represents the total retained earnings of the corporation through the end of the report period.

10.10 THE BALANCE SHEET*

A balance sheet presents a summary of the assets, liabilities, and net worth of the company at a particular moment, for example, at the close of business on the final day of a fiscal year. Balance sheets are usually prepared as of the end of each

---

* The balance sheet may also be called by other names such as financial statement, statement of financial condition, statement of worth, or statement of assets and liabilities.

fiscal year and are of a form more or less prescribed by custom. They are universally used to describe the financial condition of business concerns. A representative example of a contractor's balance sheet is depicted in Figure 10.2.

The basic balance sheet equation may be stated as follows: assets = liabilities + net worth. The balance sheet presents in analytical form all company-owned property, or interest in property, and the balancing claims of stockholders or others against this property. The foregoing equation expresses the equality of assets to the claims against these assets. Assets are defined as anything of value, tangible or intangible. Liabilities involve obligations to pay assets or to render services to other parties. Net worth is obtained as the excess of assets over liabilities and represents the contractor's equity in his business. Here, "the contractor" is used in the broad sense meaning proprietor, partners, or stockholders.

The major headings of Figure 10.2 will now be discussed.

(a) Current assets include cash, materials, and other resources that may reasonably be expected to be sold, consumed, or realized in cash during the normal operating cycle of the business. When the business has no clearly defined cycle or when several operating cycles occur within a year, current assets (and current liabilities) are construed on a twelve-months basis. Prepaid expenses represent goods or services for which payment has already been made and which will be consumed in the future course of operations.

(b) Noncurrent notes receivable are in the nature of deferred assets, representing the value of notes that become payable at some future date or dates.

(c) Property represents the fixed assets of the business. These assets are more or less permanent in nature and cannot readily be converted into cash, at least not in amounts commensurate with their true values to the contractor. These assets generally have a useful life of several years, although assets such as buildings, equipment, vehicles, and furnishings do wear out gradually. These assets are capitalized at their purchase price or in accordance with appropriate cost appraisals.

(d) Accumulated depreciation represents the total decrease in value of the property as a result of age, wear, and obsolescence. Depreciation is more fully discussed in Section 10.12.

(e) Total assets is the sum of everything of value that is in the possession of or is controlled by the company.

(f) Current liabilities are debts that become payable within a normal operating cycle of the business [see Item (a)]. Presumably, payment will be made from current assets.

(g) In our example, the Blank Construction Company, Inc., is using the completed-contract method of reporting income. Deferred credits represent the excess of project billings over related costs on current contracts that have not reached substantial completion by the end of the reporting period. There is some difference of opinion concerning the proper way to treat this item. It seems reasonable to say that under most contracts the progress billings are merely advances against the amount that will be earned when the contract is completed. Consequently, the excess of progress billings over cost is a current liability representing the amount due the owner until the contract has been completed. This is the procedure followed in Figure 10.2.

THE BLANK CONSTRUCTION COMPANY, INC.

PORTLAND, OHIO

BALANCE SHEET

December 31, 19___

ASSETS		LIABILITIES	
(a) CURRENT ASSETS:		(f) CURRENT LIABILITIES:	
Cash on hand and on deposit	$ 389,927.04	Accounts payable	$ 306,820.29
Notes receivable, current	16,629.39	Due subcontractors	713,991.66
Accounts receivable, including retainage of $265,686.39	1,222,346.26	Accrued expenses and taxes	50,559.69
		Equipment contracts, current	2,838.60
Deposits and miscellaneous receivables	15,867.80	Provision for income taxes	97,616.66
Inventory	26,530.14	Total	$1,171,826.90
Prepaid expenses	8,490.68	(g) DEFERRED CREDITS:	
TOTAL CURRENT ASSETS	$1,679,791.31	Income billed on jobs in progress at December 31, 19___	$2,728,331.36
(b) NOTES RECEIVABLE, NON-CURRENT	$ 12,777.97	Costs incurred to December 31, 19___ on uncompleted jobs	2,718,738.01
(c) PROPERTY:		Deferred Credits	$ 9,593.35
Buildings	$ 5,244.50	TOTAL CURRENT LIABILITIES	$1,181,420.25
Construction equipment	188,289.80	EQUIPMENT CONTRACTS, NON-CURRENT	7,477.72
Motor vehicles	37,576.04	(h) TOTAL LIABILITIES	$1,188,897.97
Office furniture and equipment	13,596.18	NET WORTH:	
TOTAL PROPERTY	$ 244,706.52	(i) Common stock, 4,610 shares	$ 461,000.00
(d) Less accumulated depreciation	102,722.51	Retained earnings	184,655.32
NET PROPERTY	$ 141,984.01	(j) TOTAL NET WORTH	$ 645,655.32
(e) TOTAL ASSETS	$1,834,553.29	(k) TOTAL LIABILITIES AND NET WORTH	$1,834,553.29

Figure 10.2 Balance sheet.

(h) Total liabilities is the sum of every debt and financial obligation of the company.

(i) This is the capital stock account, showing the classes and amounts of stock that have been actually issued and paid for by the stockholders. In our example, 4,610 shares of $100-par-value common stock have been purchased by the owners.

(j) This represents the net ownership interest the corporation "owes" to the stockholders. In our example, it is obtained as the sum of the common stock investments plus retained earnings (also called "earned surplus"). The book value of the common stock as of December 31, 19——, is obtained by dividing $645,655.32 by 4,610, which gives $140.06 per common share. Book value excludes intangibles of all kinds that would have no value on liquidation.

(k) The equality of (e) to (k) illustrates that total assets = total liabilities + net worth.

10.11 FINANCIAL RATIOS

Ratios of various kinds are frequently employed as quantitative guides for the assessment of a company's financial and earning position. For example, ratios can be used to analyze income statements and balance sheets. By comparing the same ratios over a series of financial reports, very significant information can be obtained regarding company financial progress over the years. When such ratios are compared with similar figures of other contractors, a comparative financial picture of the business is obtained.

Although many ratios are used in the interpretation of financial reports, the following ones are considered to be of major significance. The value of each ratio below is computed for the Blank Construction Company, Inc., using data from the company's income statement, Figure 10.1, and balance sheet, Figure 10.2. This company is represented to be a building contractor whose financial structure is relatively good. In brackets and just below each ratio for the Blank Construction Company are shown ratios for contractors recently sampled by Dun & Bradstreet, Inc. The first figure is the upper quartile, the second figure is the median, and the third figure is the lower quartile of the contractors sampled.

It should be obvious that the Dun & Bradstreet ratios are illustrative only of contractor' financial experience in general and that some ratios for an individual contractor may vary substantially from these values. In addition, some of these ratios typically vary with the type of construction; for example, fixed assets to net worth are usually much higher for heavy and highway contractors than for building contractors.

The following data are from Figures 10.1 and 10.2:

Current assets	=	$1,679,791.31
Current liabilities	=	1,181,420.25
Total assets	=	1,834,553.29
Total liabilities	=	1,188,897.97
Fixed assets	=	141,984.01

Net worth $\qquad$ = $ 645,655.32
Net working capital = current assets — current liabilities = 498,371.06
Net profits (after taxes) = 115,408.08
Annual volume = 8,859,138.39

1. Net profits on annual volume $= \dfrac{\$115,408.08}{\$8,859,138.39}$ (100) $= 1.30\%$

$$[2.98 — 1.48 — 0.85]$$

2. Net profits on net worth $= \dfrac{\$115,408.08}{\$645,655.32}$ (100) $= 17.9\%$

$$[20.1 — 11.5 — 5.7]$$

3. Net profits on net working capital $= \dfrac{\$115,408.08}{\$498,371.06}$ (100) $= 23.2\%$

$$[41.5 — 18.8 — 8.4]$$

4. Annual volume to net worth $= \dfrac{\$8,859,138.39}{\$645,655.32} = 13.7$

$$[12.2 — 7.5 — 4.4]$$

5. Annual volume to net working capital $= \dfrac{\$8,859,138.39}{\$498,371.06} = 17.8$

$$[22.4 — 12.6 — 6.6]$$

6. Current assets to current liabilities $= \dfrac{\$1,679,791.31}{\$1,181,420.25} = 1.42$

$$[2.22 — 1.53 — 1.22]$$

7. Fixed assets to net worth $= \dfrac{\$141,984.01}{\$645,655.32}$ (100) $= 22.0\%$

$$[11.6 — 26.3 — 49.8]$$

10.12 DEPRECIATION

From the day of its acquisition, most property steadily declines in value because of age, wear, and obsolescence. This reduction in value, called "depreciation," is a cost of doing business and represents the physical depletion of assets such as offices, warehouses, vehicles, accounting machines, engineering instruments, and construction equipment of all sorts. Because of the continued decline in the value of such property, its cost must be amortized over its useful and economical life so that the contractor recovers his investment and has capital available when replacement of the property becomes necessary. The following paragraphs discuss methods of amortizing, or depreciating, assets, using construction equipment for the purpose of illustration.

The useful lives of various items of construction equipment are controlled to some extent for tax purposes by the Internal Revenue Service. A suggested guideline of the U. S. Treasury Department prescribes 5 years for general contract construction equipment and 12 years for marine contract construction. Lives shorter than these may be selected by a contractor provided that his claimed deprecation is in line with his actual replacement and modernization program. It is to be noted that the guidelines just cited do not apply to office equipment or machines, automobiles, general-purpose trucks, buildings, or water transportation equipment.

There are several methods of computing depreciation costs for tax-reporting purposes. Each of these methods has its advantages and disadvantages, depending upon many operational and financial variables of the company. The advice of an experienced tax accountant should be sought when a method is being selected for use. Generally speaking, permission of the Internal Revenue Service must be obtained before an operating company can change from one method to another. For construction equipment, four different procedures are commonly recognized as being acceptable approaches to calculating annual depreciation charges:

1. Production method.
2. Straight-line method.
3. Declining-balance method.
4. Sum-of-year-digits method.

With any of these methods, the value of each piece of equipment is decreased periodically. The sum of these reductions at any time is a depreciation reserve which, when subtracted from the initial cost of the equipment, gives its current book value. The book value represents the portion of the original cost that has not yet been amortized. As previously stated, depreciation charges are a cost of doing business and correspondingly reduce the earnings reported by the income statement. At the same time, the depreciation reserve represents capital retained in the business, ostensibly for the ultimate replacement of the capital assets being depreciated.

Each of the aforementioned methods will now be discussed. Depreciation accounting is in a more or less continual state of flux because of changes being made in existing tax laws. For this reason the depreciation methods will be discussed in general terms only. For purposes of illustration and comparison of the methods, let us consider a $16,000 ditcher having a probable service life of 5 years or 10,000 operating hours and an estimated salvage value of $1,000.

10.13 PRODUCTION METHOD

In the production method, the asset's cost is prorated on a per-unit-of-output basis. One form of this procedure apportions the depreciable value over the total expected hours of operation. Under the assumption that the ditcher will have a useful service life of about 10,000 hours of field operation, the book value of the machine will be decreased by $1.50 for each operating hour. This hourly depreciation is obtained by dividing the depreciable value (initial cost minus salvage value) of $15,000 by the total estimated service life (10,000 operating hours).

In a second form of the production method, the depreciable value is apportioned over the total units of production that the equipment will be expected to produce during its useful life. This procedure is applicable to production equipment such as rock crushers, aggregate plants, concrete batch plants, and asphalt paving plants. For example, the cost of an asphalt hot-mix plant can be spread over the total expected production of the plant, the depreciation rate being expressed as a fixed cost for each ton of hot mix produced.

10.14 STRAIGHT-LINE METHOD

The straight-line method writes off the cost of an asset at a uniform rate throughout the service life. The cost of an asset, for depreciation purposes, is established as the initial outlay less the anticipated disposal value, if any. The original outlay includes not only the sale price but also the costs of taxes, freight, unloading, and assembly. The salvage value must be realistic and is subject to revision by the Internal Revenue Service. The cost, so established, is then spread uniformly over the service life of the equipment. Useful life can be expressed in any one of several time units, but annual depreciation charges are usual. Table 10.1 illustrates the workings of this method.

10.15 ACCELERATED DEPRECIATION METHODS

Both the declining-balance method and the sum-of-year-digits method give a faster write-off during the first years of equipment life than for the later years. These procedures are called "accelerated depreciation methods." The use of procedures that afford larger depreciation deductions during the earlier years of asset ownership may have important advantages for a contractor. To illustrate, rapid initial depreciation causes cash to be retained in the business. Larger depreciation charges against regular income cause a reduction of income taxes for that year. This effect may or may not represent a long-range advantage, however, because depreciation charges companywide have a tendency to stabilize over the years.

Accelerated methods provide for faster recovery of equipment value, consequently offering the contractor some measure of protection against unanticipated contingencies later in the life of the equipment, such as obsolescence, excessive maintenance, rapid wear, or need for equipment of different size or capacity. Rapid depreciation amortizes the contractor's equipment investment more quickly and simultaneously decreases the book value at the same rate. Rapid reduction of book value leaves the contractor much freer to dispose of unsatisfactory equipment and, to some degree, can also assist him in combating the problem of replacing equipment during periods of inflation.

There are some restrictions on the use of the two accelerated methods; they are not as universally applicable as the straight-line method. For example, at the present writing, the two accelerated procedures can be applied only to new equipment whose cost is in excess of a stated minimum amount and whose service life is greater than a prescribed number of years.

TABLE 10.1   Annual Depreciation Costs of Ditcher

Original cost   = $16,000   Service life = 5 years
Assumed salvage value =   1,000

End of Year	Annual Charge	Accumulated Depreciation	Book Value
Straight-Line Method			
0	$ 0	$ 0	$16,000
1	3,000	3,000	13,000
2	3,000	6,000	10,000
3	3,000	9,000	7,000
4	3,000	12,000	4,000
5	3,000	15,000	1,000
Declining-Balance Method			
0	$ 0	$ 0	$16,000
1	6,400	6,400	9,600
2	3,840	10,240	5,760
3	2,304	12,544	3,456
4	1,382	13,926	2,074
5	830	14,756	1,244*
Sum-of-Year-Digits Method			
0	$ 0	$ 0	$16,000
1	5,000	5,000	11,000
2	4,000	9,000	7,000
3	3,000	12,000	4,000
4	2,000	14,000	2,000
5	1,000	15,000	1,000

* This value cannot become less than the salvage value.

10.16 DECLINING-BALANCE METHOD

With the declining-balance method, the annual depreciation charge is calculated as a constant rate times the book value. The rate is equal to 200 percent divided by the estimated service life in years. This rate is double the straight-line rate with the same useful life. A piece of equipment having a 5-year service life would then be depreciated at a rate of 40 percent of its undepreciated balance, or book value, each year. No salvage value is deducted from the initial asset cost when using the declining-balance method, although the book value cannot decrease below the estimated salvage value.

Table 10.1 shows how this method works as applied to our $16,000 ditcher. It is to be noted that, when the declining-balance method is used, the book value never reduces to zero as with the straight-line method, and a residual value always remains unrecovered at the end of the equipment's service life. The declining-balance rate used in Table 10.1 writes off about two-thirds of the cost of an asset in the first half of its service life.

10.17 SUM-OF-YEAR-DIGITS METHOD

This method calculates the annual depreciation to be charged on the basis of the sum of the digits representing each year in the asset's life. For example, for a 5-year service life, this sum would be $1 + 2 + 3 + 4 + 5 = 15$. A proportion of this total is then taken of the depreciable value for each year. To illustrate, $\frac{5}{15}$ of the depreciable value is taken as the first year's depreciation charge; $\frac{4}{15}$ the second year; $\frac{3}{15}$ the third year; $\frac{2}{15}$ the fourth year; the remaining $\frac{1}{15}$ the last year.

Table 10.1 presents the results of applying the sum-of-year-digits method to the ditcher. This method writes off about three-fourths of the depreciable cost in the first half of the life.

10.18 CASH DISCOUNTS

Discounts are frequently offered to the contractor by material dealers and others as an inducement for early payment of bills. These are not trade discounts in the sense of adjusting a catalog price or making a concession for quantity buying. Rather, cash discounts are in the nature of a premium given in exchange for payment of an invoice before it becomes due, and the buyer is entitled to the discount only when he pays within the time specified.

Many cash discount terms are in commercial usage; three will be mentioned here. The expression "$\frac{2}{10}$ net 30" means that, if the contractor makes payment within 10 days of the invoice date, 2 percent can be deducted from the face amount of the invoice. The bill in its full amount is due and payable 30 days after the date of the invoice. Material dealers normally date their invoices the day the goods are shipped. If the customer's location is close by, he has time to check the goods before paying within the discount period. A customer who is far removed geographically, however, may have to pay before the goods are actually received if he is to take advantage of the discount. To overcome this disadvantage to distant customers, some vendors, upon request, will mark their invoices "ROG" or "AOG" to indicate that the discount period begins on "receipt of goods" or on "arrival of goods."

A cash discount provision similar to the one just discussed is termed "prox," which means that the discount period is expressed in terms of a specified date in the next month after the shipments are made or billed. The expression "$\frac{2}{10}$ prox net 30" means that a 2 percent cash discount is allowed if the invoice is paid not later than the tenth day of the month following the purchase. The net due date of the account is 30 days from the first of that month.

Another commonly used discount is expressed as "$\frac{2}{10}$ E.O.M.," which indicates that a 2 percent discount can be taken if the invoice is paid before the eleventh day of the month after the purchases are shipped. If the buyer does not make payment within this period, the bill is considered to be due net thereafter.

Cash discounts are treated as income and appear as "earned discounts" on the income statement, Figure 10.1. On the basis of a single invoice, 2 percent may appear to be inconsequential. However, if a contractor is able to take this discount on a million dollars' worth of materials in a year's time, he has increased his earnings in the amount of $20,000.

The status of cash discounts is a matter of sufficient import that it should be clearly spelled out in cost-plus contracts. It is standard policy that all cash discounts accrue to the contractor, except when the owner has advanced the latter money from which to make payments. Documents of The American Institute of Architects reflect this policy, as shown by Article 11 of Appendix I. However, some forms of cost-plus contracts stipulate that the reimbursable cost of materials shall be decreased by the amount of any cash discounts taken, regardless of who provides the funds to make payment.

10.19 TITLE OF PURCHASES

Legal difficulties for the contractor sometimes evolve from the sale and purchase of materials. When such difficulties arise, the mutual rights and responsibilities of the buyer and of the seller are largely controlled by the "law of sales." Normally, the risk of loss or damage as related to personal property rests with the person holding title. Responsibility for loss and rights of each party as buyer or seller depend upon whether or not title of the goods has passed from seller to buyer at the time the issue is raised. For this reason, the time at which title of purchases passes from the vendor to the contractor is a matter of considerable importance.

Fundamentally, title to personal property that is the basis of a sale passes from seller to buyer when the parties intend it to pass. If the purchase order either states or clearly implies at what time title is to pass, the terms of the agreement govern. Seldom, however, do the parties to a sales agreement insert any provision that controls the passage of title. For this reason various rules for determining the intention of the parties have been formulated by the courts. In the absence of any stipulation in the purchase order to the contrary, title passes in accordance with the following rules.

Cash Sales. Agreements that call for delivery and payment to take place concurrently are called cash sales. Title to the goods does not pass until they are paid for and delivery takes place.

Sale on Trial. When goods are delivered to the buyer on approval or trial, title remains in the seller until the buyer displays an intention to accept the goods.

Delivery by Vendor. If the purchase order requires the seller to deliver the goods to the buyer's destination and delivery is made by the seller himself, the seller retains title until the goods are delivered and unloaded.

Shipment by Carrier. There is a general rule that, when the goods are shipped by common carrier to the buyer, title passes to the buyer when the seller delivers the goods to the carrier for transportation, with these exceptions:

1. When the seller fails to follow shipping instructions given by the buyer, such as the buyer naming a particular carrier and the seller shipping by another.
2. When the seller is required to deliver at a particular place, as at the buyer's dock or railroad siding.
3. When the seller is required to pay freight up to a given point, as in F.O.B. agreements.
4. When the seller is required by purchase order or custom to make arrangements with the carrier to protect the buyer, as by declaring the value of the shipment or in C.I.F. agreements, and fails to do so.
5. When the goods shipped do not correspond in both quality and quantity to those ordered.
6. When the seller reserves title by retaining the bill of lading.

F.O.B. Standing for "free on board," F.O.B. indicates that the seller pays the transportation costs up to a delivery place indicated. For example, contractors' purchase orders frequently specify delivery as F.O.B. job site or F.O.B. storage yard. If the purchase order requires the seller to pay the delivery charges to a designated point, the title does not pass until the goods have been delivered there. Hence, under an F.O.B. agreement, title goes to the buyer when the carrier delivers the goods at the place indicated.

C.I.F. Standing for "cost, insurance, freight," C.I.F. indicates that the purchase-order price includes the cost of the goods, customary insurance, and freight to buyer's destination. Title passes when the seller delivers the merchandise to the carrier and forwards to the buyer the bill of lading, insurance policy, and receipt showing payment of freight.

C.O.D. Meaning "collect on delivery," C.O.D. indicates that title passes to the buyer, if he is to pay the transportation, at the time the goods are received by the carrier. However, the seller reserves the right to receive payment before surrender of possession to the buyer.

10.20 PERIODIC PAY REQUESTS

Construction contracts typically provide that the owner shall make partial payments of the contract amount to the prime contractor as the work progresses. Payments at monthly intervals is the usual proviso. The pay requests may be prepared by the contractor, the architect-engineer, the owner, or the contracting officer on a public project. The general or special conditions usually stipulate what party is to have the responsibility and authority for compiling these requests.

In any event, a periodic pay request is based upon the work accomplished since the last payment was made by the owner. Consequently, field progress must be measured or estimated at intervals, and a payment form used that clearly identifies the units of work which have been accomplished and upon which the pay request is based. The contract may prescribe a payment form for use by the contractor. When the pay request has been compiled, it is transmitted to the owner through the architect-engineer or contracting officer, who approves the request and certifies it to the owner for payment.

10.21 PROJECT COST BREAKDOWNS

Construction contracts for lump-sum projects usually require that a cost breakdown of the project be submitted by the contractor for approval before any payment request by the contractor is presented. This cost breakdown is intended to serve as the basis for the subsequent monthly pay requests. This breakdown, which is actually a schedule of costs of the various components of the structure, is prepared in sufficient detail so that the architect-engineer or contracting officer can readily check the contractor's pay requests. Figure 10.3, which presents a typical monthly pay request, illustrates in the first column of figures a cost breakdown for our hypothetical Municipal Airport Terminal Building. Occasionally, to satisfy an owner requirement, the specifications will stipulate the individual items for which the contractor is to present cost figures. In the absence of such instructions it is usual to prepare the cost schedule by using the same general items as they appear in the specifications and on the final recap sheet of the estimate. This practice minimizes the time and effort necessary to prepare the breakdown figures and ensures a maximum of accuracy in the results.

Inspection of Figure 10.3 shows that the cost figures given for the individual work classifications do not check with those indicated on the recap sheet, Figure 6.4. The explanation for the discrepancy is that taxes, overhead, equipment, markup, and bond are not shown on the cost breakdown as separate items but have been prorated back into each of the cost items. The total of these five items has not been added entirely on a pro rata basis, however. Rather, items of work completed early in the construction period, such as excavation, concrete, reinforcing steel, and forms, have been increased proportionately more. This serves the purpose of helping to reimburse the contractor for his initial costs of moving in, setting up, and commencing operations, for which a pay item is seldom provided. Moderate unbalancing of cost figures, it will be recalled, assists the contractor financially and minimizes his initial investment in the owner's project.

It should be pointed out that a cost breakdown compiled for payment purposes cannot be used for the pricing of either extra work to or deductions from the contract. Items of general expense have been prorated into the various pay items whether or not they apply directly to a given item of work. Additionally, as has been discussed, these cost breakdowns are usually unbalanced to some degree.

10.22 PAY REQUESTS FOR LUMP-SUM CONTRACTS

Figure 10.3 illustrates the form of a typical pay request for a lump-sum building contract. Usually prepared by the general contractor, it includes all subcon-

THE BLANK CONSTRUCTION COMPANY, INC.

1938 CRANBROOK LANE

PORTLAND, OHIO

PERIODIC ESTIMATE FOR PARTIAL PAYMENT

Project: <u>Municipal Airport Terminal Building</u> Location: <u>Portland, Ohio</u>

Periodic Estimate No.: <u>4</u> for Period: <u>September 1, 19__,</u> to September 30, 19__

Item No.	Item Description	(1) Total Cost	(2) Completed to Date	(3) Cost to Complete	(4) Percent Complete
1	Clearing and Grubbing	$ 11,964	$ 11,964	$ --	100
2	Excavation and Fill	37,495	31,871	5,624	85
3	Concrete and Forms				
	Footings	34,843	24,739	10,104	71
	Grade Beams	35,997	20,878	15,119	58
	Beams	22,750	2,275	20,475	10
	Columns	7,349	2,205	5,144	30
	Slab	140,823	16,899	123,924	12
	Walls	20,544	7,396	13,148	36
	Stairs	14,962	---	14,962	0
	Sidewalks	12,300	---	12,300	0
4	Masonry	555,653	16,670	538,983	3
5	Carpentry	37,871	---	37,871	0
6	Millwork	86,357	---	86,357	0
7	Steel and Miscl. Iron				
	Reinforcing Steel	108,000	56,160	51,840	52
	Mesh	23,722	3,558	20,164	15
	Joist	117,290	---	117,290	0
	Structural	225,589	38,350	187,239	17
8	Insulation	26,256	---	26,256	0
9	Caulk and Weatherstrip	5,757	---	5,757	0
10	Lath, Plaster, and Stucco	250,454	---	250,454	0
11	Ceramic Tile	22,349	---	22,349	0
12	Roofing and Sheet Metal	217,282	8,691	208,591	4
13	Resilient Flooring	26,153	---	26,153	0
14	Acoustical Tile	33,390	---	33,390	0
15	Painting	98,341	---	98,341	0
16	Glass and Glazing	72,041	---	72,041	0
17	Terrazzo	99,229	---	99,229	0
18	Miscellaneous Metals	87,520	---	87,520	0
19	Finish Hardware	55,523	---	55,523	0
20	Plumbing, Heating, Air-Cond.	615,872	55,428	560,444	9
21	Electrical	401,616	20,081	381,535	5
22	Clean Glass	3,140	---	3,140	0
23	Paving, Curb, and Gutter	93,706	---	93,706	0
		$3,602,138	$ 317,165	$3,284,973	8.8
24	Change Order No. 1	5,240	---	5,240	0
		$3,607,378	$ 317,165	$3,290,213	8.8
A.	Cost of Work Performed to Date	$ 317,165			
B.	Materials Stored on Site (Schedule Attached)	67,699			
C.	Total Work Performed and Materials Stored	$384,864			
D.	Less 10 Percent Retained	38,486			
E.	Net Work Performed and Materials Stored	$ 346,378			
F.	Less Amount of Previous Payments	180,369			
G.	Balance Due This Payment	$ 166,009			

Figure 10.3 Periodic estimate for partial payment.

tracted work as well as that done by his own forces. For each work classification that he does himself the contractor estimates the percentage completed and in place. From invoices submitted by his subcontractors suitable percentage figures are entered for all subcontracted work. These percentage figures must be realistic measures of the work actually accomplished. Otherwise, the pay request may be disapproved.

The total value of each work classification is multiplied by its percent completion and these figures are totaled. The total work completed to date expressed as a percentage of the total project cost gives the percentage completion of the entire project (8.8 percent in our example). To the total of completed work is added the value of all materials stored on the site but not yet incorporated into the work. The cost of stored materials includes that of the subcontractors and is customarily set forth in a supporting schedule. From the total of work in place and materials stored on site is subtracted the prescribed retainage. This gives the total amount of money due the contractor up to the date of the pay request. From this is subtracted the amount of progress payments already made. The resulting figure gives the net amount now payable to the contractor.

10.23 PAY REQUESTS FOR UNIT-PRICE CONTRACTS

Payment requests under unit-price contracts are based upon field measurements of quantities of work completed. Measurement of quantities is done in several ways. Quantities of materials, such as cubic yards of aggregate, tons of asphaltic concrete, and bags of portland cement, are measured as they are delivered to the job site. Representatives of both the owner and the contractor check the amounts delivered and used. Other work classifications—for example, cubic yards of compacted fill, lineal feet of pipe, and cubic yards of excavation— must be actually measured in place. Survey crews of the owner and of the contractor often make their measurements independently and adjust any differences.

After the amount of each work unit in place has been determined, it is multiplied by its respective contract unit price. These figures are totaled, and the retainage is subtracted. The resulting sum represents the entire sum of money due the contractor for his work to date. From this amount is subtracted the total of all prior progress payments, giving the net amount of money payable to the contractor. There may or may not be provision for payment for materials stored on the site. After the work quantities have been determined, the actual pay request itself is often prepared by the owner, who sends it to the contractor for his approval before payment is made.

10.24 PAY REQUESTS FOR COST-PLUS CONTRACTS

Negotiated construction contracts sometimes provide that the owner will advance the contractor money to meet payrolls and to pay other expenses associated with the work. Otherwise, the contractor furnishes his own working capital, receiving periodic reimbursement from the owner for costs incurred. In either event, the contractor must make periodic accountings to the owner of the cost of the work, either to receive direct payment from the owner or to obtain further advances of funds.

Periodic pay requests under cost-plus contracts consist primarily of the submission of records of costs incurred by the contractor in his prosecution of the work. Copies of invoices, payrolls, vouchers, and receipts are submitted in substantiation of the contractor's claims. In addition to cost records of payments made by the contractor to third parties, the periodic pay requests customarily include equipment expense, overhead, and a pro rata share of the negotiated fee.

Because of the touchy nature of cost reimbursement, it is common practice to establish a field office when the work under a cost-plus contract is substantial enough to justify this action. Representatives of both the contractor and the owner are assigned to the project. All matters pertaining to payrolls, purchasing, disbursement, and record keeping for the project are carried out in the field office. Financial documents either are routed through the owner's representative or are available for his inspection at any time. This business procedure does much to eliminate misunderstandings and facilitates the final audit. Cost-plus contracts with public agencies customarily impose special conditions upon the contractor with regard to form of payment application, affidavits, and preservation of records.

10.25 FINAL PAYMENT

After project completion, corroborated by a final inspection, the architect-engineer or contracting officer indicates his acceptance of the work and authorizes the owner to make final payment to the contractor. If the final inspection discloses inadequacies in the work, these "punch-list" items must be completed by the contractor before final payment is made. Under a lump-sum form of contract, the final payment is the final total contract amount less the total of all previous payment installments made. With a unit-price contract, the final overall contract amount is determined by the measurement of final total quantities of all payment items. Final payment by the owner includes all retainage that has been withheld by him.

The final pay request must sometimes be accompanied by a written release of all claims that the contractor may have against the owner under the contract. In lieu of this release, provision may be made that acceptance by the contractor of final payment serves as a release of such claims. This release precludes the contractor's reserving any claims under the contract but does not apply to any claims for damages that may arise from breach of contract.

10.26 THE MECHANIC'S LIEN

A mechanic's lien is a right created by law to secure payment for work performed and materials furnished in the improvement of land. This statutory right attaches to the land itself in much the same way as a mortgage. The purpose of a lien statute is to permit a lien upon the premises where a benefit has been received by the owner and where the value or condition of the property has been increased or improved by the furnishing of the labor and/or materials and where the laborer and/or material supplier has not been paid. Following the lead of Maryland in 1791, every state has enacted some form of mechanic's lien law. These laws are similar in general import but differ considerably in detail. Lien laws are strictly construed by the courts, and full compliance with all provisions of the local statute is mandatory.

Lien laws are designed to protect workmen, material men, and, under certain conditions, general contractors and subcontractors. Rights accruing to general contractors and subcontractors are the same, but there are differences in the notices required of the two parties. In order for a general contractor to obtain a lien, a usual requirement is that the owner agreed to have the work done and to pay for it. In some states, a written contract must exist. In case of default by a private owner on a construction contract, the general contractor actually has two remedies available. He can file civil suit against the owner for breach of contract, or he can exercise his right of lien. In some cases he takes both courses of action.

Public property is not subject to a statutory lien, although some lien laws provide that unpaid workers, material suppliers, and subcontractors can claim a lien on funds due the general contractor. Pursuant to such an action, the public owner must withhold payment to the contractor until the validity of the claim is established. If the lienor's claim is upheld, the money is paid to him rather than to the contractor.

10.27 FILING A CLAIM

In order for any person who contracts directly with the owner to be able to obtain a lien, the statutes typically require him to record his notarized claim for public record with the county authority within the statutorily prescribed time. In most jurisdictions, this lien claim is considered sufficient if it names the owner, describes the project, contains appropriate allegations as to the work performed or materials furnished, and states the amount and from whom it is due. The time for filing differs from state to state, but general contractors typically have 60 days after the filing by the owner of a notice of project completion or, if no notice is filed, 90 days after the physical completion of the work that is the subject of the lien.

Laborers, subcontractors, or material dealers who contract with the general contractor rather than with the owner are also entitled to liens, but the statutory requirements for these people are often different from those for the general contractor. They must not only file a notice of lien for the public record, but also are usually required to give notice in writing to the owner or his agent. The time limit for such filing is prescribed by statute and is frequently different from that required of people contracting directly with the owner. In addition, the statutory time for filing a claim may begin with the date when the last labor or materials were furnished rather than with project completion.

Mention has been made previously that a party filing a lien must be careful to adhere to all of the statutory technicalities. For this reason, it is advisable that the services of a lawyer be obtained the first time that a lien is filed. After a contractor or subcontractor becomes familiar with the requirements of the law, a lawyer is no longer necessary because the contractor can file his own claim.

10.28   FORECLOSURE OF LIEN

Once the lien claim is filed and no payment has been made, proceedings must be brought to enforce the lien, usually within 90 days after filing. The court procedure by which the claim is judicially determined is known as a foreclosure action; it varies from state to state but is always highly technical and requires the services of a lawyer. If the evidence substantiates the claim under the mechanic's lien and the court finds that there is a sum of money due and owing, the court can order the property to be sold and the proceeds used to satisfy the indebtedness. The sale of the property is made at auction by the sheriff, and a certificate of sale is executed to the successful bidder. The holder of the lien is paid from the proceeds of the sale. Some statutes give the original owner a one-year period to redeem his property upon payment of the judgment, interest, and costs.

The priority of claims is a matter treated by the pertinent state statute. A mortgage subsequent to the construction contract is inferior to a mechanic's lien that arises out of work done under the contract. Mortgages outstanding at the time of the contract may or may not be inferior, depending upon the law. As a general rule, liens stand on an equal footing regardless of the order in which they are filed. An exception is the preferred status usually given to workmen and material dealers.

10.29   WAIVER OF LIEN

The right to lien may be waived in a number of ways, depending upon the particular statute. Construction contracts sometimes include a clause whereby the general contractor agrees not to file or place any liens against the owner's premises and waives his right in this regard. After the contract has been signed, this clause is binding on the contractor. The courts have long held that a contractor, by the terms of a contract, may waive his right of lien.

A broader form of waiver of lien used in construction contracts provides that no liens shall be filed by the general contractor or any subcontractor or material dealer. This proviso can be made binding on the subcontractors and material dealers provided that it is permitted by the statute involved and provided certain actions are taken by the general contractor, these actions depending upon the requirements of the law. For example, he may be required to give timely notice of the waiver before the purchase orders and subcontracts are signed, either by direct notification in writing to the subcontractors and material dealers or by making the waiver agreement a matter of public record. Additionally, the subcontracts and purchase orders may have to include a clause that expressly provides for the waiver of lien by the subcontractors and material dealers. This is a consequence of the fact that lien statutes often provide that the right of lien may be waived only by an express agreement in writing specifically to this effect. In some states, waivers of lien in the general contract are not binding on persons who are not parties to the contract.

10.30 AFFIDAVIT OF RELEASE OF LIENS

The contract may require that, before the owner will make final payment to the general contractor, the contractor submit an affidavit certifying that all indebtedness connected with the work has been paid (see Subparagraph 9.7.3 of Appendix C). If there are exceptions, the contractor must list the persons to whom money is owing and the amounts due. When the owner has been informed of sums payable on his project, either by affidavit from the contractor or by direct notice from the unpaid party, the owner may become liable for these debts if he does not withhold sufficient funds from the general contractor to cover them. If the general contractor certifies payment of all bills and the owner has not received any notification of debt, the owner is entitled to rely on the general contractor's statement and make final payment.

Sometimes the owner requires additional assurance in the form of releases of lien from the general contractor and all of the subcontractors and material suppliers. Figure 10.4 is Document G706 of The American Institute of Architects, which serves as an affidavit of release of liens from the general contractor to the owner. This form would be accompanied by a release of lien executed by each subcontractor and material supplier on the project. Figure 10.5 is an example of a release of lien that subcontractors and material suppliers submit to general contractors and owners.

10.31 ASSIGNMENTS

Construction contracts establish rights and duties on the part of both the owner and the contractor. Under certain circumstances, a party to a contract can assign his rights or duties under the contract to a third party, provided, however, that the assignment is not contrary to public policy or does not involve a right

CONTRACTOR'S AFFIDAVIT OF RELEASE OF LIENS AND PAYMENTS OF DEBTS AND CLAIMS

AIA DOCUMENT G706

OWNER ☐
ARCHITECT ☐
CONTRACTOR ☐
SURETY ☐
OTHER

TO (Owner)

ARCHITECT'S PROJECT NO:

CONTRACT FOR:

CONTRACT DATE:

PROJECT:
(name, address)

State of:

County of:

The undersigned hereby certifies that pursuant to Subparagraph 9.7.3 of the General Conditions of the Contract for Construction, AIA Document A201, Sept. 1966 Edition, the releases or waivers of liens attached hereto include the Contractor, all Subcontractors, all suppliers of materials and equipment, and all performers of work, labor or services who have or may have liens against any real or personal property of the Owner arising in any manner out of the performance of the above-named Contract.

The undersigned further certifies that, except as listed below, he has paid in full, or has otherwise satisfied all obligations for all materials and equipment provided, and for all work, labor, and services performed and for all known indebtedness and claims for damages arising in any manner in connection with the performance of the Contract referenced above for which the Owner or his property might in any way be held responsible.

EXCEPTIONS: (If none, write "none"):

SUPPORTING DOCUMENTS ATTACHED HERETO:

1. Contractor's Release or Waiver of Liens.

2. Consent of Surety to Final Payment. Wherever Surety is involved, Consent of Surety is required. AIA DOCUMENT G707, CONSENT OF SURETY, may be used for this purpose. Indicate attachment: (yes   ) (no   ).

3. List of separate Releases or Waivers of Liens from all Subcontractors and materials and equipment suppliers.

4. Separate Releases or Waivers of Liens listed in Item 3 above.

CONTRACTOR:

Address:

BY:

Subscribed and sworn to before me this
                                        day of   19

Notary Public:

My Commission Expires:

Figure 10.4 Contractor's affidavit of release of liens. This document, copyrighted by The American Institute of Architects, is reproduced here with its permission.

_____, 19___

RELEASE*

KNOW ALL MEN BY THESE PRESENTS, that _____
of _____
for valuable consideration, the receipt whereof is hereby acknowledged does for himself and his
successors in interest and assigns, hereby release and forever discharge The Blank Construction
Company, Inc., an Ohio Corporation, and its successors and assigns, for the construction and
completion of _____
_____ at _____
from all actions, debts, accounts, bonds, covenants, contracts, agreements, damages, claims, and
demands whatsoever, in law or equity, which have arisen or may arise out of or by reason of, or
which are based on that certain contract executed on the _____ day of
_____, 19___, by and between The Blank Construction Company, Inc. and the
undersigned, or which have arisen from or by reason of any cause, matter or thing whatsoever.

The undersigned further releases the owner and the owner's property from any claim of
any kind on account of work performed or materials furnished in connection with the above
referred to contract, or in connection with construction on above referred to project.

The undersigned further warrants that he has paid and satisfied all claims for labor and
materials used by him for or in connection with the work under the said contract. The undersigned further hereby agrees to indemnify and hold the aforesaid persons, firms and corporations
free and harmless from any and all such claims and any and all expenses including attorney's
fees, which may be incurred in contesting or adjusting any thereof.

IN WITNESS WHEREOF, the said _____
has caused these presents to be executed the day and year first above written.

_____
_____

Subscribed and sworn to before me this _____ day of _____, 19___.

_____
Notary Public in and for the
County of _____ State of _____

* Reproduced by permission from William E. Coombs, Construction Accounting and Financial Management, ©
1958 by F. W. Dodge Corporation.

Figure 10.5   Release.

or duty whose nature is strictly personal. One party to a contract can assign (or
transfer) his rights under the contract with or without the consent of the other
contracting party. Freedom of assignment, however, can be regulated by the
terms of the contract itself. A person cannot assign (or delegate) a contractual
duty without the consent of the other party to the contract.

Construction contracts usually contain provisions that expressly forbid the
owner and the general contractor to assign either the contract or funds due or to
become due under the contract to third parties without the assent of the other
(see Subparagraph 7.2.1 of Appendix C). The subcontract forms of the general
contractor customarily include a similar restriction [see Article X(8)(a) of
Appendix J]. The general contractor is often requested to approve an assignment
of moneys due or to become due a subcontractor. By assignment of such funds

to a bank, for example, the subcontractor can receive a loan from the bank to finance his operations. This form of assignment, which must be accepted in writing by the general contractor, requires that he make payments jointly to the subcontractor and the lending bank. Once the general contractor has signified his acceptance of an assignment, he is obligated to adhere to its terms.

11

PROJECT COST ACCOUNTING

11.1 GENERAL ACCOUNTING SYSTEM

A contractor's business records include journals, ledgers, and assorted books of accounts. Journals are books of original entry and are used for the preliminary recording of financial transactions in their chronological order, showing for each the date, the nature of the transaction, the amount involved, and the ledger accounts to be debited and credited. Contractors typically use several special-purpose journals such as purchase journals, cash journals, invoice journals, and yard material journals.

All debit and credit items listed in the journals are periodically transferred to their respective accounts in the ledgers through a process called "posting." Postings from the journals are normally made in subsidiary or detail ledgers. Typical subsidiary ledgers in common use by contractors are an accounts receivable ledger, a subcontract ledger, an equipment ledger, and project cost ledgers.

Summary data from the subsidiary ledgers are entered in control accounts that are collected together in a general ledger. The general ledger contains the controlling accounts for income, expense, profit and loss, assets, liabilities, and net worth.

11.2 ACCOUNT CODE

It is customary that an identifying code designation be assigned to each individual account of a contractor's records. The coding systems used by contractors are not standardized, although suggested standard designations have been proposed by various groups such as the American Association of Cost Engineers and the Associated General Contractors of America. Contractors often use their own cost code systems, which they have tailored to suit their particular operations. Alphabetic, decimal, and mixed cost codes are in use. The code used in this text is a decimal code and may be considered as typical of construction accounting practice.

Appendix K contains an abbreviated list of typical ledger accounts in common usage by contractors. The asset accounts as included in the general ledger are identified by whole numbers from 10 through 39. General ledger liability accounts are designated by 40 through 49, net worth by 50 through 69, income accounts by 70 through 79, and expense accounts by 80 through 99. Subaccounts are assigned a distinctive decimal number, the first part of which identifies the general ledger or control account under which the subaccount exists. For example, consider the account 14.105. The whole number 14 indicates a Property, Plant, and Equipment account. The first decimal number, 0.1, indicates that it is associated with Real Estate and Improvements. The last two numbers identify the specific piece of real property to which this account applies.

In Appendix K, it will be noted that Project Expense is designated by account number 80.000. This is where every item of expense chargeable to a particular job is recorded. This major category of Project Expense is often subdivided into three major subdivisions:

1. Project work accounts.
2. Plant and equipment operation accounts.
3. Project overhead accounts.

A subsidiary ledger is maintained for each of these three project cost classifications. Each of these major subdivisions has an extensive internal breakdown into detailed items of cost. An abridged list of cost accounts for each of these is shown in Figure 11.1. The use of "general" or "miscellaneous" cost accounts is to be avoided.

11.3 DISTRIBUTION OF PROJECT COSTS

As previously noted, a basic accounting principle for construction contractors is that project costs are recorded by job. Cost keeping must of necessity be a function of each project, and profit or loss is evaluated at the individual job level. When a new construction contract is obtained, a ledger sheet or portion thereof is set up in the three project cost ledgers discussed in Section 11.2 for each cost item that pertains to the project. Each job expense is then posted to the appropriate cost account.

Labor, materials, supplies, equipment costs, subcontract payments, and all such expenditures are charged to the appropriate project from the original documents such as payrolls, invoices, freight bills, and equipment time reports. To ensure that each such expenditure is charged to the proper cost account, the cost code number is entered on each document before the amounts are posted.

MASTER LIST OF PROJECT COST ACCOUNTS

(SUBACCOUNTS OF GENERAL LEDGER ACCOUNT 80.000, PROJECT EXPENSE)

PROJECT WORK ACCOUNTS .100 - .499		PLANT AND EQUIPMENT OPERATION ACCOUNTS .500 - .699		PROJECT OVERHEAD ACCOUNTS .700 - .999	
100	Clearing and grubbing	500	Power shovels	700	Project administration
101	Demolition	.10	Move-in	.1	Project manager
102	Underpinning	.30	Ownership and operating	.2	Office engineer
103	Common excavation	.70	Move-out	701	Construction supervision
104	Rock excavation	510	Crawler tractors	.1	General superintendent
105	Backfill	.10	Move-in	.2	Concrete gang foreman
115	Wood sheet piling	.30	Ownership and operating	702	Project office
116	Steel sheet piling	.70	Move-out	.1	Office building
130	Excavating for caissons	520	Rubber-tired bottom dumps	.2	Office furniture
240	Concrete	.10	Move-in	.3	Office supplies
.01	Footings	.30	Ownership and operating	703	Timekeeping
.05	Grade beams	.70	Move-out	.1	Timekeeper
.07	Slab on grade	530	Concrete mixing plant	.2	Watchmen
.08	Beams	.10	Move-in	.3	Guards
.11	Columns	.30	Ownership and operating	705	Utilities
.12	Walls	.70	Move-out	.1	Water
260	Concrete forms	532	Rock crushers	.2	Gas
.01	Footings	.10	Move-in	.3	Electricity
.05	Grade beams	.30	Ownership and operating	.4	Telephone
.07	Slab on grade	.70	Move-out	710	Storage facilities
.08	Beams	535	Screening plant	711	Temporary fences
.11	Columns	.10	Move-in	712	Temporary bulkheads
.12	Walls	.20	Erection	715	Storage area rental
280	Masonry	.30	Ownership and operating	717	Job sign
.01	Common brick, 8" wall	.50	Dismantle	720	Drinking water facilities
300	Carpentry	.70	Move-out	721	Sanitary facilities
.01	Floor joist	538	Transit-mix trucks	722	First-aid facilities
310	Millwork	540	Concrete pavers	725	Temporary lighting
.01	Kitchen cabinets	545	Hoist machinery	726	Temporary stairs
320	Steel and miscl. iron	.10	Move-in	730	Load tests
.01	Structural steel	.30	Ownership and operating	740	Small tools
331	Blinds, drapes, & carpet	.70	Move-out	750	Permits and fees
340	Insulation	547	Hoist tower	755	Concrete tests
342	Caulk & weatherstrip	.10	Move-in	756	Compaction tests
360	Ceramic tile	.20	Erection	760	Photographs
362	Resilient flooring	.30	Ownership and operating	761	Surveys
370	Miscl. metals	.50	Dismantle	765	Cutting and patching
.01	Metal door frames	.70	Move-out	770	Winter operation
380	Painting	550	Air compressors	780	Drayage
430	Finish hardware	555	Wagon drills	785	Parking
455	Plumbing, heating, &	560	Rippers	790	Protection of adjoining
	air conditioning	565	Mobile cranes		property
470	Electrical	570	Pile drivers	795	Drawings
488	Clean glass	580	Paving plants	800	Worker transportation
495	Paving, curbs & gutter	590	Asphalt pavers	805	Worker housing
499	Allowances			810	General clean-up

Figure 11.1   Master list of project cost accounts.

11.4 LABOR AND EQUIPMENT COSTS

Costs associated with materials and subcontracts are of a reasonably fixed nature and can be estimated with considerable exactness when the job is bid. During construction, these costs are seldom subject to appreciable fluctuation, barring oversight or mistake during the estimating process. For this reason, they are seldom the subject of detailed cost analysis.

Labor and equipment costs, however, are subject to considerable uncertainty. These two categories of expense can vary substantially during the construction process. Labor and equipment costs in the field are variables and, to a degree, are influenced by the contractor's construction supervision and management procedures.

The inherent variability of labor and equipment costs explains the fact that contractors' project cost accounting systems are more or less confined to them. Our discussion of project cost accounting will be limited to these two cost categories, and will describe the process of determining from day to day how much work is being accomplished in relation to the amount of labor and equipment being used. Some form of unit cost is the most convenient tool for doing this. Through the medium of a unit cost, management can quickly pinpoint excessive cost items and take remedial action.

11.5 COST ACCOUNTING

Project cost accounting is but a specialized part of the contractor's overall accounting system. It involves the continuous determination of project costs, together with work quantities produced, the analysis of these data, and the presentation of the results in summary form. Cost accounting differs from the usual accounting procedures in that the information needed and produced cannot be expressed entirely in terms of dollars and cents. Construction cost accounting is necessarily concerned not only with labor and equipment costs but also with the amounts of work accomplished by these expenditures. In addition, knowledge of total costs is not sufficient. Cost performance has to be expressed and analyzed in terms of the detailed make-up of the total cost.

A cost accounting system will function properly only if it receives the sympathetic support of the entire organization, particularly of the field supervisors on the projects. These are the men responsible for gathering the basic input information consisting of labor time and equipment time, work categories to which these times are charged, and quantities of work accomplished. Each individual associated with the cost system, whether he be in the office or in the field, must be impressed with the importance of his work and the need for accuracy, promptness, and reasonable care. A slipshod cost accounting system yields nothing of real value and is a waste of time and money.

11.6 NEED FOR COST ACCOUNTING

The only justification for the expense of a contractor's cost accounting system is the value of the information that it provides. If the data produced are not used or if the information is not supplied in a usable form or timely fashion, the cost accounting system has no real value and its expense is not justified. It is difficult to imagine, however, that any contractor can be successful and not have some form of functioning cost system. Its workings depend upon his own needs and business structure, but detailed cost information is required for two very important business purposes: bidding new jobs and controlling costs on existing contracts.

As described in Chapter 6, when a project is bid, the many elements of cost must be estimated and compiled. Labor and equipment costs, in particular, are evaluated in the light of past field experience. In essence, acquired past experience is the only reliable source of information available. Consequently, contractors customarily base the bidding of new work on their experience with past projects. A company cost accounting system provides an accurate and systematic way of accumulating field costs in a form usable by estimators when bidding future projects.

A second important use of field costs is in the checking of these actual costs against the amounts estimated when the job was bid. Keeping within the cost estimate and knowing when and where a job is deviating from this estimate constitute the key to profitable operation. In effect, the original estimate of the job serves as a budget and the costs as they actually occur are continuously compared with this budget. Field costs must be kept in substantial detail and must be compiled in a timely way if they are to serve their intended purposes. Detailed cost figures are necessary because this is the way jobs are bid and also because excessive costs in the field can be corrected only if the exact cause can be pinpointed. To know that construction costs are going over the estimate is not helpful if it is impossible to identify where the trouble is occurring. Timely information is needed if effective action against excessive field costs is to be taken. To learn of such costs after the work is finished leaves the contractor with no possibility of taking corrective action.

11.7 COST ACCOUNTING AND ESTIMATING

For effective cost control, it is necessary that the project be broken down into identical work classifications for the purposes of both estimating and field cost accounting. When the estimator bids a new project, the work is subdivided into many classifications. The extent to which the breakdown is carried depends upon the nature of the work and what portions of the project the contractor expects to do with his own forces. The job is priced on the basis of the number of units of these elementary work classifications, each of which is identified by a code number. Reference to Figure 6.3 shows that the estimator identifies each work item by its code designation when he sets down the results of his quantity take-off. Throughout the construction process, a continuous record is kept of the actual cost of production of each work classification. From estimate to project completion, the same work items and their code numbers are used.

A point to be noted is that each unit of work must contain the same cost elements. For example, labor unit costs used for estimating and determined by cost accounting must consistently include or not include fringe benefits and payroll taxes and insurance.

11.8 COST RECORDS AND SUMMARIES

By what methods and in what form the field data are recorded depends upon whether the cost summaries are produced by manual procedures or whether electronic data processing equipment is used. If cost accounting reports are generated by hand, some form of ledger or notebook is needed for the recording and analysis of the detailed cost data. These data are, of course, recorded and segregated by project and by category of work or piece of equipment. Because of the considerable detail in which these costs are kept and the accompanying need for work quantities, the project cost accounting records are normally maintained separately from the usual project cost ledgers described in Section 11.2.

If data processing equipment is utilized to mechanize the clerical aspects of cost accounting, the input information concerning cost breakdowns and quantities of work accomplished may be on punched cards. Regardless of whether manual reduction of data or data processing equipment is used, however, the information that goes in and the cost reports that come out are essentially the same. Data processing methods are advantageous when the contractor's work volume is extensive and large amounts of data must be processed.

Summary cost reports must be compiled at frequent intervals so that excessive project costs can be detected while there is still time to do something about them. Daily cost reports are possible, particularly when data processing equipment is used. However, daily preparation is expensive, and there is some question about the value of so much information. It is generally considered that weekly intervals are about optimum for most construction operations, and this time period will be the basis for the discussion following.

11.9 LABOR TIME REPORTING

The source document for both payroll purposes and labor cost accounting is the labor time card. It is used to report the hours of labor time for each worker and the work categories to which the labor applies. Figure 11.2 shows a typical daily time card, and Figure 11.3 a weekly time card. Which of the two is used depends upon company preference and policy.

When daily time cards are used, a time card is filled in and forwarded each day to the company's payroll office. The head of each card provides for entry of the project name and number, date, weather conditions, and name of the person preparing the card. The body of the time card provides for the name and badge number of each man covered. Hours are reported as regular or overtime as the case may be. For each man listed, several slots are provided for the distribution of his hours to specific cost codes. It must be remembered that perfection in cost distribution is unobtainable. Nevertheless, the need for care and reasonable accuracy in ascribing costs cannot be overemphasized.

If weekly time cards are used, a separate card for each individual worker is prepared to record the hours he worked that week. Although the arrangement of

THE BLANK CONSTRUCTION COMPANY, INC.

DAILY TIME CARD

Job __Municipal Airport Terminal Building__   Job No. __669__   Weather __Cloudy-Windy__

Date __August 18, 19___   Prepared by __R. D. Jones__

Badge Number	Name	Craft	Hourly Rate	R/O	COST CODE 701.2	240.01	240.05	240.07	240.08	240.51	240.91	Total Hours	Gross Amount
316	Jones, Richard D.	CF	$6.55	R / O	4		2		2			8	$ 52.40
109	Adams, Claud	CM	6.30	R / O						6	2	8	50.40
422	Chavez, S. C.	CM	6.30	R / O				4		4		8	50.40
461	Womac, C. T.	CM	6.30	R / O		4	2			2		8	50.40
247	Craig, O. N.	L	4.90	R / O		4	4					8	39.20
356	Johnson, Clyde	L	4.50	R / O				4	4			8	36.00
393	Newmann, Stan	L	4.50	R / O		4	4					8	36.00
211	Prong, Glace	L	4.50	R / O				4	4			8	36.00
	Total Cost				$26.20	$62.80	$63.30	$61.20	$49.10	$75.60	$12.60		$350.80

Figure 11.2   Daily time card.

THE BLANK CONSTRUCTION COMPANY, INC.

WEEKLY TIME CARD

Name   Womac, C. T.

Badge No.   461

Week Ending   August 22, 19

Craft   CM   Job   Municipal Airport Terminal Building

Job No.   669

Prepared by   R. D. Jones

Cost Code	Hourly Rate		Sat.	Sun.	Mon.	Tues.	Wed.	Thurs.	Fri.	Total Hours	Total Cost
240.01	$6.30	R			4	8	8			20	$126.00
		O									
240.05	6.30	R			2				4	6	37.80
		O									
240.07	6.30	R						4		4	25.20
		O									
240.08	6.30	R						4		4	25.20
		O									
240.51	6.30	R			2				4	6	37.80
		O									
		R									
		O									
Total Hours		R			8	8	8	8	8	40	
		O									
Gross Amount					$50.40	$50.40	$50.40	$50.40	$50.40		$252.00
Weather					Cloudy-Windy	Clear-Windy	Clear	Clear-Hot	Cloudy		

Figure 11.3   Weekly time card.

the weekly time card is different from that of the daily time card, it presents the same information concerning the individual worker.

It should be mentioned here that many construction companies are automating their cost procedures and are using data processing punched cards for labor time reporting. The contractor's office or data processing service prepares cards that are prepunched and preprinted with standard information such as employee name and number. The person filling out the cards on the project need add only the hours and cost codes.

11.10   TIME CARD PREPARATION

Labor time cards are prepared on the project by a person who knows the workers and has knowledge of how each man's time should be allocated. The distribution of each individual's hours among work classifications must be a function of the foreman, and this information is probably first recorded in his pocket time book. The foreman may describe the work performed by the individuals in his crew not by code numbers but in word form. He identifies the craft and position of each man by using any simple letter or numerical code that the contractor may decide upon. For example, in Figure 11.2, CF indicates concrete foreman, CM means cement mason, and L indicates laborer. Ordinarily the foreman enters the hourly rate for each worker because it not unusual for a man during a week, or even in a single day, to be employed on work requiring different rates of pay. However, wage amounts and costs allocated to the different cost codes are normally not determined by the foreman.

It may well be that the formal time card is filled in by someone other than the foreman, such as the field office manager. One reason for this is the fact that paper work is usually the least desirable part of a foreman's job. The office manager can take the foreman's time book and fill out the time card, adding the necessary information for payroll and cost accounting, such as employee number and work cost codes, and perhaps make the extensions.

Even if a weekly time card is used, it is preferable that the information be entered on a daily basis. Setting down the time and its cost distribution as the work progresses will eliminate the practice of the foreman letting the matter go until the end of the week and then trying to enter the information from memory. It is probable that completing the labor record on a daily basis will improve the accuracy of the distribution.

11.11   MEASUREMENT OF WORK QUANTITIES

The end objective of construction cost accounting is to determine the unit costs of production. In order to compute these costs, the work accomplished must be measured periodically in the field. The frequency with which such measurements are made on the projects depends upon company policy, but measurement is usually made at the end of each weekly payroll period. Items of work measured must be identical with the elementary work classifications of the cost code and be so identified.

On most jobs, the work quantities accomplished are measured by the foreman. On large projects, however, it is often necessary to make such measurement a separate function done by someone else such as the job engineer. This may be necessary because the scope of the project is such that considerable time is required to measure work quantities or because the nature of the work requires that the measurement be made by a survey crew. An example would be work that involves excavation or compacted fill. In this regard, it is not unusual that progress of the work at any point in time be expressed as a percentage of the total rather than as actual measured quantities to date. An estimated percentage of completion can be readily translated into quantities of work done. This practice, while not ideal, yields useful information as long as accurate field measurements are made occasionally, such as for the monthly pay requests.

There must be some routine way in which the quantities of work accomplished on the projects are transmitted from the jobs to those responsible for the preparation of weekly cost summaries. The weekly reports of work done can be submitted on a form such as Figure 11.4. Prepunched and preprinted punch cards with cost code, work description, and unit of measure already entered can be used for reporting work quantities.

11.12. LABOR COST SUMMARY

For each work cost classification on each project, the weekly labor cost from the time card is now combined with the work done as reported by the weekly quantity report. As previously discussed in this chapter, this may be done manually by recording the information in notebooks, there being a separate notebook for each project and each project notebook having a separate sheet for each active labor cost code number. If data processing equipment is used, the labor costs and work quantities done are recorded on punch cards. Many contractors, when projects are remote from their central offices, transmit their time card and work quantity information automatically over telephone lines to their central offices, where the data are received and recorded in punched card form. Whether the unit labor costs are computed by hand or by machine, about the same form of labor cost summary is generated.

Labor cost summaries vary considerably in format and contents from one construction company to another. All labor reports, however, share the same objectives of providing construction management with timely information concerning the current status of every labor cost classification that the contractor is doing with his own forces and of indicating how these labor costs compare with those estimated. Figure 11.5, a typical example of a weekly labor cost summary, presents labor cost data for placing concrete. The estimated labor costs of concrete placing come from the summary sheet, Figure 6.3. It is understood that similar summaries are prepared covering all cost codes on every project under construction.

THE BLANK CONSTRUCTION COMPANY, INC.

WEEKLY QUANTITY REPORT

Job Municipal Airport Terminal Building   Job No. 669

Week Ending August 22, 19___   Prepared by R. D. Jones

Cost Code	Work Description	Unit	Total Last Report	Total This Week	Total To Date			
240.01	Concrete, footings	C.Y.	479	196	675			
240.05	Concrete, grade beams	C.Y.	208	208	416			
240.07	Concrete, slab	C.Y.	595	65	660			
240.08	Concrete, beams	C.Y.	0	60	60			
240.51	Concrete, trowel finish	S.F.	50,595	2,865	53,460			
240.91	Concrete, curing, slab	S.F.	50,595	2,865	53,460			

Figure 11.4   Weekly quantity report.

THE BLANK CONSTRUCTION COMPANY, INC.

WEEKLY LABOR COST SUMMARY

Job Municipal Airport Terminal Building

Week Ending August 22, 19___

Job No. 669

Prepared by W. W. Smith

Cost Code	Work Description	Unit	Estimated			To Date			This Week			To Date		Projected	
			Quant.	Total Cost	Unit Cost	Quant.	Total Cost	Unit Cost	Quant.	Total Cost	Unit Cost	Saving	Loss	Saving	Loss
240.01	Concrete, footings	C.Y.	1,240	$ 3,348	$2.70	675	$1,958	$2.90	196	$559	$2.85		$135		$ 248
240.05	Concrete, grade beams	C.Y.	1,055	4,115	3.90	416	1,556	3.74	208	770	3.70	$ 66		$ 169	
240.07	Concrete, slab	C.Y.	3,072	10,138	3.30	660	2,515	3.81	65	253	3.90		337		1,566
240.08	Concrete, beams	C.Y.	608	2,006	3.30	60	200	3.33	60	200	3.33		2		19
240.51	Concrete, trowel finish	S.F.	156,320	15,632	0.10	53,460	4,811	0.09	2,865	287	0.10	535		1,563	
240.91	Concrete, curing, slab	S.F.	192,400	1,924	0.01	53,460	428	0.008	2,865	29	0.01	107		385	

Figure 11.5 Weekly labor cost summary.

Figure 11.5 is a comprehensive report that summarizes the costs as estimated, costs to date, and costs for the week reported. Unit costs, obtained by dividing total costs in each category by the respective quantity, enable direct comparisons to be made between the actual costs and the costs as bid. The to-date saving or loss is developed by multiplying the quantity to date by the estimated unit cost and subtracting the total cost to date from the result. The projected saving or loss for each work item is obtained by assuming that the unit cost to date will continue to completion of the item. Multiplying the to-date unit cost by the total estimated quantity and subtracting the total estimated cost yields the projected saving or loss figure.

There is considerable difference of opinion about whether or not the management of a construction company should divulge the detailed cost information contained in Figure 11.5 to field personnel. The statement is made, for example, that field supervisors will be tempted to charge labor costs on operations showing losses to other cost codes on which performance has been good and savings have been reported. It may also be said that confidential cost information may be divulged or that a foreman may tend to relax when he knows that his costs are within the estimate. On the other hand, it seems reasonable to assume that the only way a cost system can succeed is through the complete cooperation of the field forces. Field supervisors try to achieve the best possible performance and expect to receive credit if they beat the estimated costs. If costs are running over, field personnel need to be shown where this is happening. Field costs are very much involved when companies enter into profit-sharing or incentive arrangements with their field supervisors. The answer to the question of divulging these costs must remain a matter of company policy.

11.13 EQUIPMENT EXPENSE

Cost keeping for equipment, particularly in heavy and highway construction, is an important cost accounting application. Equipment constitutes a substantial part of the assets of many contractors, and the need for control of equipment costs parallels the need for control of labor costs. The costs associated with large pieces of construction equipment are high, inherently variable, and deserving of a comprehensive record-keeping system. The objectives of equipment cost accounting are the same as those discussed for labor costs. Management requires timely information for effective project cost control, and estimators need data to use for future bids. Less expensive equipment such as power saws, concrete vibrators, and hand-operated soil compactors are normally charged to a project on a flat-rate or lump-sum basis and are not usually subject to detailed cost study.

The estimating of equipment expense and the procedures used to determine the costs of equipment on the job vary substantially from one contractor to another and also with the nature of the construction work involved. The costs of equipment are always charged to the individual projects to which they apply, but the way in which this is done varies considerably. Many companies charge equipment expense to individual equipment cost codes and this will be the general procedure discussed in the following sections. The cost codes contained in Figure 11.1 illustrate this cost-recording procedure. Another practice is the charging of certain or even all equipment costs to a single cost code with no further breakdown. Still another procedure is to consider equipment cost simply as a part of a specific work code. For example, the expense of hoisting equipment used for erecting structural steel can be charged directly to the steel erection cost code and combined with the labor costs to determine erection costs per ton.

The usual basis for expressing and recording the cost of a given piece of construction equipment is a fixed charge per hour, day, week, or month. The rate itself can be computed in a variety of ways. For purposes of discussion here, a typical method of equipment cost reporting will be used which involves an ownership rate and an operating rate. These rates show just how much it costs to own, operate, and maintain each piece of major equipment. As previously discussed in Section 6.22, ownership expense includes the cost of depreciation, insurance, taxes, storage, and interest on investment. The operating rate is computed from the costs of repairs, fuel, oil, greasing, tires, and operating labor. Ownership expense and operating expense are frequently combined into a total rate per operating hour of the equipment.

11.14 EQUIPMENT TIME REPORTS

Regardless of the procedures used in accounting for equipment costs, keeping time on equipment is essential if such costs are a substantial part of the total cost of a project. Because most equipment costs are related to time, equipment time records are the starting point for equipment cost accounting. If equipment is rented or leased, the charges are usually based on time. If equipment is owned, ownership and operating costs are clearly time dependent.

The best source of equipment time information is probably payroll time, the origin of which may be the foreman's pocket time book or the individual operator's daily time card. The situation here is much the same as for labor time, discussed in Section 11.9, except that equipment is now involved and additional information concerning idle time is required. Figure 11.6 shows an operator's time card that he fills in and submits daily to his foreman.

The foreman, office engineer, or other knowledgeable person enters the daily time card information on a daily or weekly equipment time summary. Figure 11.7 presents an example of a daily equipment time report. This report is customarily prepared in the field and transmitted to the contractor's main office weekly so that equipment charges can be assessed against the project and permanent equipment records brought up to date. It is to be noted that Figure 11.7 categorizes equipment time by cost code and differentiates idle time (I) from working time (W). Excessive equipment idle time may indicate management problems such as too much equipment on the job, improper balance of the equipment spread, poor field supervision, inadequate equipment maintenance, or worn-out equipment. On the other hand, substantial downtime can be caused by severe working conditions or extended periods of bad weather.

```
┌─────────────────────────────────────────────────────────────────┐
│                                                                 │
│                    THE EXCELLO COMPANY, INC.                    │
│                        DAILY TIME CARD                          │
│                                                                 │
├─────────────────────────────────────────────────────────────────┤
│                                                                 │
│  Name    John Jones              Classification  Operator       │
│                                                                 │
│  Machine and Number      D7 - #16                               │
│                                                                 │
│  Date  October 16, 19__    Start  8:00 A.M.   Total Hours   8   │
│  Weather   Warm-Clear      Quit   4:30 P.M.                     │
│                                                                 │
├─────────────────────────────────────────────────────────────────┤
│                                                                 │
│  Jobs and Moves  Holloman Taxiways - Excavation    Hours   4    │
│                                    Demolition              4    │
│                                                                 │
│                                                                 │
│                                                                 │
│  Repair Time _____  Stand by Time _____  Remarks _____ │
│                                                                 │
└─────────────────────────────────────────────────────────────────┘
```

Figure 11.6   Equipment operator's daily time card.

The rates per hour shown in Figure 11.7 are total use rates for each piece of equipment, including both the ownership rate and the operating rate. The cost information yielded by Figure 11.7 can now be used to charge the project with the equipment expense indicated and to up-date the equipment records. In essence, the daily equipment report is an equipment payroll, and the equipment costs are charged directly to the project by posting them to the appropriate plant and equipment operation account, 80.500-80.699, as shown in Figure 11.1. The costs of move-in, erection, dismantling, and move-out are also charged to the project in a similar manner.

The hours of equipment time are posted to the individual equipment ledger sheets, where cumulative totals of operating hours and expenses are kept. This matter is discussed in Section 11.17. Whether only actual working hours or total hours including idle time are posted to the permanent equipment records depends upon how the contractor obtains the production rates (see Section 6.24) of his equipment. There is a "normal" idle time associated with most equipment types. Use of the "50-minute hour" automatically assumes that 10 minutes of each hour will be nonproductive. How much idle time should be considered as normal depends upon many variables. Operating time is commonly taken to be equal to total shift time unless the idle time experienced is unusually large.

THE EXCELLO COMPANY, INC.
DAILY EQUIPMENT REPORT

Job __Holloman Taxiways__   Job No. __868__   Prepared by __G. Brown__

Date __October 16, 19___   Weather __Warm-Clear__

Machine No.	Machine	Rate per Hour	W/I	101	103					Total Hours	Total Cost
16	Tractor, dozer	$11.80	W / I	4	4					8	$ 94.40
17	Air Compressor	6.50	W / I	8						8	52.00
2	Shovel	14.50	W / I		8					8	116.00
9	Bottom Dump	12.75	W / I		8					8	102.00
			W / I								
			W / I								
Total Cost				$99.20	$265.20						$364.40

Figure 11.7 Daily equipment report.

11.15 WORK QUANTITY REPORT

In order to compute equipment expense as a cost per unit of production, quantities of the elementary work classifications put into place are measured and reported on a weekly basis. As previously discussed in Section 11.11, such measurement may require the services of a survey crew. If weekly measurement of work units put into place imposes an undue burden on the field forces, such quantities can often be estimated with reasonable accuracy as percentages of the total. These can be adjusted when accurate field measurements are made at the end of each month for purposes of progress payments to the contractor by the owner.

Work units accomplished by equipment must, therefore, be reported in the same way that they are reported when done by labor. Quantities of the elementary work classifications, identified by the proper cost code numbers, can be reported by a form similar to or the same as Figure 11.4.

11.16 EQUIPMENT COST SUMMARY

By following very much the same process that has already been described in Section 11.12, the reported equipment costs are combined with the work quantities reported done. On a summary form such as that shown in Figure 11.5, management is apprised weekly of the equipment cost per unit of production for each of the various elementary work classifications on every project under construction.

The checking of costs on a unit-price contract can involve some additional computation. A typical bid item such as rock excavation per cubic yard involves several elementary labor and equipment cost codes, as well as material cost. In order to check the actual field cost of rock excavation against the cost as bid, the contractor must make a detailed analysis in which he collects together all of the rock excavation costs and quantities moved. Figure 11.8 illustrates how such a cost analysis can be made.

11.17 EQUIPMENT LEDGER SHEET

A separate ledger sheet is set up for each piece of construction equipment under general account 14.000, Property, Plant, and Equipment (see Appendix K). These ledger sheets serve to maintain cumulative records of use and expense of each piece of equipment. They are the source of the up-to-date ownership rates and operating rates that the contractor uses to estimate new work and that he charges to the project during construction as described in Section 11.14. All charges against a piece of equipment, such as depreciation, taxes, insurance, fuel, oil, grease, repairs, tires, and operating labor, are entered periodically on its ledger sheet. At regular intervals, weekly or monthly, the number of hours of equipment usage is entered. By dividing the hours of usage into the costs to date, the actual

BID ITEM COST ANALYSIS

Job No. _____   Date __October 31, 19___.

Job Name_____   Work Classification ___Rock Excavation___

Quantities: This Period ___5,720 C.Y.___   To Date _22,165 C.Y._ ⸱ _ % Complete __78__

Operation	Unit Cost		Total Cost	
	This Period	To Date	This Period	To Date
Wagon Drill, Ownership & Operating	$0.924	$1.011	$5,285	$22,409
Jackhammer, Ownership & Operating	0.760	0.633	4,347	14,030
Drill Steel and Bits	0.126	0.132	721	2,926
Sharpening - Labor & Expense	0.417	0.440	2,385	9,753
Air - Compressor Plant, Ownership & Operating	0.958	0.947	5,480	20,990
Blasting Labor	0.380	0.385	2,174	8,534
Blasting Explosives and Expense	0.481	0.476	2,751	10,551
Loading Labor	0.521	0.505	2,980	11,193
Loading Equipment, Ownership & Operating	0.766	0.798	4,382	17,688
Trucks, Ownership & Operating	0.929	0.909	5,314	20,148
Shop Facilities	0.106	0.110	606	2,438
Clean up Labor	0.417	0.614	2,385	13,609
Clean up Equipment, Ownership & Operating	0.236	0.311	1,350	6,893
Haul Road Maintenance	0.370	0.273	2,116	6,051
Total to date	$7.391	$7.544	$42,276	$167,213

Figure 11.8 Bid item cost analysis.

costs of ownership and operation can be obtained. Also entered on the ledger sheet as equipment rental income is the ownership and operating expense that has been charged against a project. Figure 11.9 shows a typical equipment expense ledger sheet.

If a contractor has little equipment, it may pay him to have repairs done by an outside agency. On the other hand, a contractor who uses a substantial amount of equipment in his business normally repairs it in his own shops. Parts and repair labor are charged directly to the equipment unit involved, and repair overhead (shop supervision, heat, etc.) is prorated to the equipment on the basis of repair labor. The cost of fuel, oil, and grease is also posted to each equipment item from service truck records.

An equipment ledger sheet such as that shown in Figure 11.9 serves many useful purposes. Already mentioned is the fact that it provides up-to-date ownership and operating costs useful both for estimating and project cost control. When repair and maintenance charges begin to increase or when there is a considerable decrease in hours of operation, it may be time to dispose of the equipment item.

THE EXCELLO COMPANY, INC.

EQUIPMENT LEDGER SHEET

Cost Summary, Account No. __14.509__

Equipment No. ____9____   Description ____Bottom Dump____

Date Acquired ___June 30, 19__   Estimated Life ___5 years___

Initial Cost ___$25,226.00___   Estimated Salvage ___None___

Estimated Use per Year _2,000 hrs._   Annual Depreciation ___$3,756.00___

Avg. Annual Investment ___$15,135.60___

Year	Item	Charge	Operating Hours	Cumulative Hours	Cost per Hour
First Year (6 mos.)	Depreciation	$ 1,878.00			
	Interest, Taxes, Insurance	756.78			
	Fuel, Oil, Lube	832.30			
	Repairs, Parts	432.37			
	Tires	1,630.80			
	Operating Labor	5,610.00			
	Total	$11,140.25	1,020	1,020	$10.92
Second Year	Depreciation	$ 3,756.00			
	Interest, Taxes, Insurance	1,409.22			
	Fuel, Oil, Lube	1,588.04			
	Repairs, Parts	1,191.24			
	Tires	2,598.24			
	Operating Labor	10,764.80			
	Total	$21,307.54	1,856	2,876	$11.48
Third Year	Depreciation	$ 3,756.00			
	Interest, Taxes, Insurance	1,013.71			
	Fuel, Oil, Lube	1,998.28			
	Repairs	3,712.45			
	Tires	3,109.73			
	Operating Labor	13,066.20			
	Total	$26,656.37	2,142	5,018	$12.44

Figure 11.9   Equipment ledger sheet.

If the current cost of ownership and operation of a piece of equipment exceeds the rental or lease rate of a similar item, the contractor should not own it. Although some companies keep equipment costs by categories of equipment rather than by individual units, information of the type just discussed illustrates the value of keeping equipment cost records on an individual-machine basis.

12

PROJECT PLANNING AND SCHEDULING

12.1 INTRODUCTION

The matter of project cost control is presented in Chapter 11. To be discussed in this chapter is the planning and time scheduling of construction projects. Such projects are complex, and a large job will involve literally thousands of separate operations. If these tasks were to follow one another in single-file order, job planning and scheduling would be relatively simple but this is not the case. Each operation has its own time requirement, and its start depends upon the completion of certain preceding operations. At the same time, many tasks are independent of one another and can be carried out simultaneously. Thus, a typical construction project involves many mutually dependent and interrelated operations that, in total combination, comprise a tangled web of individual time and sequential relationships. When individual task requirements of materials, equipment, and labor are superimposed, it becomes obvious that project planning and scheduling is a very complicated and difficult management function.

Traditionally, contractors have scheduled their construction projects largely on the basis of experience and intuition. Bar graphs (Gantt charts) have been used for many years in conjunction with project scheduling. These graphical representations of work versus time are easily read and undoubtedly will continue to serve as a simple and understandable way of scheduling construction and recording its progress. However, the bar chart is very limited in its usefulness because it does not show the interrelationships and interdependencies between operations that effectively control project progress. In addition, it is difficult to modify the usual bar chart to include revisions made as the project proceeds.

Modern conditions of intense competition, soaring costs, tight time schedules, and increasing complexity of construction procedures have lent great impetus to the development of more efficacious ways of planning and scheduling construction projects.

12.2 DEVELOPMENT OF CPM AND PERT

During the years since 1957, a new concept of planning and scheduling has been developed and put into practice. The new management techniques involved analyze the sequential and time characteristics of projects by the use of networks. Although these new procedures have not by any means entirely supplanted the traditional approach, they are already widely used and are rapidly becoming an indispensable part of a contractor's project management system. It is not unusual for contract documents to require that the contractor utilize certain of these procedures in his planning and scheduling of projects.

The first of these techniques originated in 1957 when the Remington Rand UNIVAC Division of the Sperry Rand Corporation joined with the E. I. du Pont de Nemours Company to develop a planning and scheduling technique for the construction, maintenance, and shutdown of chemical process plants. The technique devised by James E. Kelley, Jr., of Remington Rand (UNIVAC) and Morgan Walker of Du Pont is called the Critical Path Method (CPM). The Du Pont company successfully applied CPM to a variety of large and complex engineering projects involving design, construction, and maintenance and generally established the power and efficacy of the new procedure. CPM is now widely used in the construction industry.

In 1958, the Program Evaluation Research Task was formed by the United States Navy. A project team was established to study and formulate improved methods for the planning and control of the complex programs associated with the development of the Polaris missile system. The method developed by this group is called Program Evaluation Review Technique (PERT). The PERT procedure is widely used as a management system on military and aerospace projects.

Although CPM and PERT are similar to one another in several important respects, the two methods differ somewhat in their applications and objectives. PERT is particularly useful when applied to research and development tasks in which the work is entirely or largely new in concept and is being attempted for the first time. In such cases time requirements can seldom be predicted accurately and probabilistic principles are used in conjunction with the estimation of time requirements. The PERT procedure is concerned with estimating the probability of completing a project within a specified time.

CPM, on the other hand, lends itself well to projects on which costs and time can be predicted with a higher degree of certainty. It is a method for achieving improved schedule and cost control over projects such as construction jobs whose many elements are susceptible to reasonably accurate estimates of cost and time.

The differences between CPM and PERT as discussed above are becoming less distinct because of a merging of the two techniques. There are many examples of network-based management systems that are referred to as PERT-type although they utilize most if not all of the basic CPM concepts. Exact nomenclature is not really important at this point.

For most of its applications, the construction industry has found the original CPM procedure to be the better of the two methods. For this reason, the discussion in this chapter will be limited to this method, which, for purposes of discussion, will be referred to as CPM. The technique is still in a stage of development, and new mutations and applications undoubtedly will continue to be devised. With a good understanding of the basic CPM method, the reader can easily assimilate new developments as they appear. This chapter will confine itself to a discussion of basics.

12.3 ESSENTIALS OF CPM

The Critical Path Method is a project management system that provides a basis for informed decision making on projects of any size. It provides information necessary for the time scheduling of a construction project, guides the contractor in selecting the best way to expedite the job, and predicts future manpower and equipment requirements.

The CPM procedure starts with project planning. This phase consists of identifying the elementary items of work necessary to achieve job completion, establishing the logical order in which these work items must be done, and preparing a graphical display of this planning information in the form of a network diagram.

The scheduling phase which follows requires an estimate of the time required to accomplish each of the work items identified. By using the network diagram, computations are then made that provide information concerning the time schedule characteristics of each work item and the total time necessary to achieve project completion.

The procedure just described may suggest that CPM must follow a definite step-by-step order of development. In actual practice, this is seldom exactly the case. For example, the three planning steps often proceed more or less simultaneously. However, for the purposes of discussion, the three steps described will be treated separately in the order mentioned.

The computations associated with the scheduling phase of CPM are simple additions and subtractions. Manual computation is easy and logical but can become tedious and very time consuming on large projects. For this reason, many contractors utilize electronic computers to produce their CPM schedules and to monitor the projects during construction in the field. The computer's role in the process is merely to perform the many arithmetic operations in a faster and more economical manner than would be possible with human effort alone. For proper understanding, however, it is necessary that the practitioner be familiar with how the calculations are made. Consequently, the following discussion of fundamental concepts is based on manual procedures.

12.4 GENERAL CONSIDERATIONS

Although some preliminary CPM study of a project may take place during the estimating or negotiation process, it is usual that the contractor start his detailed CPM planning immediately after he has been awarded the construction contract. A characteristic of CPM is that its effectiveness depends upon the accuracy of the input information and the skill and judgment with which the generated data are used. Consequently, the development and application of a CPM project plan must be made the responsibility of people who are experienced in and thoroughly familiar with the type of field construction involved.

A project plan is usually the result of a study made by a group of people. Key persons involved with the job such as estimators, field supervisors, and project manager may be participants. A CPM consultant might also be involved, particularly when the contractor's own staff planners have no background of practical CPM application. Because the prime purpose of CPM is to produce a coordinated project plan, key subcontractors must also be brought into the planning. Their input information is vital to the development of a workable construction schedule. Normally, the prime contractor sets the general timing reference for the project. The individual subcontractor then reviews the portions of the plan relevant to his work and needed alterations are made in the plan when mutually agreeable.

The basic procedure followed by such a planning group is to talk the project through from start to finish. In so doing, the job is subjected to careful, detailed advance planning. This planning alone probably justifies the time spent on CPM. It is usual that the network diagram be developed in rough form as the job is dissected into its basic elements and the sequential order of construction operations is discussed. It is often helpful to list the major operations of the project and to use them to develop a preliminary diagram. This diagram can serve as a basis for discussion and as a basic framework for the subsequent development of a fully detailed network. The activity list needed for scheduling purposes may be taken from the network diagram after it has been developed. It is important that the plan prepared be the one that the contractor actually expects to follow. This means, therefore, that the people preparing the plan must have full authority to make decisions concerning methods, procedures, equipment, and manpower.

12.5 PROJECT PLANNING

The initial phase of CPM is that of planning. The project must first be broken up into its elemental, time-consuming activities. An activity is a single identifiable work step in the total project. The extent to which the project is subdivided into activities depends upon a number of practical considerations, but the following factors should be taken into account:

1. Different areas of responsibility, such as subcontracted work, which are distinct and separate from that being done by the prime contractor directly.

2. Different categories of work as distinguished by craft or crew requirements.
3. Different categories of work as distinguished by equipment requirements.
4. Different categories of work as distinguished by materials such as concrete, timber, and steel.
5. Distinct and identifiable subdivisions of structural work such as walls, slabs, beams, and columns.
6. Location of the work within the project which necessitates different times or different crews to perform.
7. Owner's breakdown for bidding or payment purposes.
8. Contractor's breakdown for estimating or cost accounting purposes.

The activities chosen may represent relatively large segments of the project or may be limited to small steps. For example, a concrete slab may be a single activity, or it may be broken down into the erection of forms, placing of reinforcing steel, pouring of concrete, finishing, curing, and stripping of forms. If the activity breakdown is too gross, the job plan developed will not yield information in sufficient detail to be optimally useful. However, if the subdivision of the work is carried to the other extreme, the excessive detail tends to obscure the really significant planning factors. Experience with CPM is probably the best tutor in this regard.

After the separate activities have been identified and defined, the sequential relationships between them are determined. This is sometimes referred to as "job logic" and is an enumeration of the necessary time order of construction operations. When the time sequence of activities is being determined, restraints must be recognized and be taken into consideration. Restraints refer to practical limitations such as the approval of shop drawings, delivery of materials, special labor needs, equipment requirements, or availability of completed contract drawings. It is usual to consider these restraints as activities and to represent them as such on the arrow diagram.

12.6 ACTIVITIES

The overall job plan can now be depicted graphically in the form of a network diagram showing the sequence in which individual tasks must be done and the extent to which they can be performed in parallel. There is more than one way in which such a diagram can be prepared. This chapter will discuss the widely used method of showing each activity as an arrow with the tail of the arrow representing the beginning of the activity and its head, the completion. Not surprisingly, the resulting network diagram is commonly called an "arrow diagram," and the two terms are used synonymously. The arrows depicting activities are not vectors, their lengths and orientations are not significant, and they can be curved or bent as required. The essence of the diagram is the manner in which the activities are joined together into a total operational pattern or network.

Each activity of an arrow diagram is depicted as an arrow in the following fashion:

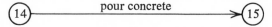

This activity is designated as activity 14-15. In many CPM applications, the letter i is used as a general term to designate the tail of an activity and the letter j to designate the head. The activity above has an i of 14 and a j of 15. To obviate errors in identification, it is usual that each activity be assigned a unique i-j designation.

For illustrative purposes, consider a simple project consisting of only a few steps, such as the construction of a heavy reinforced concrete slab on grade. This will be called Example Problem 1. Let us assume the job to be subdivided into eight activities as listed in Table 12.1. The activity "Procure Reinforcing Steel" will be recognized as a job restraint.

TABLE 12.1   Job Logic

EXAMPLE PROBLEM 1:   REINFORCED CONCRETE SLAB ON GRADE

Activity	Symbol	Activity Immediately Following
Excavate	EX	FG, SF
Build Forms	BF	SF
Procure Reinforcing Steel	PS	PR
Fine Grade	FG	PR
Set Forms	SF	PR
Place Reinforcing Steel	PR	PC
Pour Concrete	PC	FC
Finish Concrete	FC	- - -

12.7 JOB LOGIC

The job logic or the time-sequence relationships between the activities of Example Problem 1 must now be determined. The sequence of operations will be the following. The procurement of reinforcing steel, excavation, and the building of forms are all opening activities that can proceed independently of one another. Fine grading will follow excavation, but forms cannot be set until both the excavation and form building have been completed. The placing of reinforcing steel cannot start until fine grading, form setting, and steel procurement have all been carried to completion. Concrete will be poured after the steel has been placed, and finishing will be the terminal operation, proceeding after the concrete pour. In elementary form, this is the kind of information generated as a project is "talked through."

When establishing job logic, three criteria must be identified for each activity: (1) the activities immediately preceding it that must be completed before it can start, (2) the activities immediately following it that cannot be started until it is complete, and (3) the activities that can proceed concurrently. Every activity in the network must have a definite event to mark its starting. This event may be either the start of the project or the completion of preceding activities. It is not possible in CPM to have the finish of one activity overlap beyond the start of a succeeding activity. Where such a condition exists, the work must be further subdivided.

As has already been mentioned, the arrow diagram is normally drawn concurrently with the development of the job plan and the operational sequence is not otherwise recorded, listed, or written down. There are occasions, however, when it is useful to list the job logic. One such instance, certainly, would be in a textbook presentation of CPM fundamentals. For this reason, if no other, job logic is listed herein in conjunction with example problems.

Job logic can be expressed in several different ways, no one procedure necessarily being any better than another. A common way of expressing the necessary activity sequence is to list, for each activity, those following activities that can start immediately after and only after the given activity is finished. This is a sufficient system for enumerating job logic and will be used herein. Table 12.1 presents the previously discussed job logic of Example Problem 1. The arrow diagram describing the prescribed sequence of activities is shown in Figure 12.1.

12.8 LOGICAL CONNECTIONS

In Figure 12.1, the dashed arrow 2-3 is an example of a logical connection, usually called a "dummy." It is required because of the prescribed sequence of activities. The logic of Table 12.1 stipulates that the start of activity FG depends only upon the completion of EX, while SF cannot be begun until both EX and BF have been completed. The dummy arrow 2-3 is not an activity but does show that the start of SF depends on the completion not only of BF but also of EX. Project logic cannot back up against the arrowhead, and the direction of the dummy arrow designates the flow of activities. For example, dummy arrow 2-3 does not establish any dependence of FG upon the completion of BF.

Another common usage of dummy arrows is to give each activity a unique

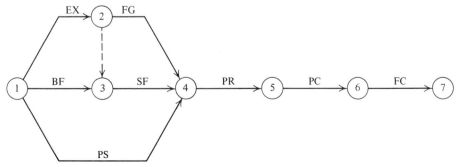

Figure 12.1   Arrow diagram, Example Problem 1: reinforced concrete slab on grade.

i-j designation. In the figure just below are shown three activities that can proceed in parallel with one another and that have the same start and finish points.

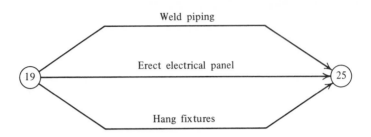

In the case shown, each of the three activities has the same *i-j* designation and each would be designated as 19-25. This circumstance would not necessarily occasion great difficulty if only manual computations were involved because the human operator could differentiate between the different activities. However, if a computer is used, activities are normally identified only by their *i-j* numbers for computational purposes, and most computer programs require that each activity have a unique *i-j* designation.

When a situation as just described is encountered (and they are relatively frequent), dummy activities are used. The following illustrates how dummies can be utilized to give each activity its individual numerical designation:

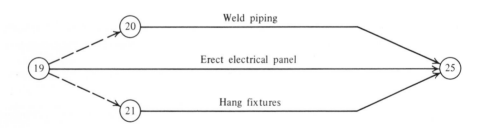

12.9 LOGICAL LOOPS

A logical loop involves the impossible requirement that an activity be followed immediately by another activity that has already been accomplished. The figure below presents a simple example of a logical loop.

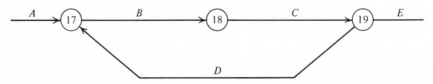

A logical loop is, of course, completely illogical. Although this fact may be perfectly obvious, logical loops are sometimes inadvertently included in large or complex networks. Because these loops are impossible in actuality and have no place in an arrow diagram, safeguards must be used to prevent their inclusion.

12.10 EVENTS

In Figure 12.1 the circles at the junction of the arrows are called "nodes" or "events." An event is the interval of time between completion of the latest incoming activity and the earliest start of a following activity. CPM is not event-oriented; that is, CPM does not usually emphasize or name events but merely designates them by numbers. If there are some events that are particularly important, they can be named and so designated on the arrow diagram. These events are commonly referred to as "milestones." Milestones are important intermediate goals within the network. An example might be the point in time when a new structure is finished so that an existing structure can be vacated and remodeled.

It is customary that the event at the head of an arrow be numbered higher than the event at its tail; that is to say, j is normally greater than i. Originally this was done primarily to facilitate computer usage, although it is no longer necessary. Nevertheless, the practice persists because such a system makes it easier to locate events and activities on a diagram and protects against the inclusion of logical loops. Numbers need not be used in sequence nor need all numbers be used. Usual practice is that event numbers are not entered until the network has been completed. Leaving gaps in the numbers is often desirable so that spare numbers are available for subsequent refinements and revisions. It is standard procedure that arrow diagrams have only one initial event and only one terminal event.

12.11 NETWORK DIAGRAM FORMAT

Use and custom have evolved a horizontal diagram format that has become relatively standard in the construction industry. When the job logic and the network diagram are developed simultaneously, the general synthesis of the diagram is from start to finish, working from project beginning on the left to project completion on the right. During the preliminary development of a diagram, trial layouts are sketched with emphasis on the activity relationships rather than on the appearance or style of the diagram. This first stage, which frequently utilizes random direction lines and wide sweeping curves, is commonly done on a blackboard, where corrections and revisions are easily made. An attempt is often made to identify a central chain of significant events that will form a network backbone with branching activities appearing both above and below.

When the diagram is prepared from a listing of job logic, such as that shown in Table 12.1, there appears to be some advantage in developing the arrow diagram starting with the project end and working backward to the project start. After the diagram is drawn, it is advisable to run through the diagram from start to finish and check it against the designated logic.

Usually at least a part of each activity arrow is drawn horizontally. This horizontal portion is used for the entry of activity identification and activity time. The topic of activity time will be discussed subsequently. The horizontal convention, however, does not apply to dummy activities. The use of symbols for activities rather than entering the full name of each activity on the arrow diagram is questionable. Symbols are convenient in listing job logic and preparing the diagram, but they can make the final diagram difficult to read. Activity symbols are used in the example problems of this chapter only as a convenience for discussion and as an aid in the presentation of job logic.

In the preparation of the working network diagram, arrow size and spacing deserve attention. If the arrows are too long and too widely spaced, the diagram is likely to become so large that it is unwieldy. On the other hand, if the spacing is too compact, the small scale makes the diagram difficult to read and inhibits corrections and modifications. With experience, the practitioner can adjust the size of the diagram to the scope and complexity of the project involved.

It is generally agreed that backward arrows are to be avoided. Because they act against the time flow of activities, they are confusing to those reading the diagram. In addition, backward arrows increase the chances of unintentional logical loops appearing in the diagram. Crossovers are instances in which one arrow must cross over another in order to satisfy the prescribed job logic. These are not arrow intersections because activities can come together only at the nodes. Crossovers can be minimized by careful layout, but there are usually some that cannot be avoided. Several different symbols are in use to designate such crossovers.

12.12 PROJECT SCHEDULING

In the discussion thus far, the vital concern has been with sequential constraints. Before the CPM procedure can be carried further, attention must be given to time requirements. This is called the "scheduling phase" of CPM.

The essential input information for project scheduling is the network diagram and a time duration estimate for each activity. These estimated durations are very important and the usefulness of CPM depends in large measure on their accuracy.

Project scheduling is accomplished by carrying out a series of simple computations that yield valuable project control information. An overall project completion time is first established. Assuming, for the moment, that the resulting project completion date is acceptable, we then determine times or dates within which each activity must start and finish if the established project completion date is to be met.

12.13 ACTIVITY DURATIONS

The first step in the scheduling process is to estimate the time necessary to carry out each activity. These durations are generally expressed as working days and do not include nonproductive periods such as holidays and weekends. Other units of time may be used, (e.g., hours, calendar days, or shifts). The only requirement is that the same unit of time be used consistently throughout. The process of estimating activity durations will usually result in a certain amount of network refinement and activity redefinition.

Much of the value of the CPM process depends on the accuracy of the estimated activity durations. The following rules constitute the basis for this important step:

1. Each activity duration is based on the "normal" level of manpower and equipment that the estimator usually assumes when he prices the job. This normal level is about optimum in the sense that it represents the activity duration for minimum direct cost. Direct cost refers to the costs of materials, labor, and equipment and does not include indirect costs such as overhead, liquidated damages, penalty and bonus clauses, or interest. Presumably larger or smaller crews could be used, but the direct costs will increase if greater times (dragout) or lesser times (expediting) are allowed.

2. It is important that each activity be evaluated independently of all the others; for example, if an activity might take longer than usual because of an anticipated delay in material delivery, delivery should be made a separate activity with a realistic duration of its own.

3. A normal work day or week is assumed. Overtime or multiple shifts are not considered unless this is standard practice or a part of a normal work period.

4. Activity durations must be estimated without regard to predetermined contract completion dates. Otherwise unconscious adjustments may be made to fit the activities into the time available. Quite obviously this defeats the entire scheduling process.

5. Consistent time units must be used throughout. To illustrate, delivery of materials is commonly quoted in terms of calendar days. However, a 30-day delivery period will involve only 21 or 22 working days and even less if weekday holidays occur. The curing of concrete is another familiar example. A seven-day curing period will usually involve only five working days.

Quantitative information is available to assist in the estimation of activity durations; for example, the estimating sheets compiled when the job was bid will yield the man-hours or equipment-hours for each activity. By making assumptions concerning size of work crew or number of equipment units, activity durations can be computed. Practice has shown, however, that experienced field personnel and estimators can usually make informal time estimates that are just as accurate as those obtained from presumably more exact means. It must be remembered that the seemingly more formal procedure also involves an element of uncertainty —that of estimating crew size or equipment spread. Up to a point the accuracy of duration estimates can be improved by subdividing the work into smaller units. For obvious reasons dummy activities have zero times. Activity durations are normally shown on the diagram below their respective arrows.

It is not desirable to add a contingency factor to any individual activity duration to allow for unpredictable project delays caused by strikes, late material deliveries, fires, or accidents. Such a contingency is better included in the time required for overall project completion. Weather delays can be predicted to some degree, and it is appropriate to include a factor when estimating the durations of those activities susceptible to delay by weather when such an eventuality appears to be a strong possibility.

12.14 EXAMPLE PROBLEM 2

To illustrate subsequent discussion, let us now consider a somewhat more involved construction project which will be Example Problem 2. Although much simplified from an actual construction project, it will serve to illustrate the essential workings of the CPM scheduling procedure.

The project to be discussed is a natural gas compressor station involving a prefabricated metal building, compressor foundation, stand-by butane fuel system, and compressor appurtenances such as piping, electrical services, and controls. Table 12.2 presents the job logic and the estimated activity durations, and Figure 12.2 shows the completed arrow diagram. It should be noted that activity

TABLE 12.2 Job Logic and Activity Times

EXAMPLE PROBLEM 2: COMPRESSOR STATION

Activity	Symbol	Duration (working days)	Activity Immediately Following
Grading	GR	7	CF, EXB
Granular Fill	GF	21	CC, BP, SF
Run-in Electrical	RE	42	EC
Procure Building	PB	28	ERB
Compressor Foundation	CF	8	CC, BP, SF
Excavate Butane	EXB	17	BUS
Butane Storage	BUS	34	PS
Connect Cooling	CC	11	PS
Bolts and Plates	BP	6	SC
Slab and Footings	SF	14	SC, ERB
Piping Systems	PS	15	CP
Set Compressor	SC	13	SCP
Electrical to Compressor	EC	20	SCP
Erect Building	ERB	29	WB
Wire Building	WB	17	TC
Set Control Panel	SCP	14	CP
Connect Piping	CP	10	TC
Test and Clean	TC	4	—

times are indicated on the diagram. This is a convenience for computing and other diagram usage.

12.15 TIME COMPUTATIONS

To be effective, a scheduling system must yield information in sufficient detail so that it is possible to determine where the project is lagging and how serious the delay may be to overall project completion. In CPM, it is possible to obtain this information by computing limiting times either for each of the activities (arrows) or for each of the events (nodes). The activity computations, which form the basis of discussion in this chapter, are carried out with the assistance of the arrow diagram and normally appear in table form such as Table 12.3. However, activity and event computations can be carried out directly on the arrow diagram.

Preparing the network diagram and estimating the activity durations call for considerable experience and judgment. The computations, however, are routine and can be delegated to a clerk or to an electronic computer. On projects involving more than a few hundred activities, digital computers are generally utilized to develop the necessary data.

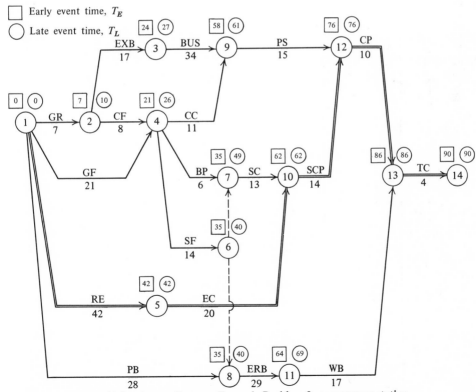

Figure 12.2 Arrow diagram, Example Problem 2: compressor station.

TABLE 12.3 Time Analysis

EXAMPLE PROBLEM 2: COMPRESSOR STATION

Activity	Arrow i-j	Estimated Duration (working days)	Earliest		Latest		Float		Critical Activity
			Start	Finish	Start	Finish	Total	Free	
(1)	(2)	(3)	(4)	(5)	(6)	(7)	(8)	(9)	(10)
GR	1-2	7	0	7	3	10	3	0	
GF	1-4	21	0	21	5	26	5	0	
RE	1-5	42	0	42	0	42	0	0	*
PB	1-8	28	0	28	12	40	12	7	
CF	2-4	8	7	15	18	26	11	6	
EXB	2-3	17	7	24	10	27	3	0	
BUS	3-9	34	24	58	27	61	3	0	
CC	4-9	11	21	32	50	61	29	26	
SF	4-6	14	21	35	26	40	5	0	
BP	4-7	6	21	27	43	49	22	8	
PS	9-12	15	58	73	61	76	3	3	
Dummy	6-7	0	35	35	49	49	14	0	
Dummy	6-8	0	35	35	40	40	5	0	
SC	7-10	13	35	48	49	62	14	14	
EC	5-10	20	42	62	42	62	0	0	*
ERB	8-11	29	35	64	40	69	5	0	
WB	11-13	17	64	81	69	86	5	5	
SCP	10-12	14	62	76	62	76	0	0	*
CP	12-13	10	76	86	76	86	0	0	*
TC	13-14	4	86	90	86	90	0	0	*

The contractor need know nothing about computer operation or programming if he rents time at a commercial computer center. He merely makes up the arrow diagram and estimates the various activity times. This information is then summarized on a standard-form data sheet, which the contractor submits to the computer center. These data, combined with a computer program, are fed through the machine, and the contractor receives back a print-out of the information that he desires. Many kinds of programs, each of which will produce certain schedule information for the contractor's use, are available. For example, there is a standard CPM program that will produce a machine print-out of Table 12.3. It is to be re-emphasized that the computer cannot produce anything that the contractor cannot himself obtain manually. The computer can simply do the job much faster. Although rental rates of digital computers are high, their speed is so great that the cost involved with CPM is quite reasonable.

12.16 ACTIVITY START AND FINISH TIMES

Computations are made to determine the earliest and latest start times and the earliest and latest finish times of each activity. The earliest start time of an activity is the earliest time at which it can be started considering the preceding activities that must be finished before the given activity can begin. The earliest finish time is the earliest possible completion time for the activity and is obtained by adding the activity duration to its earliest start time. The latest start time for an activity is the latest possible time at which it can begin and not delay overall project completion. The latest finish time is the latest the activity can be completed and not delay project completion. The difference between the latest start and finish times is the activity duration.

Table 12.3 shows the earliest start and finish times and the latest start and finish times for each activity of Example Problem 2. The computation of the earliest start and finish times will be discussed first. Activities GR, GF, RE, and PB are all initial activities, and their earliest possible start is at zero elapsed time. Activity GR has a duration of 7 days, and hence the earliest it can be finished is at the end of the seventh working day (or at a time of 7). All of the start and finish times in Table 12.3 represent elapsed working days from the start of the project at time zero. The earliest possible finish date for GF is 21.

Neither EXB nor CF can start until GR has been completed. The earliest that GR can be finished is at the end of the seventh day, so the earliest that EXB or CF can be started is after the expiration of 7 working days (or at time 7). The earliest that CF can be finished would be its earliest start (7) plus its duration (8) or at time 15. The start of CC, BP, and SF must await the completion of *both* CF and GF. The earliest that CF can be finished is 15, but GF cannot be completed until 21. Because CC, BP, and SF cannot start until *both CF* and GF are finished, the earliest possible start dates for these three activities would be time 21. It is easy to see, therefore, that the earliest possible start date of any activity is the latest of the earliest finish times of immediately preceding activities. Computing the earliest start and finish times of each activity is a simple arithmetic process proceeding from start to finish of the project, or from top to bottom of columns 4 and 5 in Table 12.3. In the literature, this series of computations is often referred to as "the forward pass."

It will now be noted in Table 12.3 at the bottom of column 5 that the earliest possible finish time of terminal activity TC is 90 working days. Consequently, with the job logic established and the estimated activity durations, the earliest possible overall project completion time will be 90 days. The matter of project completion time will be discussed more fully in Section 12.20. For the purposes of continuing the discussion of activity times, let us assume that 90 working days is an acceptable figure for job completion.

Columns 6 and 7 of Table 12.3 show the latest times at which the several activities can be started and finished and still achieve overall project completion in 90 working days. To determine the latest possible finish date for each activity, and from this the latest start date, times are computed from finish to start of the project or from bottom to top of columns 6 and 7 in Table 12.3. This is sometimes referred to as "the backward pass."

The latest possible finish date of activity TC is set equal to 90 (column 7). With a duration time of 4, the latest possible start time of TC is, therefore, time 86. The latest possible time for the finish of CP is 86 if TC with a duration of 4 is to be completed in time 90. Commensurately, the latest start date for CP must be 76. The latest finish time for WB is also 86, and its latest start is 69. When a given activity is followed immediately by two or more other activities, the latest finish date of the activity is the earliest of the latest start times of the succeeding activities. In all cases, the latest start times are obtained by subtracting the activity durations from the latest finish times.

12.17 TOTAL FLOAT

Examination of Table 12.3 discloses that the earliest and latest start times (also earliest and latest finish times) are the same for some activities and not for others. The significance of this fact is that there is some leeway in the scheduling of certain activities and no leeway at all in the scheduling of others. This leeway of an activity is a measure of the additional time available for the activity above and beyond its estimated time duration. This slack time is called "float," two classifications being in general usage.

The "total float" of an activity is the difference between its earliest finish time and its latest finish time and is shown in column 8 of Table 12.3. Subtracting the earliest start time from the latest start time gives the same result. An activity with zero total float has no slack time and is, therefore, one of the operations that controls project completion time. Any delay in the finish date of such an operation automatically introduces the same delay in overall project completion. For this reason, activities with zero total float are called "critical."

12.18 THE CRITICAL PATH

Inspection of Table 12.3 discloses that there are five activities; RE, EC, SCP, CP, and TC, each of which has zero total float. In the arrow diagram in Figure 12.2, it is seen that these five activities form a continuous path from project beginning to project end. Expressed in terms of node numbers, this path is 1-5-10-12-13-14. This chain of critical activities, called the "critical path," determines the overall project completion time. The critical path is normally indicated on the arrow diagram in some distinguishing way such as with colors, heavy lines, or double lines.

Inspection of the network diagram in Figure 12.2 discloses that numerous paths exist between the start and the end of the diagram. Each of these paths must be traversed during the actual construction process. If the time durations of the activities forming a continuous path were to be added for each of the many possible paths, a number of different project durations would be obtained. The longest of these durations is the critical or minimum time for project completion because each path must be traveled, and the longest of these paths thereby determines the length of time to complete *all* of the activities in accordance with the operational sequence dictated by the network diagram.

The continuous path with the longest cumulative sum of activity durations is the so-called "critical path," and the activities forming this path are the "critical activities." If this process were to be applied to the arrow diagram in Figure 12.2, it would be found that the path 1-5-10-12-13-14, consisting of activities RE, EC, SCP, CP, and TC, is the longest and that its total time duration is 90 days. This is the same critical path that was found previously by means of zero total floats of activities. All other continuous paths through this network have a summation of activity times less than 90 days. The next two longest chains through the network are 1-2-3-9-12-13-14 (87 days) and 1-4-6-8-11-13-14 (85 days). It is possible to determine the critical path and hence the critical activities of an arrow diagram by merely determining the longest path. However, this is not usually a practical procedure. The critical path is normally located by means of zero total float times or by the computing of event times, a subject that is discussed in Section 12.28.

Although there is only one critical path in Figure 12.2, more than one path is always a possibility in network diagrams. One path can branch out into a number of paths, or several paths can combine into one. In any event, the critical path or paths must constitute a continuous chain of activities from start to finish. There must be at least one such critical path, and it cannot be intermittent. A break in the path indicates an error in the computations.

12.19 FREE FLOAT

Free float is another category of slack time. The free float of an activity is found by subtracting its earliest finish date from the earliest of the earliest start dates of the activities directly following. Column 9 of Table 12.3 lists the free float for each activity of Example Problem 2.

To illustrate how the free-float values were computed, let us consider activity CF. Table 12.3 shows the earliest finish date of CF to be at time 15. The immediately following activities are CC, BP, and SF, and their earliest start dates are 21, 21, and 21, respectively. The difference between the earliest finish date of CF (15) and the earliest of the earliest start dates of the immediately following activities (21) is 6. Hence activity CF has a free float of six days.

12.20 PROJECT COMPLETION TIME

In Example Problem 2 the project completion time of 90 working days is a result of the job logic and the assumed activity times. It is normal practice that the estimated time of an activity makes no allowance for contingencies other than possibly the weather. Labor disputes, difficult site conditions, accidents, delayed material deliveries, and other contingencies can and do cause delays, but it is difficult to predict in advance which activities may be affected and by how much. In general practice no allowance is made for delays caused by such contingencies when estimating the various activity times. More generally, contractors add perhaps a 5 percent contingency to the project duration to compensate for the usual tendency of the actual completion time to exceed the computed CPM end date.

To illustrate, using Example Problem 2, the contractor will probably add something like five days to the indicated 90-day project duration and ascertain the suitability of a 95-working-day construction period. If this is acceptable, he will proceed to make up a project calendar based on 90-day completion. No reworking of the arrow diagram or Figure 12.2 will be necessary. If everything goes as planned, he will probably finish the project in about 90 days. However, if the usual contingencies arise, he has allowed for a 95-day operating period.

If the 95-working-day construction time is, for some reason, not satisfactory, the contractor must re-examine his operational plan. Before CPM was devised, the construction manager's first impulse was to expedite most, if not all, of the job operations when the construction time for a project had to be reduced or when a project was falling behind schedule. This procedure is neither necessary nor economical because there is seldom any need to speed up any but the critical job activities. As we have already seen, most job activities are floaters; that is, more time is available for them than is required by their estimated durations. There is nothing to be gained by shortening even further the durations of such noncritical activities. Only the shortening of the critical path will produce any reduction of the project duration. On large networks, it is unusual that more than 10-20 percent of the activities turn out to be critical.

Because the critical path determines the overall job duration, the only way in which job duration can be shortened is to reduce the length of the critical path, either by rearranging the critical activities or by shortening some of the individual critical activities or perhaps both. The first action is to determine the possibility of performing some of the critical activities in parallel with one another rather than in series. Sometimes a localized reworking of job logic will make possible a shortening of the critical path. One caution is needed at this point: any rearrangement of the network diagram may result in the appearance of new critical paths. Thus, when the critical path is being shortened, the network must be continuously re-examined to ensure that all critical operations have been identified.

If the time reduction achieved by reworking the job logic is not sufficient, the durations of the critical activities themselves must be examined with the intent of shortening certain of them. This shortening of critical activities cannot be done arbitrarily. It must be both practicable and feasible in the field.

12.21 CPM COST PHASE

When the job duration is to be reduced by shortening the times of selected critical activities, the process becomes one of identifying the critical activities that can actually be expedited and their comparative costs. Up until this point, the element of project cost has been only incidental to the discussion. The basic CPM procedure includes a means of determining the variation of total project cost with project completion time. Total project cost is the sum of all direct and indirect costs. Theoretically, this cost versus time information enables the contractor to determine a project completion time that will minimize his total construction cost. This procedure has not been an unqualified success in practice, however, and will not be discussed herein. Nevertheless, some elements of the method do have practical application in assisting the contractor to expedite the project at the least additional direct cost.

12.22 LEAST-COST EXPEDITING

Assume that it has become necessary to shorten the job duration of Example Problem 2 by means of expediting critical activities. Each of the five critical activities (RE, EC, SCP, CP, TC) must first be studied to ascertain whether it can be shortened and, if so, what the additional direct cost will be. When necessary, most activities can be completed in less than the normal time. Speed-up actions do increase the direct cost of the activity, however, because they involve the additional expense of overtime work, multiple shifts, more equipment, payment of premiums for quick delivery of materials, or larger but less efficient crews. There is a point, of course, beyond which an activity cannot be expedited further. The process of shortening an activity is known as "crashing."

Suppose the contractor on the compressor station of Example Problem 2 ascertains that he can shorten activity RE (Run-in Electrical) by as much as 3 days by sending in another pole-setting truck with crew. The additional expense of moving the extra truck and crew to and from the job site will be a single lump sum of $1,000 whether 1 day or 3 days is saved. Activity EC (Electrical to Compressor) can be expedited by 1 day if the electricians work overtime. The additional cost of premium time will amount to $200. Activity SCP (Set Control Panel) can be shortened by 1 day if the manufacturer's installation engineer does part of his work at night. This will require special lighting that will cost about $300 to install and remove. Activity CP (Connect Piping) can probably be expedited by a day or two by renting additional welding and cutting equipment, but the cost is considered to be prohibitive. Activity TC (Test and Clean) is already scheduled as a 24-hour-a-day operation and cannot be shortened.

The contractor's analysis discloses, first of all, that the original critical path can be shortened by a maximum of five days. This means that the probable job duration can be shortened from 95 to 90 days or the CPM time from 90 to 85 days, assuming that any new critical paths created during the shortening process can also be shortened. The project cannot be shortened more than five days, however, because the original critical path remains a critical path during the entire expediting process.

The critical activities to be shortened will be selected on the basis of least cost. The exact activities selected will depend on the number of days the project is to be reduced. In our Example Problem 2 the expediting pattern and cost for the first three days reduction would be as follows:

If Reduction in Days Is	Activity Reduced– Days	Total Additional Direct Cost
1	EC-1	$ 200
2	EC-1, SCP-1	500
3	RE-3	1,000

This now reduces the critical path 1-5-10-12-13-14, hence the CPM duration of the project to 87 days. In so doing path 1-2-3-9-12-13-14, whose total length is also 87 days, now becomes a second parallel critical path. To shorten the project further it is necessary to shorten both critical paths simultaneously. This could be done by diminishing either activity CP or TC because they are common to both critical paths. However, it has already been established that neither of these can be reduced. Further expediting, therefore, depends upon shortening simultaneously the least costly of activities EC or SCP (RE has already been expedited its full 3 days) and of activities GR, EXB, BUS, or PS. Without going into detail, suppose that activity BUS is the cheapest of the latter group and can be expedited as much as 4 days at an extra cost of $150 per day. The expediting pattern and cost for the next 2 days' reduction of project duration would be:

If Reduction in Days Is	Activity Reduced– Days	Total Additional Direct Cost
4	RE–3, $\left\{\begin{array}{l} \text{EC-1} \\ \text{BUS-1} \end{array}\right.$	$1,350
5	RE–3, $\left\{\begin{array}{l} \text{EC-1, SCP-1} \\ \text{BUS-2} \end{array}\right.$	1,800

This now reduces the CPM project duration to 85 days, and this is the most that can be achieved. When there is more than one critical path (our example now has three), all critical paths must be shortened simultaneously to achieve overall project reduction. Since the original critical path has now been decreased to an irreducible minimum, no further project expediting is possible.

12.23 SIGNIFICANCE OF FLOATS

The float of an activity represents potential scheduling leeway. When float is available, the earliest start of an activity can be delayed, its duration can be extended, or a combination of both can occur. To do a proper job of rescheduling noncritical activities, it is important that the practitioner understand the workings of float times.

The total float of an activity is the maximum time that its actual completion date can go beyond its earliest finish date and not delay the entire project. It is the time leeway available for that activity if the activities preceding it are started as early as possible and the ones following it are started as late as possible. The free float of an activity is the maximum time by which its actual completion date can exceed its earliest finish date and not affect either overall project completion or the floats of any subsequent activities. If an operation is delayed to the extent of its free float, the following activities are not affected and they can still start at their earliest start times.

It is to be noted that free float is a part of total float. That is to say, when free float is used, total float is also being utilized in like amount. If float in excess of the free float but less than the total float of an activity is used, the floats of following activities in the network are reduced commensurately. The difference between the total float and the free float of an activity is called "interfering float" and indicates the range of floats that, when used, has a tightening effect on subsequent activities. If all the total float of any one acitvity is utilized, a new critical path is created.

12.24 TIME-SCALED NETWORK

The arrow diagram, when drawn to a horizontal time scale, is very useful for scheduling purposes. In particular, such a network clarifies the workings of float times, especially when the rescheduling of noncritical activities is involved.

Figure 12.3 is the same network diagram as Figure 12.2 except that it is drawn to a horizontal time scale of elapsed working days. Each activity in Figure 12.3 is started at its earliest start time as given by Table 12.3. Vertical solid lines indicate sequential dependence of one activity on another. A time-scaled plot of this type automatically yields to scale the free float of each activity. Free floats are shown as horizontal dotted lines. When the activity has no free float, no dotted extension of that activity arrow appears.

Examination of Figure 12.3 will clarify the nature of free float. To illustrate, activity CC has a duration of 11 days and a free float of 26 days. Figure 12.3 clearly shows that there is a total of 37 days in which to accomplish CC. Within its two boundaries CC can be delayed in starting, have its duration increased beyond 11 days, or a combination of the two without disturbing any following activity.

The significance of total float is equally obvious from a study of Figure 12.3. In working with total float it is necessary to consider the connected solid lines as rigid frames and the dotted lines as elastic connections; for example, consider the rigid framework that consists of activities GR, CF, EXB, BUS, and PS. Not only is the free float of PS equal to three days but the total float of each activity GR, EXB, BUS, and PS is also three days. The diagram shows that if any one of these four activities is allowed to consume an additional three days the succeeding activities will be pushed along and all of the elasticity in path GR-EXB-BUS-PS-CP-TC is gone. Consequently, it becomes a second critical path. The result would be the same if any three of activities GR, EXB, BUS, and PS were each extended one additional day.

Figure 12.3 clearly shows the interrelated and shared nature of floats along a path or paths through a network. Again considering the activities GR, CF, EXB, BUS, and PS, the free float of PS will be reduced, that of CF may be reduced, and that of CC could be increased, depending on which of GR, EXB, BUS, and PS are extended. The delay of any one of these four activities will reduce the total float of each of the others in like amount.

12.25 RESOURCES PLANNING AND SCHEDULING

An important consideration associated with establishing a final time schedule of construction operations is the effect of activity sequence on limited resources such as equipment or manpower. It is usual that the initial arrow diagram is developed on the assumption of unlimited resources. When activities requiring the same

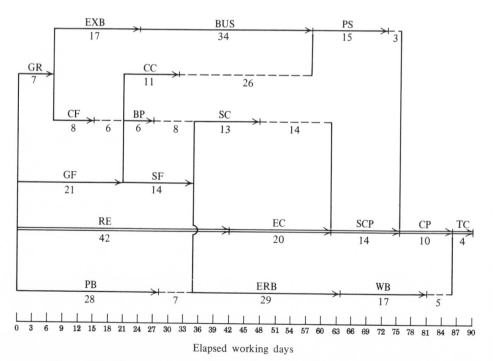

Figure 12.3 Time-scaled arrow diagram, Example Problem 2: compressor station.

limited resource are scheduled for the same calendar period, a conflict exists that must be resolved either by revising the job logic or utilizing the float times of the activities affected.

To illustrate a simple case of activity revision suppose the following appeared as a part of an arrow diagram for the construction of a two-span bridge:

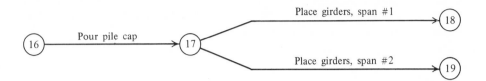

To place the girders for both spans simultaneously would require twice the equipment that would be needed to place the girders one span at a time. Assuming that the contractor's equipment is limited and that overall job conditions do not actually require both spans to be set at the same time, we could reschedule these operations as follows:

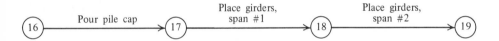

In a case such as the one just discussed, the equipment conflict should be detected and corrected while the arrow diagram is still being developed. However, when operations requiring the same resource at the same time are more distantly removed from one another in a large or complex diagram, the conflict may not come to light until the activity time computations in Table 12.3 have been made.

A time-scaled plot of the arrow diagram is valuable and convenient for the scheduling of construction resources such as equipment. The mechanics of "equipment leveling" are simple and straightforward. By using the time-scaled diagram, a table is made showing the equipment requirements for each day. The table quickly detects equipment conflicts and points out areas where rescheduling of activities is necessary or desirable. By the judicious use of float times, noncritical activities can usually be rescheduled to spread out peak equipment needs to a more reasonable level. Decisions concerning buying new equipment or renting are made easier as well.

As a simple illustration, suppose that the start of activity SC in Example Problem 2 requires the use of the same heavy-duty crane already engaged on activity BUS. Two cranes on the project simultaneously would be difficult and expensive to arrange. Figure 12.3 shows that the start of SC can easily be deferred by as much as 14 days. Rescheduling the start of SC undoubtedly will remove the equipment conflict.

The procedure just discussed can easily be applied to the leveling of manpower requirements also. Sharp fluctuations in labor needs on a project are undesirable and often impossible to arrange. Although a constant work force is not usually possible, fluctuations can be minimized by making a table of day-to-day labor requirements in a manner similar to that for equipment. To illustrate, let us assume that pipefitters are in short supply and that Figure 12.4 represents the anticipated need for this craft as obtained from the first version of the project schedule. The extreme peaks and valleys of demand are very objectionable, and more than 8 or 9 pipefitters probably will not be available anyway. The dotted line representing a constant work force of 5 men represents the ideal situation. Although it probably is not attainable, judicious rearrangement of activities and the use of float times can do much to smooth out manpower requirements.

12.26 PROJECT CALENDAR

When a final schedule of activities has been determined, it is desirable to translate this information into a summary project calendar. Thus far, project times have been expressed only in terms of elapsed working days. For purposes of project control, it is necessary to express these times as the calendar dates on which each activity is expected to start and finish. This is easily done with the aid of a calendar on which the working days are numbered consecutively, starting with number 1 on the anticipated start date and skipping all weekends, holidays, and vacation periods.

When making up a job calendar, the true meaning of elapsed days must be kept in mind. For example, if the start of an activity is to be 24, this means at the *expiration* of 24 working days, so that the *start* of the activity will be on the twenty-fifth day. It is important that the project calendar include job restraints shown on the arrow diagram, such as approval of shop drawings, delivery of materials, and availability of key construction equipment.

The project calendar must reflect the shortening of critical activities, rearrangement of job logic, and use of float times as required to expedite the project or to

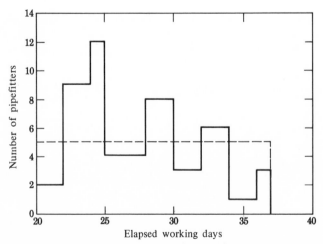

Figure 12.4   Manpower-time requirements.

smooth out resource needs. Activities not affected are scheduled to take place for their estimated durations and to start at their earliest start dates. Table 12.4 is a project calendar for Example Problem 2. It is based on the durations and earliest start dates contained in Table 12.3.

Once again, the scheduling information must be examined for reasonableness. In this case, certain activities must be compared with the weather to be expected during the calendar dates established. If concrete placing, for example, is concentrated into the coldest periods, some revision of the schedule may be needed. In addition, it is to be emphasized that although CPM is a valuable management guide it is not a cure-all. It cannot and should not replace skilled project supervision. The project calendar must be viewed as allowing the construction superintendent reasonable latitude to exercise his experience and judgment.

12.27 PROJECT MONITORING

Once the project schedule has been determined and construction is underway, the CPM plan must be monitored and updated as operations proceed. One of the nice features of CPM is its ability to incorporate changes as the project goes along. No project plan is ever perfect, and deviations from the CPM program are in-

TABLE 12.4 Project Calendar

EXAMPLE PROBLEM 2: COMPRESSOR STATION

Activity	Scheduled Duration (working days)	Scheduled Starting Date	Scheduled Completion Date
GR	7	April 29, 19—	May 7, 19—
GF	21	April 29, 19—	May 27, 19—
RE	42	April 29, 19—	June 26, 19—
PB	28	April 29, 19—	June 6, 19—
CF	8	May 8, 19—	May 17, 19—
EXB	17	May 8, 19—	May 31, 19—
BUS	34	June 3, 19—	July 19, 19—
CC	11	May 28, 19—	June 12, 19—
SF	14	May 28, 19—	June 17, 19—
BP	6	May 28, 19—	June 5, 19—
PS	15	July 22, 19—	August 9, 19—
SC	13	June 18, 19—	July 5, 19—
EC	20	June 27, 19—	July 25, 19—
ERB	29	June 18, 19—	July 29, 19—
WB	17	July 30, 19—	August 21, 19—
SCP	14	July 26, 19—	August 14, 19—
CP	10	August 15, 19—	August 28, 19—
TC	4	August 29, 19—	September 4, 19—

evitable. The arrow diagram itself provides a useful medium for recording day-to-day progress. Entry in colored pencil of the daily advancement of each activity provides a visible, current status report of the job. Arrow diagrams plotted to a horizontal time scale are especially useful for job monitoring.

Periodic updating of the CPM plan is necessary during the construction period. Updating involves revising the plan at periodic intervals to incorporate actual activity durations and changes made in the job logic as the work proceeds. The objective is to compute revised values of the project completion date, activity start times, floats, and critical activities.

How often the network should be recomputed depends upon the project and the degree of control desired. For the general range of projects, updating intervals of 2 weeks to 1 month are commonly used. On a project of considerable size, it is difficult to keep up with the schedule changes when using the manual method of data reduction. To incorporate changes at reasonable updating intervals, the use of a computer becomes a practical necessity.

12.28   EVENT TIMES

The computational procedures discussed thus far have been based on the determination of activity times. An alternative is to compute similar limiting times for the events. These two times are called the "early event time" and the "late event time," and the computations are usually carried out directly on the arrow diagram itself. Event times are shown in Figure 12.2.

The early event time, T_E, is defined as the earliest possible time that the event can occur. The early event time is the latest of the earliest completion times of the entering activities. Reference to Figure 12.2 will illustrate the procedure. For example, assume that node 4 is under discussion. The earliest that CF can finish is 15 days and the earliest that GF can finish is 21 days. Because the early event time does not occur until the instant that all incoming activities are finished, the early event time of node 4 will be 21. Normally, values of T_E are computed by working from project start to project finish.

The late event time, T_L, is defined to be the latest time at which an event may occur without delaying the computed project duration. The late event time is the earliest of the latest start times of all activities leaving the node. To compute the values of T_L, it is usual to work backward through the network from finish to start. To illustrate the procedure let us consider node 4 again. Three activities, CC, BP, and SF, immediately follow this event. The latest start times of these three are 50, 43, and 26, respectively. Consequently, the late event time of node 4 is 26.

Reference to the event times in Figure 12.2 shows that for some events T_E equals T_L. At event 10, for example, $T_E = T_L = 62$. Therefore the earliest that event 10 can possibly occur is time 62. However, the latest time that event 10 can occur and not delay project completion beyond 90 days is also time 62. This is a critical event, since zero time may elapse between its start and finish. Inspection of Figure 12.2 shows that all the critical events lie along the critical path 1-5-10-12-13-14. Thus computation of event times is another way of locating the critical path.

Occasionally there is more than one path of activities between critical events, which makes it necessary to identify the activities that are indeed critical. A critical activity must first start and finish at critical events. In addition, the duration of a critical activity will equal the difference between the late event time T_L at its head event and the early event time T_E of its tail event. This is simply saying that the total float of a critical activity must equal zero.

12.29 PRECEDENCE DIAGRAMS

There is another method of constructing a network besides the arrow-activity mode discussed in this chapter. The basic concept of the alternative procedure is that the activities (not events) are represented by circles and the dependencies between activities are indicated by lines or arrows. This method is called by several names, including "precedence diagraming" and "circle notation."

To illustrate how this method works, some common logic relationships are shown in Figure 12.5 for both arrow notation and circle notation. Figure 12.6 presents the network of Figure 12.2 drawn in circle notation.

Precedence diagraming has both advantages and disadvantages when compared to arrow diagraming. In concept, circle notation seems to be simpler and faster to learn, particularly for field and operating personnel. For many people, it is easier to plot and analyze. There are no dummies in a precedence diagram. The big disadvantage of circle notation is that it is nonstandard. Arrow notation greatly predominates in general practice. Also, events are sometimes of great importance, and precedence diagraming eliminates events. Computer programs applicable to circle notation are much more limited than those for arrow notation, and some say that precedence diagraming is more cumbersome to update. The calculations for the two techniques are quite similar.

12.30 CPM-BASED COST CONTROL

The discussion of construction cost-accounting presented in Chapter 11 did not give consideration to the basing of project cost reporting and control upon network activities. Such a procedure might well afford contractors with a means for improved project cost control. Department of Defense Agencies, NASA, and their aerospace contractors have developed cost reporting procedures called PERT/Cost which are based upon network activities. In the construction industry, however, interest in CPM-based cost control has been slow to develop with almost all such applications being at the instigation of owners.

Despite the fact that the use of activities for purposes of progress payments, cost reporting, and cash forecasting would seem to be advantageous, there are very real problems in implementing such procedures. A cost system based upon activities is not consonant with traditional estimating and cost accounting procedures.

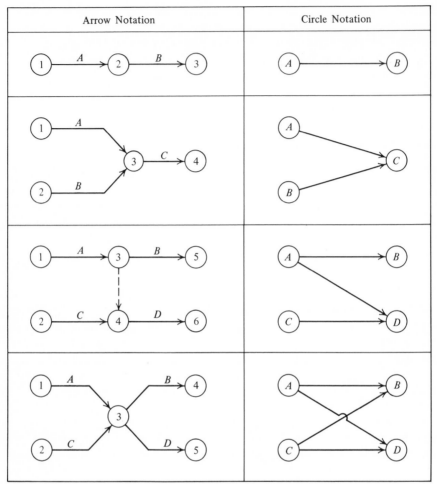

Figure 12.5   Arrow and circle notation.

Consequently, conversion to an activity-based cost system is a change of imposing proportions for most contractors. Although construction cost systems based upon CPM activities may well develop in future years, significant differences between project control by time and by cost must first be resolved.

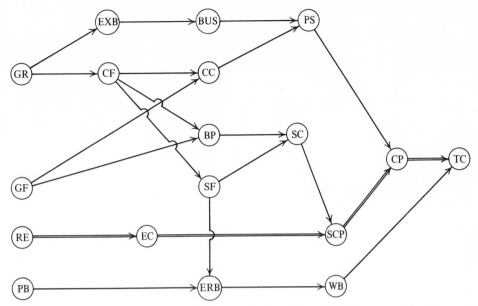

Figure 12.6 Network using circle notation, Example Problem 2: compressor station.

13

LABOR LAW

13.1 CONSTRUCTION AND LABOR LAWS

The employment of labor by the contractor is subject to the provisions of an imposing array of both federal and state statutes. These laws have such an important bearing on the conduct of a contracting business that the construction manager must have at least a general grasp of their workings and implications. It is the intent of this chapter to discuss the important features of the principal federal statutes that apply to the employment of construction workers. Federal laws are discussed because of their broad applicability and the fact that many state labor statutes are patterned after federal law. Emphasis is placed more on the broad implications of these laws than on the intricacies of case studies.

For purposes of discussion in this chapter, the labor laws are separated into two general categories. One category includes the laws that control and regulate the actions of management and labor in their mutual relationships with one another. The second classification establishes minimum standards with respect to wages and other conditions of employment. The first of these categories will now be discussed. The second will be treated in the latter part of this chapter.

13.2 HISTORY OF LABOR-MANAGEMENT LEGISLATION

In many respects, labor-management law is in a relatively early stage of development. For this reason it is in a continual state of flux. To better understand the present state of affairs, it is necessary to know something of the historical background of American labor law.

From their very inception, labor unions have been subjected to examination and regulation by the courts. Before 1842, unions were severely curtailed and were sometimes referred to as "unlawful conspiracies." However, in the year 1842, the Massachusetts Supreme Court held that unions were legal organizations and that strikes were a permissible means of exerting economic pressure on employers, provided that the end object being sought by the strike was legal. For the next 90 years, until the early 1930's, unions pursued a steady course of betterment of wages and hours, although the general judicial attitude continued to favor the strict regulation of organized labor. During this period, the organizing activities of unions were severely curtailed by court injunctions.

During the early and middle 1930's, however, popular opinion concerning unions underwent a remarkable metamorphosis, and the judicial attitude became pointedly sympathetic and permissive to organized labor. Thus, during the New Deal era, labor enjoyed unprecedented freedom of action and was actively encouraged and assisted by the federal government in the attainment of its goals. In recent years, federal labor legislation has been concerned primarily with the regulation of the activities of labor organizations.

The following sections present the major pieces of federal labor-management legislation. Although some of these laws are no longer vital, it is felt that their inclusion has value in illustrating the significance of the present public attitude toward organized labor and in understanding the trend of future labor legislation.

13.3 THE SHERMAN ANTITRUST ACT

The Sherman Antitrust Act of 1890 made statutory provisions against the restraint of trade. The act was primarily intended to limit the growth of business cartels, and it is debatable whether or not it was ever intended to apply to labor unions. However, the Supreme Court ruled in 1908 that labor organizations were covered by the provisions of the act. The Sherman Act provided a broad new basis for the use of court injunctions against unions and also placed another effective weapon of unions in jeopardy, that is, the boycott. By decision of the Supreme Court, it was ruled that a union could be sued for damages suffered by reason of boycott, and that the union and its members individually were liable.

1n 1914, Congress passed the Clayton Act, which was intended to give unions legislative relief from the Sherman Act. However, the Supreme Court interpreted the Clayton Act as pertaining only to cases involving employers and their own employees. Consequently, the injunction remained a powerful weapon in the hands of nonunion employers who wished to resist unionization of their workers. Thus, the Clayton Act was largely abortive and was of little consequence in the opinion of organized labor.

In retrospect, laws and judicial opinion were strongly discriminatory against unions until the advent of the New Deal. The eras of the conspiracy doctrine, the injunction, and the Sherman Act followed in succession, all displaying the absence of restrictions on the efforts of employers to inhibit or vitiate unions.

13.4   THE NORRIS-LA GUARDIA ACT

In 1932, Congress passed the Norris-LaGuardia Act, which substantially accomplished what the Clayton Act had attempted to do many years earlier. Fundamentally, the Norris-LaGuardia Act, also called the Anti-Injunction Act, provided that the federal courts would no longer be the agents of employers who were resisting the unions. It severely curtailed the powers of the federal courts to issue injunctions in labor disputes and protected the right of workers to strike and picket peaceably. Employment contracts in which a worker promised not to join a union during his tenure of employment ("yellow-dog contracts") were made unenforceable in federal courts. Although the act itself pertained only to federal courts, many states enacted similar injunction-control legislation. Subsequent court interpretations of the Norris-LaGuardia Act virtually freed organized labor from the Sherman Act.

13.5   THE NATIONAL LABOR RELATIONS ACT

The National Labor Relations Act, also known as the Wagner Act, was passed by Congress in 1935. Enacted in an atmosphere of depressed business conditions and extensive unemployment, the central purpose of the Wagner Act was to protect union organizing activity and to foster collective bargaining. Employers were required to bargain in good faith with the properly chosen representatives of their workers. The employer was forbidden to practice discrimination against his employees for labor activities or to influence their membership in any labor organization. These and other unfair labor practices were defined as they pertained to employers. However, no such prohibitions were applied to employees or unions in their relations with employers. Enforcement of the law was vested in a National Labor Relations Board (NLRB), which the Wagner Act created. Under the shelter of this piece of legislation, union strength and membership increased enormously during the 1937-1945 period. A number of state acts followed, which were more or less patterned after the federal law.

It was almost inevitable that the sudden removal of the traditional restraints would result in union excesses. Starting in about 1938, public opinion concerning organized labor began to undergo another reversal and became increasingly antagonistic with the mounting incidence of union restrictive practices, wartime strikes, and criminal activities of some labor leaders. Congressional resentment against organized labor's high-handed actions resulted in the War Labor Disputes Act (Smith-Connally Act) of 1943. The provisions of this act proved to be largely ineffective and accomplished little. If nothing else, however, the act reflected the mounting popular sentiment for the enactment of positive union-control legislation. During this period, several state legislatures passed statutes that regulated and curbed union activities. By 1947, thirty-seven states had passed some form of labor-control bill.

13.6 THE LABOR MANAGEMENT RELATIONS ACT

In 1947, Congress passed the Labor Management Relations Act, commonly known as the Taft-Hartley Act. This was the first federal law that imposed comprehensive controls over the activities of organized labor. It amended the National Labor Relations Act in several important respects and added new legal provisions of its own. The National Labor Relations Board was reconstituted, and its authorities were redefined. Section 7 of the Taft-Hartley Act established the basic right of every worker to participate in union activities or to refrain from them, subject to authorized agreements requiring membership in a union as a condition of employment. To protect such rights, Section 8 of the Taft-Hartley Act defined unfair labor practices for employers and labor organizations alike. The act established the Federal Mediation and Conciliation Service, gave the President of the United States certain powers regarding labor disputes imperiling national health or safety, and restricted political contributions by labor organizations.

In contradistinction to the Wagner Act, the Taft-Hartley Act was designed to curtail the freedom of action of unions in several different ways. Actually, it has not made any real inroads on labor strength, because, among other reasons, of continued prosperity and high-level employment since its passage. Nevertheless, the provisions of the Taft-Hartley Act have had far-reaching effects upon the labor-management scene.

Experience with the provisions of the act quickly revealed several imperfections and shortcomings. Some features of labor employment peculiar to the construction industry proved to be inadequately covered. However, the act's extremely controversial nature and the appreciable strengths of both its backers and opponents made revision of the law a very touchy and difficult matter.

13.7 THE LABOR-MANAGEMENT REPORTING AND DISCLOSURE ACT

In 1959, Congress passed the Labor-Management Reporting and Disclosure Act, also known as the Landrum-Griffin Act, which made the first really significant changes in the Taft-Hartley Act. The principal thrust of this new law was to safeguard the rights of the individual union member, to ensure democratic elections in unions, to combat corruption and racketeering in unions, and to protect the public and innocent parties against unscrupulous union tactics. Under the act, reports pertaining to union organization, finances, activities, and policies are required from unions, union officials and employees, employers, labor relations consultants, and union trusteeships. It was made illegal for an employer to pay or lend money to any labor representative or union of his employees. Provided for, however, are employer contributions to qualified funds for paid vacations, paid holidays, severance pay, and apprenticeship training programs.

Additionally, the Landrum-Griffin Act amended the National Labor Relations Act and the Taft-Hartley Act. The 1959 law enumerated additional union unfair labor practices and remedied several inadequacies of the Taft-Hartley Act with respect to pressures that unions and their agents can legally apply to employers and their employees. So-called "hot-cargo" labor agreements (see Section 13.11, item 6) were forbidden with an exception made for the construction industry. Limitations were applied to organizational picketing of employers by labor organizations. Most of the restrictions on union-security agreements in the construction industry were removed, and union hiring halls (see Section 13.16) were made legal.

13.8 COVERAGE OF THE NATIONAL LABOR RELATIONS ACT

The National Labor Relations Act as amended plays a dominant role in national labor relations policy. Its declared purpose is to state the legally recognized rights of employees, employers, and labor unions in their relations with one another and with the public, and to provide machinery to prevent or remedy any interference by one with the legitimate rights of another. In particular, it protects employees in the free exercise of their rights to join or not to join a union, to bargain collectively through representatives of their own choosing, and to act together with other employees for mutual aid and protection. Any violation of these rights, whether by management or by labor representatives, is declared to be an unfair labor practice.

The National Labor Relations Act applies to employers and employees engaged in interstate commerce or the production of goods for such commerce. It does not apply to employment in a business or industry in which a labor dispute does not affect interstate commerce. The interpretation of what interstate commerce is has been so liberal that the act's authority extends to almost all employment except for purely local enterprises. The act specifically excludes the following employers and employees from its coverage:

1. Employees of an employer subject to the Railway Labor Act.
2. Agricultural laborers.
3. Domestic servants.
4. Any individual employed by his parent or spouse.
5. Government employees, federal or state or any political subdivision of either.
6. Employment in nonprofit hospitals.
7. Independent contractors.
8. Supervisors.

Certain selected portions of the National Labor Relations Act, as amended, have been selected for discussion. These are presented in Sections 13.9 through 13.21.

13.9 THE NATIONAL LABOR RELATIONS BOARD

Administration of the National Labor Relations Act is the responsibility of the National Labor Relations Board (NLRB), which is composed of five members, and the General Counsel of the board. The NLRB has two primary functions: (1) to establish, usually by secret-ballot elections, whether or not certain groups of employees wish to be represented by labor organizations for collective-bargaining purposes, and (2) to prevent and remedy unfair labor practices, whether committed by labor organizations or employers.

Members of the NLRB are appointed by the President, with consent of the Senate, for terms of 5 years. The General Counsel is appointed by the President, with consent of the Senate, for a term of 4 years. The General Counsel and his staff in the regional offices investigate and prosecute unfair labor practice cases and conduct elections to determine employee representatives. The NLRB decides cases involving charges of unfair labor practices and determines representation election questions that come to it from the regional offices.

Much of the day-to-day work of investigating and processing charges of unfair labor practices and handling representation proceedings has been delegated by the board and the General Counsel to the various NLRB regional offices located in major cities throughout the nation. All cases coming to the NLRB must be initiated and processed in the regional offices.

By statute, the NLRB exercises its powers over all enterprises whose operations affect interstate commerce. It does not act, however, on every case over which it could exercise jurisdiction. The Landrum-Griffin Act authorized the NLRB to limit its cases to enterprises whose effect on commerce is, in the board's opinion, substantial. As a guide to when it will exercise its power, the board has established minimum measures of the annual volume of business that must be met before the NLRB will accept the case. These standards are expressed in terms of gross dollar volume of business or sales and vary for different kinds of enterprises. The Landrum-Griffin Act further provided that state courts can assume jurisdiction over labor disputes that the NLRB declines to hear.

13.10 PETITION FOR ELECTION

The principle of majority rule applies in the determination of the bargaining representative of a group of employees. The representative may be an individual or a labor union but cannot be a supervisor or other representative of the employer. The National Labor Relations Act requires that an employer bargain with the representative selected by a majority of his employees but does not stipulate a selection procedure. The only requirement is that the representative clearly be the choice of the majority.

In order for the employees to select a majority representative, it is usual for the NLRB to conduct representation elections. However, such an election can be held only when a petition has been filed by the employees, by an individual or a labor organization acting in their behalf, or by an employer who has been confronted with a claim of representation from an individual or labor organization.

In a representation election, the employees are given a choice of one or more bargaining representatives or no representative at all. To be chosen, a labor organization must receive a majority of the valid votes cast. The NLRB will certify the choice of the majority of employees for a bargaining representative only after a secret-ballot election.

Elections to select bargaining representatives are not common in the construction industry. The construction trades unions traditionally represent construction workers, and there is seldom any doubt concerning what union or unions will represent a contractor's employees. This fact is recognized by Section 8(f) of the National Labor Relations Act, which authorizes employers in the building and construction industry to enter into labor agreements with construction labor unions without holding employee elections. This proviso is called the "prehire contract" provision of the act.

13.11 EMPLOYER UNFAIR LABOR PRACTICES

Under the National Labor Relations Act, as amended, an employer commits an unfair labor practice if he:

1. Interferes with, restrains, or coerces employees in the exercise of rights protected by the act, such as their right of self-organization for the purposes of collective bargaining or other mutual assistance [Section 8(a)(1)].
2. Dominates or interferes with any labor organization in either its formation or its administration [Section 8(a)(2)]. Thus, "company" unions that are dominated by the employer are prohibited, and employers may not unlawfully assist any union financially or otherwise.
3. Discriminates against an employee in order to encourage or discourage union membership [Section 8(a)(3)]. It is illegal for an employer to discharge or demote an employee or to single him out in any other discriminatory manner simply because he is or is not a member of a union.
4. Discharges or otherwise discriminates against an employee because he has filed charges or given testimony under the act [Section 8(a)(4)]. This provision protects the employee from retaliation if he seeks help in enforcing his rights under the act.
5. Refuses to bargain in good faith about wages, hours, and other conditions of employment with the properly chosen representatives of his employees [Section 8(a)(5)]. Matters concerning rates of pay, wages, hours, and other conditions of employment are called "mandatory" subjects about which the employer and the union must bargain in good faith, although the law does not require either party to agree to a proposal or to make concessions.
6. Enters into a "hot-cargo" agreement with a union [Section 8(e)]. Under a hot-cargo agreement, the employer promises not to do business with or not to handle or otherwise deal in the products of another person or employer. Only in the garment industry and the construction industry (to a limited extent) are such agreements now lawful. This unfair labor practice can be committed only by an employer and a labor organization acting together.

It is interesting to note that the Taft-Hartley Act has a free-speech provision that establishes the employee's right to hear the arguments of both labor and management. The expressing or dissemination of any views, arguments, or opinions by either side does not constitute an unfair labor practice so long as it contains no threat of reprisal or force or promise of benefit.

13.12 UNFAIR LABOR PRACTICES OF LABOR ORGANIZATIONS

Under the National Labor Relations Act, as amended, it is an unfair labor practice for a labor organization or its agents:

1. To restrain or coerce employees in the exercise of their rights guaranteed in Section 7 of the Taft-Hartley Act [Section 8(b)(1)(A)]. In essence, Section 7 gives an employee the right to join a union or to assist in the promotion of a labor organization or to refrain from such activities. This section further provides that it is not intended to impair the right of a union to prescribe its own rules concerning membership.
2. To restrain or coerce an employer in his selection of a representative for collective bargaining purposes [Section 8(b)(1)(B)].
3. To cause an employer to discriminate against an employee in regard to wages, hours, or other conditions of employment for the purpose of encouraging or discouraging membership in a labor organization [Section 8(b)(2)]. This section includes employer discrimination against an employee whose membership in the union has been denied or terminated for cause other than failure to pay customary dues or initiation fees. Contracts or informal arrangements with a union under which an employer gives preferential treatment to union members are violations of this section. It is not unlawful, however, for an employer and a union to enter an agreement whereby the employer agrees to hire new employees exclusively through the union hiring hall so long as there is no discrimination against nonunion members. Union-security agreements that require employees to become members of the union after they are hired are also permitted by this section.
4. To refuse to bargain in good faith with an employer about wages, hours, and other conditions of employment if the union is the representative of his employees [Section 8(b)(3)]. This section imposes on labor organizations the same duty to bargain in good faith that is imposed on employers.
5. To engage in, or to induce or encourage others to engage in, strike or boycott activities, or to threaten or coerce any person, if in either case an object thereof is:
   a. To force or require any employer or self-employed person to join any labor or employer organization, or to enter a hot-cargo agreement that is prohibited by Section 8(e) [Section 8(b)(4)(A)].
   b. To force or require any person to cease using or dealing in the products of any other producer or to cease doing business with any other person [Section 8(b)(4)(B)]. This is a prohibition against secondary boycotts, a subject discussed further in Section 13.17 of this chapter. This section of the National Labor Relations Act further provides that, when not otherwise unlawful, a primary strike or primary picketing is a permissible union activity.

c. To force or require any employer to recognize or bargain with a particular labor organization as the representative of his employees that has not been certified as the representative of such employees [Section 8(b)(4)(C)].

d. To force or require any employer to assign certain work to the employees of a particular labor organization or craft rather than to employees in another labor organization or craft, unless the employer is failing to conform with an order or certification of the NLRB [Section 8(b)(4)(D)]. This provision is directed against "jurisdictional disputes," a topic discussed in Section 13.21 of this chapter.

Item 5 permits union publicity, other than picketing, provided that the business operations of neutral employers are not disrupted.

6. To require of employees covered by a valid union shop membership fees that the NLRB finds to be excessive or discriminatory [Section 8(b)(5)].

7. To cause or attempt to cause an employer to pay or agree to pay for services that are not performed or not to be performed [Section 8(b)(6)]. This section forbids practices commonly known as "featherbedding."

8. To picket or threaten to picket any employer to force him to recognize or bargain with a union:

a. When the employees of the employer are already lawfully represented by another union [Section 8(b)(7)(A)].

b. When a valid election has been held within the past 12 months [Section 8(b)(7)(B)].

c. When no petition for a NLRB election has been filed within a reasonable period of time, not to exceed 30 days from the commencement of such picketing [Section 8(b)(7)(C)]. This section does not apply to picketing or other publicity for the purpose of truthfully advising the public that a dispute exists unless it has the effect of inducing work stoppages by employees of persons doing business with the picketed employer.

Although the contribution or expenditure of funds by a labor organization in connection with the election of federal officials is not defined as an unfair labor practice, such union activity is prohibited by the Taft-Hartley Act. This restriction has not proven to be effective, and unions continue to be active in political matters through affiliate organizations to which their members voluntarily contribute. The AFL-CIO Committee on Political Education (COPE), for example, has become extremely active in politics, both locally and nationally. Technically, COPE does no collective bargaining and obtains its finances from sources other than union dues or assessments, with the result that it is not considered to be a labor organization under the Taft-Hartley Act.

13.13 FILING A CHARGE

Charges of unfair labor practices can be filed by an employer, a union, or the individual worker. These charges must be filed in the NLRB regional office that serves the area in which the case arose within 6 months from the date of the alleged unfair activity. After charges are filed, field examiners investigate the circumstances and a formal complaint is issued if the charges are found to be well grounded and the case cannot be settled by informal adjustment.

When a complaint is issued, a public hearing is held before a trial examiner whose findings and recommendations are served upon the parties and are sent to the NLRB in Washington, D. C. If no exceptions are filed by either party within a statutory period, the examiner's judgment takes the full effect of an order by the NLRB. If exceptions are taken, the NLRB reviews the case and makes a decision.

If an employer or a union fails to comply with an order of the NLRB, the board has no statutory power of enforcement of its own but can petition the U. S. Court of Appeals for a decree enforcing the order. If the court issues such a decree, failure to comply may be punishable by fine or imprisonment for contempt of court. Parties aggrieved by the order may seek judicial review.

13.14 REMEDIES

When the NLRB finds that an employer or a union has engaged in unfair labor practices, it is empowered to issue a cease and desist order and to take such affirmative action as deemed necessary. The purpose of the board's orders is remedial, and it has broad discretion in fashioning remedies for unfair labor practices. Typical affirmative actions ordered by the NLRB may include reinstatement of persons discharged, reimbursement of wages lost, or refund of dues or fees illegally collected.

The law provides that, whenever a charge is filed alleging certain unfair labor practices relating to secondary boycotts, hot-cargo clauses, or organization or recognition picketing, the preliminary investigation of the charge must be given first priority. The board or the General Counsel is authorized to petition the appropriate federal district court for an injunction to stop any conduct alleged to constitute an unfair labor practice. If the preliminary investigation of a first-priority case reveals reasonable cause to believe that the charge is true, the law requires that the General Counsel seek such injunctive relief or temporary restraining order as seems proper under the circumstances.

13.15 UNION-SHOP AGREEMENTS

The National Labor Relations Act outlaws the closed shop but permits the establishment of a union shop. A closed shop requires that a worker be a union member at the time he is hired. Under a union shop, the new employee need not be a union member at the time he is employed, but he must join within a stipulated period to retain his job. Therefore a union-security agreement cannot require that applicants for employment be members of the union to be hired but can only stipulate that all employees covered by the agreement must become members of the union within a certain period of time. This grace period cannot be less than 30 days after hiring except in the building and construction industry, where a shorter grace period of 7 days is permissible. Originally, a union-shop contract could be negotiated only when authorized by a majority of the employees eligible to vote. This requirement was repealed in 1951, however.

The National Labor Relations Act allows an employer engaged primarily in the building and construction industry to sign a union-security agreement with a union that has not yet been designated as the representative of his employees. The agreement can be made before he has hired any employees for a project and will apply to them when they are hired. (This is the same prehire provision discussed in Section 13.10.) As noted previously, the workers must be allowed at least 7 days within which to join the union.

Section 14(b) of the Taft-Hartley Act provides that the individual states have the right to forbid negotiated labor agreements that require union membership as a condition of employment. In other words, any state or territory of the United States may, if it chooses, pass a law making a union-shop labor agreement illegal. This is called the "right-to-work" section of the act, and such state laws are termed "right-to-work" statutes. At the present writing, nineteen states have such laws in force.*

It is interesting to note that most of these state right-to-work laws go beyond the mere issue of compulsory unionism inherent in the union shop. Most of them outlaw the agency shop, under which workers, in lieu of joining a union, must pay it the equivalent of union dues to hold their jobs. Some explicitly forbid unions to strike over the issue of employment of nonunion workers.

13.16 UNION HIRING HALL

The National Labor Relations Act provides that, in the building and construction industry, a labor agreement can require the contractor to notify the union of opportunities for employment or to give the union an opportunity to refer qualified applicants to the contractor. The agreement may also specify minimum training or experience qualifications for employment or provide for priority in job referrals based upon length of service with such employer, in the industry, or in the particular geographical area.

Contracts or informal arrangements with a union under which an employer gives preferential treatment to union members are illegal. It is not unlawful, however, for an employer and a union to enter into an agreement whereby the employer agrees to hire new employees exclusively through the union hiring hall, so long as there is no discrimination against nonunion members in favor of union members. Both the agreement and the actual operation of the hiring hall must be nondiscriminatory; referrals must be made without reference to union mem-

---

* Alabama, Arizona, Arkansas, Florida, Georgia, Iowa, Kansas, Mississippi, Nebraska, Nevada, North Carolina, North Dakota, South Carolina, South Dakota, Tennessee, Texas, Utah, Virginia, and Wyoming now have right-to-work legislation in effect.

bership. The employer must not discriminate against a nonunion employee if union membership is not available to him under the usual terms or if membership is denied him for reason other than nonpayment of union dues and fees.

The courts have held that a lawful hiring hall is a mandatory subject of bargaining between employers and unions and that a union can strike and picket to press its demands for an exclusive nondiscriminatory hiring-hall referral system. It is important to note that contractors who were parties to a labor agreement providing for exclusive union-hall referrals have in certain circumstances shared the union's guilt when the system has been found guilty of using discriminatory practices.

Construction hiring halls or referral systems that discriminate against minorities are illegal under civil-rights statutes, even though they may appear to be legal under the Taft-Hartley Act. The matter of contractor responsibility has become particularly troublesome with regard to the hiring of workers from minority groups. In this regard the NLRB has held that hiring is a management responsibility and cannot be delegated to a union. The contractor, not the union, must be the judge of a worker's competency and a worker's access to a construction job cannot be conditioned upon his ability to pass a union examination. If a contractor hires or retains a man that the union will not accept, the union is liable for the consequences if it strikes to force him off the job.

13.17 SECONDARY BOYCOTTS

A primary boycott arises when a union, engaged in a dispute with an employer, exorts his employees and customers to refrain from all dealings with him. A secondary boycott occurs if a union has a dispute with Company A and attempts to exert pressure on this company by causing the employees of Company B to stop handling the products of Company A, or otherwise forces Company B to stop doing business with Company A. The primary employer, in this case Company A, is the employer with whom the union has the dispute. Company B is the neutral secondary employer and hence the name "secondary boycott."

Primary boycotts generally have been viewed in a favorable light by the courts, whereas secondary boycotts have a turbulent legal history. Illegal at common law, secondary boycotts were ruled to have been forbidden by the Sherman Act in a decision by the Supreme Court. This prohibition was reversed by the Norris-LaGuardia Act and the Wagner Act, which gave unions almost complete immunity from liability for damages arising out of secondary boycotts. The pendulum has since returned almost to its original position, with the Taft-Hartley Act forbidding secondary boycotts.

Secondary boycotts in construction can assume many forms, and the dividing line between a legal primary boycott and an illegal secondary boycott is sometimes hazy and difficult to establish. The wording of the law is strictly construed in determining the legality of a boycott action. Three aspects of secondary boycotts in construction are of particular significance, these being common-situs picketing, subcontractor clauses, and product boycotts. These are discussed in the sections following.

13.18 COMMON-SITUS PICKETING

A common situs is a given location such as an industrial plant or a construction project at which several different employers are simultaneously engaged in business activities. A dispute between one of these employers and a union is likely to involve the other neutral employers, especially if picketing is involved. Decisions of the NLRB and of the courts have evolved some rules for establishing whether or not such "common-situs picketing" constitutes an illegal secondary boycott action.

In an attempt to give effect to both the union's right to picket the primary employer and the right of the secondary employer to be free from disputes that are not his own, the NLRB established in 1950 the Moore Dry Dock tests, which determine when a union may picket a common site without committing an illegal secondary boycott. These rules are:

1. That the picketing be limited to times when the employees of the primary employer are working on the premises.
2. That the picketing be limited to times when the primary employer is carrying on his normal business there.
3. That the picket signs clearly indicate the identity of the primary employer with whom the union is having the dispute.
4. That the picketing be carried on reasonably close to where the employees of the primary employer are working.

In 1951, the Supreme Court decided the Denver Building and Construction Trades Council case. This dispute involved a general contractor whose employees were union members and a nonunion subcontractor. The project was picketed and shut down by the construction unions, which demanded that the subcontractor be discharged. The Supreme Court found that the unions were guilty of an illegal secondary boycott because the object of the picketing was to force the general contractor (secondary employer) to quit doing business with the nonunion subcontractor (primary employer).

Subsequent to the Denver Building Trades case, the use of separate gates on multiemployer construction sites has become common practice if labor trouble is experienced. The usual pattern is that one gate is reserved and marked for the contractor involved in the labor dispute, and another gate for the contractors not involved. On the basis of the Moore Dry Dock standards traditionally applied to common-situs picketing and the Denver Building Trades case, the NLRB has held that the craft unions cannot picket separate gates reserved for employees of neutral secondary contractors if the effect is to keep them off the project. In essence, this decision says that construction contractors at the site are separate and distinct employers and union picketing must be limited to the primary contractor involved in the dispute. It is unlawful for a union to picket a gate reserved for the exclusive use of contractors not involved in the dispute. Such picketing constitutes an illegal secondary boycott because it tends to force one company to cease doing business with another.

The Supreme Court, in the General Electric case, decided that the matter is different, however, when the construction work is being done at an industrial plant. The court ruled that picketing by plant strikers of gates reserved exclusively for the contractor can be banned only if there is a separate marked gate set apart for the contractor, if the work is unrelated to the normal operations of the industrial company, and if the work is of a kind that will not curtail normal plant operations.

13.19 SUBCONTRACTOR CLAUSES

The Landrum-Griffin Act made it an unfair labor practice for an employer and a union to enter into an agreement whereby the employer agrees to refrain from handling the products of another employer or to cease doing business with any other person. As has already been pointed out, such a contract provision is called a "hot-cargo" clause. However, the construction industry was exempted from the ban under certain circumstances. Under the law, contractors can agree to restrictions on subcontracting or can agree not to handle certain products, as long as the restrictions relate to the contracting or subcontracting of work to be done at the site. Such a provision in a labor contract is called a "subcontractor clause."

Subcontractor clauses are widely used in construction labor contracts and typically require that work be awarded only to subcontractors who will comply with all the terms and conditions of the prime contractor's labor agreement, who are under agreement with the appropriate building trades union, or who employ only union labor and use union-made materials. The NLRB and the courts have ruled that construction unions may strike to obtain subcontractor clauses in their labor contracts if no secondary boycott is involved. To illustrate, picketing to induce a general contractor to accept a subcontractor clause is legal, but picketing is illegal as a secondary boycott if it is designed to force a neutral general contractor to stop doing business with an existing and identified nonunion subcontractor. The courts have held that unions cannot enforce subcontractor clauses by strikes or picketing but that such labor contract provisions can be judicially enforced by the courts.

13.20 PRODUCT BOYCOTTS

Both the NLRB and the courts have ruled that under certain circumstances construction unions can negotiate and enforce clauses in their labor agreements to ban certain prefabricated products that, if used, would eliminate some on-site construction work. Such provisions are commonly called "prefabrication clauses."

Examples of these construction products are precut and prefitted wooden doors, precut pipe insulation, prefabricated trusses, and prepackaged boilers. Such product boycotts have been construed to fall within the construction industry exemption from the ban on hot-cargo clauses and can be legal work-preservation clauses in a labor agreement if the prefabricated products replace work customarily and traditionally performed on the site by the union members.

13.21 JURISDICTIONAL DISPUTES

A jurisdictional dispute arises when more than one union claims jurisdiction over a given item of work. The construction industry in particular, has been plagued with this type of dispute, primarily because each of its many craft unions regards a certain type of work as a proprietary right and jealously guards against any encroachment of its traditional sphere by other unions. Lines of demarcation between the various jurisdictions are sometimes indistinct, and the development of new products and methods often brings with it jurisdictional clashes between unions whose members claim exclusive right to the work assignment.

Section 8(b)(4)(D) of the National Labor Relations Act makes a jurisdictional strike a union unfair labor practice unless the employer is failing to conform to an order of the NLRB. An accusation under this section, however, is handled differently from charges alleging other types of unfair labor practices. Section 10(k) of the Taft-Hartley Act requires that parties to a jurisdictional dispute be given 10 days, after filing of charges with the NLRB, to adjust their dispute. If, at the end of that time, the disputants have not resolved their differences or agreed upon methods for a voluntary settlement, the board is empowered and directed to hear the dispute and make an assignment of the work under contention. The matter is then handled in the same way as any other unfair labor practice.

Shortly after the Taft-Hartley Act was enacted, responsible elements in the construction industry feared that chaos might result if established practices, customs, and traditional methods of operation that had been built up over a long period of years were to be completely disregarded. Because the Taft-Hartley Act does not require the NLRB to rule on jurisdictional matters when the disputants have agreed to voluntary methods of adjustment, a decision was made to set up machinery to settle such disputes within the construction industry itself. In 1948, the National Joint Board for the Settlement of Jurisdictional Disputes was formed by specialty contractor associations, the Associated General Contractors of America, and the AFL building trades unions. In this way, the experience and knowledge of the construction industry could be utilized to arrive at equitable settlements of disputes while at the same time recognizing traditional craft skills and jurisdictional claims.

Although a construction jurisdictional dispute can be presented to the NLRB, most such disputes continue to be referred to the National Joint Board, which, despite some ups and downs, has enjoyed reasonably good success over the years in settling them. Although adjudication of disputes by the Joint Board is a voluntary process, the participants have largely accepted its awards and continue to abide by them. The plan has been strengthened by the support of the building trades unions and the inclusion of provisions in labor agreements that jurisdictional questions will be submitted to the Joint Board and that the unions involved will abide by its decision.

Under the rules of the Joint Board, the contractor is required to assign disputed work in accordance with agreements and decisions of record as contained in the "Green Book" or the "Gray Book."* If no such agreement or decision exists, the work must be assigned according to prevailing trade or area practice. If there has been no local precedent, the contractor must use his best judgment in assigning the work. After the assignment is made, no change can be effected unless so directed by the Joint Board, whose decision the contractor is obligated to accept. Unions have a parallel obligation to refrain from strikes or work stoppages pending decision of the Joint Board. Generally speaking, the Joint Board makes awards of disputed work only on a specific project basis. There is an independent Appeals Board to which decisions of the Joint Board can be appealed. The Joint Board will make national jurisdictional awards that are final and binding if so requested by the unions involved.

13.22 CIVIL RIGHTS ACT OF 1964

In passing the Civil Rights Act of 1964, Congress confirmed and established certain basic individual rights pertaining to voting; access to public accommodations, public facilities, and public education; participation in federally assisted programs; and opportunities for employment. Title VII of this act, "Equal Employment Opportunity," prohibits discrimination in employment. It is an unlawful practice for an employer to (1) refuse to hire or to discharge any individual or otherwise discriminate against him regarding conditions of employment because of his race, color, religion, sex, or national origin, or to (2) limit, segregate, or classify employees in any way that would deprive the individual of employment opportunity or adversely affect his status as an employee because of race, color, religion, sex, or national origin.

Administration and enforcement of the Civil Rights Act is made the responsibility of the Equal Employment Opportunity Commission (EEOC) that the act created. The responsibility of the commission is to assure that consideration for hiring and promotion is based on ability and qualifications, without discrimination. Title VII prohibits discriminatory practices on the part of employers, employment agencies, labor organizations, and apprenticeship or training programs. The Civil Rights Act applies to interstate commerce and covers employers with 25 or more employees and labor organizations with a hiring hall or 25 or more members. There are several exemptions from the act, some of which are local, state, and federal agencies, government-owned corporations, Indian tribes, and certain employees of

---

* The "Green Book" is a small, green, paperbound booklet published by the National Board for Jurisdictional Awards, which contains the national agreements and decisions rendered that affect the building industry. The "Gray Book," a similar booklet published by the Associated General Contractors of America, contains jurisdictional agreements between unions.

educational institutions. The law requires that employers, labor unions, employment agencies, and joint labor-management apprenticeship committees keep such records and submit such reports as the Equal Opportunity Employment Commission may require. Special rules apply in states that have enforceable fair employment practice laws.

The National Labor Relations Board has ruled that discrimination by a labor union because of race is an unfair practice under the Taft-Hartley Act. This has made possible the filing of unfair labor practice charges against a union because of alleged racial discrimination. A union found guilty of such practices faces cease and desist orders as well as possible rescission of its right to continue as the authorized employee representative.

13.23 EXECUTIVE ORDER 11246

Issued in 1965, Executive Order 11246 applies to contracts and subcontracts exceeding $10,000 on federal and federally assisted construction projects. Contractors are prohibited from discriminating against any employee or applicant for employment because of race, creed, color, or national origin. The contractor must take positive action to ensure that applicants are employed, and that employees are treated during employment, without discrimination. Actions pertaining to employment, promotion, transfer, recruitment, layoff, rates of pay, training, and apprenticeship must not be discriminatory. Executive Order 11375 (1968), as an extension of Executive Order 11246, prohibits discrimination in employment because of sex in the performance of federal and federal-aid contracts.

Executive Order 11246, administered by the Office of Federal Contract Compliance (OFCC), U. S. Department of Labor, states that each federal contracting agency shall be primarily responsible for obtaining compliance with its provisions. In addition, each administering agency is made responsible for compliance by the recipients of federal financial assistance. Federal agencies have compliance officers whose duties are to seek adherence to the objectives of the Order, including compliance reviews. A compliance review is a procedure used to check an ongoing contract. The contractor is required to give information to show that he is complying with the nondiscriminatory requirements of his contract, including affirmative action taken.

In the event of noncompliance with the Order, the contract may be canceled or suspended and the contractor can be declared ineligible for further government or federally assisted construction contracts. Compliance reports from contractors are required, and the general contractor must include suitable provisions concerning compliance with the Executive Order in his subcontracts and purchase orders.

It is to be noted that federal and state laws pertaining to specific programs of public works can also include provisions for equal employment opportunity; for example, the Federal-Aid Highway Act of 1968 requires assurances from the states that employment on individual federally aided highway projects will be available without regard to race, color, creed, or national orgin.

13.24 THE AGE DISCRIMINATION IN EMPLOYMENT ACT

Becoming effective in June 1968, the Age Discrimination in Employment Act of 1967 prohibits arbitrary age discrimination in employment. This act protects individuals 40 to 65 years old from age discrimination by employers of 25 or more persons in an industry affecting interstate commerce. Employment agencies and labor organizations are also covered.

By the terms of the act, it is against the law for an employer to:

1. Fail or refuse to hire, to discharge, or to otherwise discriminate against any individual as to conditions of employment because of age.
2. Limit, segregate, or classify his employees so as to deprive any individual of employment opportunities or to adversely affect his status as an employee because of age.
3. Reduce the wage rate of any employee in order to comply with the act.

The prohibitions against discrimination because of age do not apply when age is a bona fide occupational qualification, when differentiation is based on reasonable factors other than age, when the differentiation is caused by the terms of a bona fide seniority system or employee benefit plan, or when the discharge or discipline of the individual is for good cause.

Employers must post an approved notice of the Age Discrimination in Employment Act in a prominent place where employees can see it, and maintain records as required by the Secretary of Labor. The act is enforced by the Secretary of Labor, who can make investigations, issue administrative rules and regulations, and enforce its provisions by legal proceedings.

13.25 EMPLOYMENT STANDARDS LEGISLATION

In the foregoing sections, several federal laws that regulate and control various aspects of labor-management relations have been discussed. The subsequent sections discuss federal statutes that prescribe certain minimum working conditions. These laws are quite complex and have many areas of overlap. In total combination, they have an important impact upon the construction industry. The several laws will be discussed in the chronological order of their first passage by Congress.

13.26 THE DAVIS-BACON ACT

The Davis-Bacon Act (1931), as subsequently amended, is a federal law that determines the wage rates, including fringe benefits, that must be paid workers on all federal construction projects and on a host of federally assisted jobs. The law applies to contracts in excess of $2000 and states that the wages of workmen shall not be less than the wage rates specified in the schedule of prevailing wages as determined by the Secretary of Labor for similar work on similar projects in the vicinity in which the work is to be performed. The contractor and his subcontractors are required to pay at least once a week all workmen employed directly on the site of the work at wage rates no lower than those prescribed. Full payment must be made with the exception of such payroll deductions as are permitted by the Copeland Act (Section 13.27). The law's purpose is to protect the local wage rates and local economies of each community and presumably to put union and nonunion contractors on a more nearly equal footing, competitively, in bidding on federal and federally assisted projects.

The Davis-Bacon Act originally applied only to construction contracts made directly with the federal government for public buildings or public works. Over the years Congress, through separate laws, has extended the scope of the Davis-Bacon Act to a wide variety of public works projects that are merely financed in some way by the federal government. The prevailing wage principle now applies, for example, to slum clearance, urban rehabilitation, certain types of FHA housing, projects to alleviate water polution, the interstate highway system, and federally assisted school, hospital, and airport projects.

The Davis-Bacon Act is administered by the U. S. Department of Labor. Contractors whose projects are covered must keep certain records, file periodic reports, and comply with various regulations in respect to the use of apprentices. Restitution is secured for workers found to have been underpaid, and penalties are assessed for violations of the overtime requirements. Violators can be denied the right to bid on other federal or federal-aid projects. The act does not provide for judicial review of Labor Department wage determinations, but a Wage Appeals Board operating under delegated authority from the Secretary of Labor has been established to hear appeals from findings or decisions of the Davis-Bacon Division.

13.27 THE COPELAND ACT

As passed in 1934 and since amended, the Copeland Act makes it a punishable offense for an employer to deprive anyone employed on federal construction work or work financed in whole or in part by federal funds of any portion of the compensation to which he is entitled. Other than deductions provided by law, the employer may not induce "kickbacks" from his employees by force, intimidation, threat of dismissal, or any other means whatever. This portion of the Copeland Act is commonly known as the Anti-Kickback Law, violation of which may be punished by fine, imprisonment, or both. Regulations issued by the Secretary of Labor allow the contractor or subcontractor to make additional deductions from wages provided that he obtains the approval of the Department of Labor by showing that the proposed deductions are proper. Union dues may be deducted by the employer if such holdback is consented to by the employee and is provided for in a collective bargaining agreement.

The law stipulates that payroll records shall be maintained and reports submitted by contractors as the Department of Labor may require. The Copeland Act covers all work for which prevailing wages are determined by the Secretary of Labor as discussed in Section 13.26. The contracting agency is responsible for enforcing compliance with the act.

13.28 THE NATIONAL APPRENTICESHIP ACT

In 1937, Congress passed the National Apprenticeship Act, authorizing the establishment of the Bureau of Apprenticeship and Training of the U. S. Department of Labor. The bureau has the responsibility to encourage the establishment of apprenticeship programs and to help improve existing ones, but it does not conduct them itself. One of its prime objectives is to promote cooperation between management and organized labor in the development of such programs. Since its establishment, the bureau has provided technical assistance in developing and improving apprenticeship and other industrial training programs. In the performance of its function, the bureau is guided by the Federal Committee on Apprenticeship, comprised of leaders of management, labor, and vocational education. The bureau works closely with state apprenticeship agencies, trade and industrial education institutions, and management and labor. Through its field staff, it cooperates with local employers and unions in developing apprenticeship programs to meet specific needs.

In order to implement apprentice training on a local level, the states have passed laws that provide for the establishment of state apprenticeship agencies. These state agencies function cooperatively with the Federal Committee and are made up of labor, management, and public representatives, perhaps with the addition of members from the state labor departments and others. Using the standards recommended by the Federal Committee on Apprenticeship as a guide, the various state laws have established detailed standards and procedures to which apprenticeship and training programs in the state are expected to conform. The state agency becomes a part of the national apprenticeship program by securing recognition of its standards and procedures by the Bureau of Apprenticeship and Training.

The actual employment and training of apprentices in the construction industry is essentially a local matter supervised by joint apprenticeship committees that are made up of representatives of both contractors and labor unions. For local programs to be approved by and registered with the Bureau of Apprenticeship and Training, the operating standards adopted by the local body must be acceptable under the general standards established by the Federal Committee. Because apprentices are employed in a wide variety of trades, the standards recommended by the Federal Committee are general in scope, leaving to the joint committees of the different trades the responsibility for working out details. Thus the joint committee performs many important services. It selects the apprentices, determines the length of training, supervises the training and instruction, and sees that standards are maintained. In general, a construction trade requires 2 to 5 years of on-the-job training and a minimum of 144 hours a year of related classroom instruction. In most instances, this instruction is given in trade or vocational schools or by local union groups.

13.29 THE FAIR LABOR STANDARDS ACT

First enacted by Congress in 1938 and since amended several times, the Fair Labor Standards Act, also known as the "wage-hour law," contains minimum wage, maximum hours, overtime pay, equal pay, and child labor standards. Workers whose employment is related to interstate commerce or consists of producing goods for interstate commerce are covered without regard to the dollar volume of business.

The Fair Labor Standards Act provides for a minimum wage for all employees covered, this minimum wage having been steadily increased during recent years. Also required is payment of an overtime rate of 1½ times the regular hourly rate of pay for all hours worked in excess of 40 hours in any work week. However, no limit is set on the number of hours that may be worked in any one day or during any one week. The law does not require premium pay for Saturday, Sunday, or holiday work or vacation or severance pay.

An employer who violates the wage and hour requirements is liable to his employees for double the unpaid minimum wages or overtime compensation plus associated court costs and attorney's fees. Willful violation of the law is made a criminal act, and the errant employer can be prosecuted. Several classes of employees are exempted from coverage under the act, such as bona fide executive, administrative, and professional employees who meet certain tests established for exemption.

The Fair Labor Standards Act provides that an employer must not discriminate on the basis of sex by paying employees of one sex wages at rates lower than he pays employees of the other sex for doing equal work on jobs requiring comparable skill, effort, and responsibility and performed under similar working conditions. Pay differentials can be justified by a seniority system, a merit system, a piece-work pay system, or other system based on factors other than sex.

The basic minimum age for employment covered by the act is 16 years except for occupations declared to be hazardous by the Secretary of Labor, to which an 18-year minimum age applies. Construction per se is not designated as hazardous, but specified work assignments such as truck driving, wrecking and demolition, and power tool operation are so designated.

13.30 THE HOBBS ACT

Also known as the Anti-Racketeering Law, the Hobbs Act, which was enacted in 1946, makes it a felony to obstruct, delay, or affect commerce by robbery or extortion. To attempt or conspire to do so is also made a felony. The underlying motive behind the act was to put an end to the use of threats, force, or violence by union officials to obtain payments from employers under the guise of recompense for services rendered. Prosecution of violators is placed in the hands of the U. S. Department of Justice.

Because of the wide publicity given to congressional labor investigations, the popular conception of labor racketeering involves only the internal affairs of unions, such as the embezzlement of union moneys or the misappropriation of welfare funds. Unfortunately, the victimization of employers by unscrupulous labor leaders has received far less attention. Extortion in many guises has been practiced against contractors, payments to union officials being required as a condition of avoiding "labor trouble." These payments have been concealed behind many subterfuges such as "gifts," "commissions," "equipment rentals," and "services." When interstate commerce is involved, the Hobbs Act is available to combat this sort of nefarious practice.

13.31 THE CONTRACT WORK HOURS STANDARDS ACT

The Congress passed in 1962 the Contract Work Hours Standards Act, also known as the Work Hours Act of 1962. This act applies to federal construction projects and to projects financed in whole or in part by the federal government. Not included, however, is federal assistance that is in the nature of a loan guarantee or insurance.

The main requirement of this law is that every mechanic and laborer shall be paid at a rate not less than 1½ times the basic rate of pay for all hours worked in excess of 8 hours per day or 40 hours per week. In the event of violation, the contractor or subcontractor responsible is liable for unpaid wages to the employees affected and for liquidated damages to the federal government. Willful violation of the Work Hours Act is punishable by fine or imprisonment. Enforcement of the law and withholding of funds from the contractor to secure compliance with the act are made the responsibility of the governmental agency for which the work is being done.

14

LABOR RELATIONS

14.1 THE CONSTRUCTION WORKER

The average construction worker has no fixed relationship with any one employer, and his tenure of employment is indefinite and temporal. He is tightly bound to his occupation and is only loosely associated with any given contractor or locality. He may work for several different employers during the course of a year and is known as a carpenter or cement mason rather than as the employee of any particular contractor. Although these generalities are much less true for workers in the specialty trades, such as electricians and plumbers, than they are for carpenters, iron workers, and others in the basic trades, they still typify employment in the construction industry.

Most construction workers are unionized, and their wages and other conditions of employment are dictated by labor agreements. Some areas of the country are more heavily organized than others, and union strength varies widely with locality. Some contractors work open-shop, and others operate under union-shop contracts. No attempt is made here to argue the merits of either system. Considering the country as a whole, however, there can be little doubt but that a large majority of the nation's contractors employ unionized construction workers. Relations with labor unions are, therefore, simply an everyday fact of life for most construction concerns.

14.2 ORGANIZED EMPLOYEES

As a general rule, relations between the contractor and his unionized employees are casual and impersonal. There is little direct contact between the construction worker and his employer. The employee is assumed to know his trade and is expected to perform any task that is assignable to his craft. If he does not measure up to expectations, the employer is free to dismiss him and hire someone else. Personal contact is almost nonexistent because negotiations for rates of pay, holidays, overtime, and other employment conditions are conducted, not with the employee himself, but with his union. The most important area of a contractor's labor relations involves his dealings with the craft unions whose members he employs. For this reason, it is important that the contractor be knowledgeable about the unions with which he must work.

14.3 ROLE OF THE UNIONS

Despite personal feelings in the matter, there is no denying the fact that unions make an important contribution to the operation of the construction industry. The unions have a stabilizing influence upon a basically unstable area of business, an influence which, from the point of view of the contractor, has both its good and bad points. Through the medium of negotiated labor contracts, fixed wage rates are established, and much uncertainty associated with the employment of labor is removed. The unions provide a pool of skilled and experienced labor from which the contractor can draw as his needs dictate. In addition, they help to police the industry on both sides of the fence, serving to maintain discipline among their own members and helping to control the entry and actions of irresponsible, fly-by-night contractors.

Belonging to a union can offer many compensations to the working man. A prime consideration is the leading role that organized labor takes in raising wages and establishing some form of job security for its members. Although the bargaining power of the individual worker is weak, that of an organization of workers can be very strong. The worker is secure in his belief that his union will protect him from unfair treatment and will exert every effort to improve his situation. He enjoys a sense of belonging to a group with the common purpose of mutual help, and through his elected union representatives he has a voice in the determination of his wages and conditions of employment.

It is true that some union members belong, not of their own volition, but as a matter of necessity to keep their jobs. However, available evidence incontrovertibly indicates that the average union man is not an unwilling captive of organized labor but belongs because it is his desire. Of course, not all members are enthusiastic unionists. Many of them do not participate actively in union affairs or even attend meetings regularly. However, this passive attitude cannot be interpreted as a lack of union patriotism.

14.4 UNION HISTORY

Unions are worldwide, and their origins go back at least one hundred and fifty years. However, organized labor has become a stable, responsible element in America only within the past half-century. Before that time, unions pursued a stormy course of expansion with prosperity and emaciation in times of recession. In 1886, the first enduring union association was founded after a long era of repeated failures. The American Federation of Labor (AFL) was organized in that year with Samuel Gompers as its first president. From the time of its inception, the AFL has traditionally been identified with the skilled craft worker, an underlying philosophy that has pervaded its policies throughout the years. The AFL is a loose confederation of many sovereign national unions, each of which remains free to manage its own internal affairs. The construction trades were charter members of the AFL.

At the time the AFL was founded, semiskilled and unskilled factory workers were largely unorganized. The Knights of Labor, an organization of polyglot membership, had made some progress in that direction but was waning rapidly so that the field was wide open. Nevertheless, the general sentiment of the AFL simply was not concordant with organization of the industrial worker. In 1905 the Industrial Workers of the World (IWW) was organized to fill the void left by the AFL's failure to act. The IWW advocated the elimination of capitalism, engaged frequently in violent strikes, and declined rapidly in the post-World War I era. Once again no central force existed for the organization of the mass-production worker, although several independent industrial unions were leading a somewhat precarious existence.

Enactment of the Norris-LaGuardia and Wagner Acts encouraged and assisted union activity. The AFL bestirred itself to extend a lukewarm welcome to some industrial unions but relegated them to a second-class position known as "federal locals." This scheme enjoyed no great success because the AFL craft unions, apprehensive that they would be obliterated in a huge mass of industrial workers, pressed demands on the federal locals for jurisdiction over members who were engaged in craft occupations. In 1935, the disgruntled leaders of eight industrial unions associated with the AFL formed the Committee for Industrial Organization for the avowed purpose of organizing the mass-production industries. This committee was organized within the AFL and sought to induce it to assume the dual personality of both craft and industry. This was nothing short of treason in the eyes of the AFL hierarchy, and the committee was summarily ordered to disband or be expelled from the federation. In 1936, the AFL executive council suspended the Committee for Industrial Organization. In 1938, after two fruitless years of attempts at reunification, the committee became the Congress of Industrial Organizations (CIO), an association of autonomous industrial unions, with John L. Lewis of the United Mine Workers as its first president.

In the following years, the AFL and the CIO engaged in a bitter struggle for the leadership of American labor and both sides came to recognize the need for reconciliation. However, personal animosities and conflict of interests proved difficult to resolve, and the merger was delayed for many years. Not until 1955 were the two groups able to patch up their differences and reassociate.

14.5 AFL-CIO CRAFT UNIONS

A large proportion of the organized construction workers belong to one of the international unions that form the Building and Construction Trades Department of the AFL-CIO. These unions are listed in Table 14.1. Not included in the table is the International Brotherhood of Teamsters, Chauffeurs, Warehousemen, and Helpers of America. This is an independent union that includes construction teamsters as a part of its membership. As used here, the term "international" refers merely to the fact that such unions have jurisdiction over members in Canada and Mexico.

Construction is traditionally the domain of the AFL craft unions. However, some intrusions by CIO and independent unions into the field of construction have been made. For example, plant employees who belong to industrial unions (CIO) sometimes claim jurisdiction over construction work that is done at the plant site. The labor contract between the employer and an industrial union may prevent the company from contracting out any work, maintenance or new construction, when the company has the construction capability itself. Although the jurisdictional conflict over industrial construction has been troublesome, there is general agreement that new construction be allocated to the building trades and maintenance be done by members of the industrial union involved. Renovation, remodeling, dismantling, equipment moving and installation, and rearrangement of facilities remain shady areas of conflict.

TABLE 14.1   International Unions Affiliated with the Building and Construction Trades Department, AFL-CIO

1. Bricklayers, Masons and Plasterers' International Union
2. Brotherhood of Painters, Decorators, and Paperhangers of America
3. Granite Cutters' International Association of America
4. International Association of Bridge, Structural and Ornamental Iron Workers
5. International Association of Heat and Frost Insulators and Asbestos Workers
6. International Association of Marble, Slate and Stone Polishers, Rubbers and Sawyers, Tile and Marble Setters Helpers and Terrazzo Helpers
7. International Brotherhood of Boiler Makers, Iron Ship Builders and Helpers of America
8. International Brotherhood of Electrical Workers
9. International Union of Elevator Constructors
10. International Union of Operating Engineers
11. Laborers International Union of North America
12. Operative Plasterers and Cement Masons' International Association
13. Sheet Metal Workers' International Association
14. United Association of Journeymen and Apprentices of the Plumbing and Pipe Fitting Industry of the United States and Canada
15. United Brotherhood of Carpenters and Joiners of America
16. United Slate, Tile, and Composition Roofers, Damp and Waterproof Workers' Association
17. Wood, Wire, and Metal Lathers' International Union

14.6 DISTRICT 50

The International Union of District 50 is an independent union whose membership embraces a wide variety of industries, including construction, chemicals, paper, public utilities, mining, and steel. District 50 had its beginnings at the time the CIO spun off from the AFL as a vehicle of industrial unionism. Out of the schism between craft and industrial unions came a CIO attempt to organize construction workers without regard to jurisdictional lines. The vertical-type industrial union for construction workers in the CIO, called the United Construction Workers (UCW), was established in 1939. Subsequently, the UCW joined District 50, a department of the United Mine Workers of America. The UCW retained its identity, first as an affiliate and then as a division of District 50, until 1960, when the charters of the construction locals were replaced by those of District 50. In 1968, the International Union of District 50 was dissociated from the United Mine Workers and became an independent union.

Most of the contractors who hire District 50 construction workers are engaged in heavy and highway construction or are specialty contractors. The union has construction locals scattered over the United States and Canada. District 50 does not divide its members into separate crafts or jurisdictions. Contractors can shift District 50 workers about in any occupational classifications as long as the workmen are able to perform the work and are paid the wages established for it. Charters of the locals forbid strikes without approval of the international union, members can transfer freely from one local to another, and union membership is open to anyone the contractor hires. Labor contracts with District 50 specifically give contractors control over the management of the work, assignment of the men, source of the construction materials, and use of tools. Grievance machinery that can terminate in binding arbitration is written into all labor contracts.

It is not surprising that the AFL-CIO construction craft unions are bitter foes of District 50, an antagonism that has precipitated much labor strife. Nevertheless, District 50 is representing more and more construction workers each year on a national basis. The courts have protected the right of District 50 to organize, to contest raids by other unions, and to participate in NLRB-supervised union elections. The NLRB has used the ban on jurisdictional strikes to protect District 50 operations from harassment by other unions.

In terms of total numbers, however, the AFL-CIO craft unions represent a very large majority of the organized construction workers. For this reason, the discussion in the following sections pertains principally to these unions.

14.7 THE LOCAL

The basic unit of a construction union is the "local," each local exercising jurisdiction over a defined geographical area such as a borough, city, county, or state. A carpenter's local, for example, is the headquarters for all union carpenters working in the area. The local is responsible for all union activities of that craft within its boundaries. The membership elects local officers, these usually consisting of a president, vice-president, secretary-treasurer, and sergeant-at-arms. These officials may or may not be salaried; a typical arrangement is that they are paid only for time actually spent on union business. An executive board or some equivalent body is also established, which is concerned primarily with the admission of new members, discipline, financial matters, and contract negotiation. If there is only one paid union representative, he is the business agent, who devotes his time to administering the detailed work of the local and who is paid at the top rate of his craft. Business agents are typical of unions, such as the building trades, that deal with many different employers and in which union members are employed in scattered groups. The local is represented on each project by a job steward, who is expected to see that union rules are observed and to report any violations or grievances to his business agent. The steward for each project is appointed by the local.

The locals of the same international union are commonly grouped together to form divisions on a district, state, county, or city basis. For example, carpenter's locals within designated regions band together to form District Councils of Carpenters, which serve to coordinate the activities of all member locals into a unified approach to common problems.

Locals of the different construction unions unite on a regional basis to form building and construction trades councils. These councils are formed of delegates from each member local and serve as agencies for regional cooperation. An important function of these councils is to present a united front to employers during periods of collective bargaining.

14.8 UNION POLICIES

The local is chartered by its international union and is subject to the constitution and bylaws of the parent organization. Beyond this, however, the decentralized nature of construction requires that the locals possess a high degree of independence and freedom of action. Construction locals typically have the authority to negotiate their own labor agreements and call strikes without the formal approval of the international union. Each local has its own set of bylaws that governs the election of local officers, ratification of labor contracts, conduct of meetings, payment of dues, expulsion of members, and other union business.

The legislative body of almost all union groups is the membership. Elected officers have only the responsibility for carrying out union rules as ratified by majority vote of the members. Correspondingly, all matters of union policy, demands for contract changes, decisions to strike, and other basic issues must be approved by the voting membership.

14.9 WORKING RULES

Most building trades locals publish booklets of working rules that pertain to the employment of the locals' members. These rules vary considerably from craft to craft but cover such general issues as work hours per day, jurisdiction of work, multiple shifts, overtime and holidays, apprentices, prohibition of piece-work, pay days, reporting time, foremen, crew size, safety provisions and devices, tools, stewards, and drinking water. Employers often criticize working rules, charging that they increase costs of production, are unduly severe on the small contractor, interfere unnecessarily with freedom of management, and unjustly restrict entry into the union. Unions defend their working rules on the grounds that they make the employment of their members more secure, defend against the loss or subversion of hard-won gains, protect the members from unfair or arbitrary treatment by the employer, and ensure the safe employment conditions to which their members are entitled.

Actually, there is truth on both sides. Working rules do have some legitimate objectives, though at the same they may be uneconomic and autocratic in nature. These rules, moreover, are not completely unilateral, since some of them represent benefits gained by past bargaining. Others are solely matters of union policy, such as the ban on piecework and restrictions on admission into the local. A few can cause unnecessary expense by intruding on managerial discretion. Rules that require unnecessarily high-quality workmanship, time-consuming methods, the hiring of skilled journeymen for unskilled tasks, and the employment of more men than are really necessary to do a given job cause additional expense with no compensating benefit.

Depending upon the general level of employment within the local, union work rules are subject to highly flexible interpretations. Full employment tends to produce a considerably more tolerant viewpoint concerning enforcement. However, should a number of members be out of work, local officials feel compelled to broaden the employment opportunities by compelling more rigid compliance with work rule provisions.

14.10 THE BUSINESS AGENT

Large locals often have more than one full-time business agent; small locals may have one of their number act as part-time business agent. The business agent is the contractor's only direct contact with a local. He helps negotiate agreements, enforces them, ameliorates grievances, protects his union's work jurisdiction, and serves as a general go-between for the local members and the employers. To the contractor, the business agent *is* the local union.

The business agent has substantial authority to make decisions for the local and bears almost the entire responsibility for management of its affairs. Obviously such freedom of action is a necessary condition in the construction industry, where jobs are scattered and can be of short duration. To be effective, the business agent must be empowered to act quickly without having to await approval of a higher body. Even though he can act freely, however, he must remain responsive to members of his local because he is elected by them, and his job depends upon how well he pleases the group.

The business agent, in many respects, is the middleman of the industry who strives to reconcile the conflicting demands of the employers on the one side and the union rank and file on the other. Contractors look to the business agent to find qualified men for the jobs and to curb recalcitrant workers. Members of the local depend on him for such services as finding jobs for them and settling disputes with employers. He must manage his local's office, act as secretary, and supervise the finances. He must also police the jobs and check employer compliance with union work rules and contract provisions.

14.11 COLLECTIVE BARGAINING

The National Labor Relations Act requires management and labor to bargain in good faith with one another. Failure to do so by either party is an unfair labor practice. The law does not require that concessions be made or even that the two sides come to an agreement. Nevertheless, the parties must exert a genuine effort to arrive at a compromise settlement that is mutually acceptable. To illustrate, lack of good faith on the part of the employer may be indicated by ignoring a bargaining request, failure to appoint company bargaining representatives, delaying and evasive tactics, attempting to deal directly with employees during negotiations, refusal to consider each and every proposal, failure to respond with counterproposals, and refusal to sign an agreement.

Collective bargaining between contractors and the construction unions has a long history, with multiemployer bargaining now being almost universal practice. Although the make-up of the bargaining units of both sides is variable, a reasonably stable pattern of negotiations has emerged. Local associations of general contractors typically negotiate with the locals of the basic trades: carpenters, cement masons, laborers, operating engineers, and construction teamsters. In some areas, iron workers are also included. The basic trades may choose to bargain as individual locals, as a group of locals affiliated with the same international union, or through organizations of locals of different unions such as building trades councils. Labor contracts negotiated with building trades councils are generally referred to as master labor agreements, because they cover the employment of several different crafts.

In general, the specialty trades unions do not subscribe to the principle of master labor agreements. Although locals of these crafts associate to form district councils and other cooperative units, these units have not been widely utilized for bargaining purposes. Local specialty contractor groups generally negotiate with the individual union locals whose members they employ. For example, a city or regional association of painting subcontractors will negotiate with the proper local or locals of the Brotherhood of Painters, Decorators, and Paperhangers of America. In a similar manner, locals of plumbers, plasterers, roofers, electricians, and the other specialty trades bargain with organizations of their subcontractor counterparts.

Collective bargaining contracts in the construction industry, with few exceptions, are only local in coverage. The geographical areas covered by these agreements range from single communities to an entire state or more.

14.12 THE BARGAINING PROCESS

The actual bargaining is done by representatives appointed by the contractors and by the unions. If there is any doubt concerning which union represents the employees, a representation election must be conducted and the results certified by the NLRB. However, as mentioned in Chapter 13, such elections are not often held in the construction industry.

Invariably, the labor side demands more than it actually expects to obtain. The resulting sessions assume somewhat the characteristics of a poker game, involving a complex strategy of offers and counter offers. By bluff, bluster, and compromise, the contest slowly and carefully picks its way toward the ultimate settlement. Often, an informed alertness concerning the internal political situation within the union can be useful in assisting the employers toward a favorable agreement. A knowledge of labor law has become a necessity. The experienced negotiator will hold back some concessions that are almost sure to be made eventually but that are useful to "horse-trade" in obtaining the final agreement. It takes experience and skill to recognize the psychological moment at which the most propitious deal can be made. As a general rule, union negotiators do not have final authority to consummate binding agreements but must obtain ratification by the union membership. It is not unusual for the members to refuse the proposed settlement, sending the negotiators back to the bargaining table.

A fatal mistake that management must constantly guard against is entering into negotiations without thorough preparation. It must be remembered that the primary purpose of unions is to establish favorable working conditions for their members. The periodic negotiations with employers are the focal point for union activity and are not taken lightly by union representatives. By the same token, these negotiations are a serious matter for management also, and a poorly informed and inadequately prepared negotiating team can be at a serious disadvantage when faced by their union adversaries, who spend a great deal of their time in constant association with labor-management matters. The highly specialized art of labor negotiation has led to the increasing practice of hiring professional assistance for this purpose. As a matter of fact, most of the large contractors and many of the contractor associations have labor relations specialists on their staffs.

14.13 BARGAINING AGREEMENTS

Once a settlement is reached between contractors and labor unions, a written instrument is prepared that contains the essentials of the agreement and is signed by the parties. This instrument, referred to as a "labor agreement" or "labor contract," is a binding and legal document. At the present time, most labor contracts in the construction industry extend from 3 to 5 years, providing for periodic pay increases during the life of the contract. As a general rule, employers favor the long-term contract because it has a stabilizing influence and removes much of the uncertainty associated with the bidding of future work.

Bargaining agreements in the construction industry, although not nearly so long and involved as the average industrial union contract, nevertheless have many provisions covering a wide range of subjects. Such contracts stipulate wages, hours, fringe benefits, overtime, and a wide variety of working conditions. Most agreements are negotiated to cover a particular category of construction. For example, separate agreements can be negotiated for the same geographical area between the same unions and different contractor groups to cover building, heavy and highway, industrial, and housing construction. Most agreements provide that jurisdictional disputes shall be settled, without stoppage, under the plan and procedure established by the National Joint Board for the Settlement of Jurisdictional Disputes and that the unions will abide by the decision.

Section 8(d) of the National Labor Relations Act provides that the party desiring to terminate or modify an existing labor contract covering employees in an industry affecting interstate commerce must:

1. Serve written notice on the other party of the termination or modification 60 days before the termination date or date of modification.
2. Offer to negotiate a new or modified contract.
3. Notify the Federal Mediation and Conciliation Service and any similar state agency that a dispute exists, if no agreement has been reached 30 days after the notice was served.
4. Continue to live by the existing contract terms without resort to slowdowns, strike, or lockout until expiration of the 60-day notice period.

Any employee who engages in a strike within the 60-day period loses his status as an employee of the struck employer and is no longer protected by the National Labor Relations Act.

14.14 THE FEDERAL MEDIATION AND CONCILIATION SERVICE

Established in 1917, the U. S. Conciliation Service functioned as a division of the Department of Labor until 1947. At that time the Taft-Hartley Act replaced it with the Federal Mediation and Conciliation Service, an independent agency of the federal government that is charged with the responsibility of assisting employers and labor organizations in promoting labor peace. As discussed in Section 14.13, employers or unions who wish to modify or terminate existing collective bargaining agreements must serve notice on the other party 60 days before the effective date of these changes. Should the matter not be resolved within 30 days, notice is required to the Federal Mediation and Conciliation Service and any similar state agency having jurisdiction. The service is automatically notified when negotiations threaten to lead to a dispute.

Mediation by the Federal Mediation and Conciliation Service is a voluntary process. The parties to a dispute are encouraged to settle their differences by themselves, but either side may request a mediator's assistance at no charge. The aim of the service is reconciliation of conflicting views without intervention or dictation into the affairs of either party. Mediators cannot compel either side in a labor dispute to do anything, but they bring experience and dispassionate advice to the bargaining table to help the disputing parties reach a mutually acceptable area of agreement. Thus the Federal Mediation and Conciliation Service functions to keep the parties bargaining, offers helpful suggestions, and otherwise assists in the ultimate achievement of collective bargaining agreements. In no way altered, however, is the fact that the resulting agreement is both the product and the responsibility of the signatories.

The service employs a staff of mediators who are located over the country and who are recruited from both management and labor. Through the years, the Federal Mediation and Conciliation Service has established a reputation for impartiality and devotion to duty while occupying a most difficult role. As a general rule, it concentrates its energies on the resolution of disputes that have an appreciable impact on interstate commerce. Should the parties agree to arbitrate their differences, the service will furnish them with a list of qualified arbitrators.

14.15 EMPLOYER LOCKOUTS

Employer lockouts are sometimes called "strikes in reverse." A lockout occurs when an employer or, more commonly, an association of employers closes its establishment against its employees during negotiations and ceases operations until a settlement has been reached.

Labor's right to strike or to engage in concerted activity for bargaining purposes is protected. The law does not, however, give employers the parallel right to engage in a lockout. Federal labor law does not expressly permit or forbid lockouts, and they are legal under certain circumstances that are not spelled out in the law. On the other hand, the National Labor Relations Act gives workers the right to bargain collectively and makes it an unfair labor practice for employers to interfere with that right. Hence it is up to the NLRB and the courts to decide whether or not a particular lockout amounts to "interference." The guideposts to legality are vague, and contractors who engage in protective lockouts assume the risk of being able to prove that the circumstances justify their actions.

Over the years some guidelines have emerged that are useful in judging the legality of a lockout action. Generally speaking, the following circumstances could justify a lockout:

1. Unusual economic circumstances exist such that a strike would cause substantial loss to the contractors.
2. A strike would pose a serious threat to the public health and welfare.
3. A lockout by members of an employer association is necessary to prevent "single-shoting" and "whipsawing" by the union.
4. A union is engaging in selective strikes against individual members of an employers' association.

In addition, the Supreme Court has held that the lockout is a valid counter-weapon after an impasse has been reached in a bargaining dispute even if the employer is not anticipating an immediate strike. The lockout cannot be used in situations where there is anti-union intent but only in support of a legitimate bargaining position as an economic tool to counter a union's strike weapon.

14.16 NATIONAL AGREEMENTS

A few construction unions negotiate labor agreements that apply nationally. For example, the elevator constructors and the sprinkler fitters work under terms stipulated by such labor contracts. As an illustration of how such agreements work, the rate of pay of an elevator constructor journeyman is determined on the basis of the local union scales of seven designated crafts. The average of the five highest of these rates constitutes his wage scale, which is adjusted every six months to reflect any changes. The general aspects of wages, hours, and working conditions are prescribed by the national agreements.

Many of the large contractors who perform work in widely scattered localities throughout the country negotiate and sign agreements directly with the international unions. Under such a "national agreement," the company agrees to recognize the jurisdiction of the union and to work the hours, pay the wages, and observe the working conditions established and agreed upon by the union local and the recognized contractor bargaining group in the locality where the company is working. In addition, other terms peculiar to the agreement are frequently negotiated. For example, often stipulated is the number of union members who are regular company employees that the company can bring from the outside into a local's jurisdiction. Also national agreements usually provide a clause under which the union agrees not to strike the national contractor and the national contractor agrees not to participate in a lockout. This means, of course, that in the event of a local strike, union members can continue to work for a national contractor but not for the local contractors. In return, the national agreement requires the national contractor to pay retroactively any increase in wages subsequently agreed upon during local bargaining. It suffices to say that local contractors sometimes find some aspects of national agreements to be objectionable and disruptive to local collective bargaining efforts.

14.17 WAGES AND HOURS

Details associated with wages and hours are generally the crucial bargaining issues; negotiations on other matters are more in the nature of skirmishes around the edge of the major area of battle. Actually, wages and hours are broad subjects, covering such considerations as fringe benefits, overtime rates, show-up time, premiums for high work, travel time, subsistence, and coffee breaks.

It is universal practice for overtime rates to be required for all hours worked in excess of 8 per day, 40 per week, or for work done on Saturdays, Sundays, or holidays. However, standard work weeks of 35 or 30 hours, and even of 25 hours, have been established in some metropolitan areas. Many of the agreements that provide for such shortened work weeks also include additional guaranteed hours of employment per week at overtime rates. Overtime rates are usually 1½ or 2 times the regular rate of pay, depending upon the craft and the labor agreement involved.

Travel time and subsistence pertain to projects located in remote areas. Most bargaining agreements establish machinery to determine the status of a given project. If a job is found to have a remote classification, special rules apply regarding contractor-furnished transportation, field camp facilities, payment of subsistence, and travel reimbursement.

The wage rates of construction workers have risen steadily since the late 1930's, and have far outstripped those in industry. This upward trend gives every appearance of being a permanent condition when one considers the underlying philosophy of the trade unions. Labor believes that constantly rising wages are necessary to provide increased consumer buying power in an expanding economy. In the eyes of the average union member, the success of his union is measured in terms of a constant increase in wages and other benefits. Fringe benefits, steadily becoming the rule rather than the exception, add further to already high construction costs. Long-term labor contracts tend to perpetuate the upward rise of labor costs. Automatic increases preclude any voluntary curbs on wage escalation, and negotiations by the various labor unions have become a game of "catching up" with the other fellow.

As has been mentioned previously, it is not unusual that different wage structures exist in the same geographical area. Where this occurs, the building construction rates are generally somewhat higher than the heavy-highway rates. In most instances, an individual contractor confines himself to work within one of these categories and therefore will normally be a signatory to only one of the existing labor agreements. There are, however, many contractors who do both kinds of work during their normal business operations. Accordingly, such contractors may be signatories to more than one labor contract covering the same crafts.

14.18 FRINGE BENEFITS

Industrial unions have a long history of negotiating pension, welfare, and other extra benefits for their members. The construction trades have been more circumspect in this regard, being traditionally less inclined to accept nonwage benefits in lieu of higher pay rates. This attitude changed, however, during World War II, when the War Labor Board imposed comprehensive controls on wages. Although the wage stabilization regulations limited the amount of pay increases that employers could grant, they did permit various forms of fringe benefits. Thus fringe benefits came into extensive usage as a means of supplementing wages. In this way, the construction trades got a taste of such benefits and liked the flavor, whereby the stage was set for continuing fringe-benefit demands.

The intervening years have seen fringe benefits become a usual bargaining issue in the construction industry. Construction labor agreements now typically provide for pension plans, profit sharing, health and welfare funds, insurance, paid vacations, paid holidays, employee education, employee thrift plans, and many other benefits. A recently published national study reported that employer contribution to fringe benefits for construction workers now averages over 20 percent of direct payroll. In fact, fringe benefits have been increasing faster than basic wage rates during recent years. Normally, fringe benefts provided by the employer are paid into special funds and are established as a predetermined amount per hour worked by each employee covered by the agreement.

14.19 INDUSTRY ADVANCEMENT FUNDS

For many years, labor and management in the construction industry have joined together in cooperative programs designed to advance some aspect of construction. The funds established for this purpose are called "industry advancement funds." Until about 1960 these funds were generally limited to the specialty trades such as lathing and plastering. Since that time, however, a number of general contractor groups have created such funds by agreement with the basic construction trades unions. Under the agreement, each employer deposits a specified amount for each hour worked by union members whom he employs. The employer's group acts as the administrator of the fund, which is used to finance programs in education, public relations, safety, apprenticeship, market development, labor relations, building codes, specification writing, and other relevant areas.

The courts have ruled that Section 302 of the Taft-Hartley Act prohibits joint administration of industry advancement funds by labor and management but that such funds are legal so long as they are managed by employers alone. This section of Taft-Hartley bans employer payments to union representatives except for certain listed purposes such as union membership dues and contributions to specified funds, for example, health and welfare, pension, vacation, apprenticeship, and various types of insurance. Several bills to legalize jointly administered industry funds have been considered by Congress, but to date such an amendment to the Taft-Hartley Act has not passed. The National Labor Relations Board has ruled that such funds are not mandatory subjects of bargaining. Consequently, contractor refusal to negotiate on this issue is not an unfair labor practice, and a union cannot strike an employer in an effort to obtain his agreement to such a fund in a labor contract.

14.20 ADMINISTRATION OF THE CONTRACT

The signing of the negotiated contract does not close the matter of contractor-union relationships. Rather, the status of the agreement merely changes from that of bargaining to one of interpretation and administration. It goes without saying that a carefully considered and clearly worded contract will do much to minimize contract misunderstandings.

Labor agreements in the construction industry typically contain procedures for the settlement of disputes that may arise during the life of the contract. When a dispute occurs that cannot be resolved by a conference of the steward, business agent, superintendent, and any other party directly involved, the grievance procedure set forth in the agreement is followed. This procedure usually provides for meetings between successively higher echelons of contractor and union officials, during which time no work stoppage is to occur. Should the grievance procedure not resolve the dispute, arbitration of the matter may or may not be provided for in the labor agreement. Historically, unions have resisted the concept of binding arbitration, preferring to remain free to select their own course of action to suit the situation. Nevertheless, many labor contracts now provide for the arbitration of contract disputes with no resort to strikes or lockouts.

It is worthwhile to note that an agreement to arbitrate can be enforced against management by federal court injunctions, but there is no comparable means in federal courts to enforce such agreements by unions. The Supreme Court in 1962 ruled that the Norris-LaGuardia Act bars federal court injunctions against unions even if only to enforce no-strike agreements to arbitrate. Where state courts have jurisdiction, this matter depends upon the laws of the individual state. The Supreme Court also ruled that an employer can sue a union for damages resulting from violation of a no-strike arbitration agreement but may not sue union officials or members.

Because administration of the contract is an everyday requirement for the contractor, a carefully selected individual should be appointed to handle the labor relations for the firm. If a specific person is assigned to this duty, even if only as one of several responsibilities, he can become versed in the complexities of labor law and the provisions of the local labor agreements. He becomes, in fact, the labor relations expert for the company. In this way, company labor policy is at least consistent and informed. The contractor is obligated to live up to the terms of the agreement, and he must be insistent that the unions do likewise.

14.21 DAMAGE SUITS

Section 301 of the Taft-Hartley Act provides that suits for violation of labor contracts between an employer and a labor union representing employees in an industry affecting interstate commerce can be brought in the federal district court having jurisdiction. The law provides that any labor organization or employer subject to the Taft-Hartley Act is bound by the actions of its agents, and that a labor organization may sue or be sued as an entity and in behalf of the employees whom it represents. Any money judgment so obtained against a union is enforceable only against the organization as an entity and against its assets and not against any individual member or his assets.

The enactment of the Taft-Hartley Act thus made it easier for either an employer or a union to sue the other for damages suffered by reason of an unfair labor practice or for willful violation of a negotiated labor agreement. Consequently, an employer who is injured in his business or property by a secondary boycott or jurisdictional dispute has the right to sue the responsible union for damages. Actually, there is quite a long history of successful suits by employers against unions for damages caused by boycotts, sitdown strikes, and other such actions. However, union responsibility for breach of collective bargaining contracts is a new concept of labor liability. In practical fact, damage suits against unions have proven troublesome to prosecute because of difficulty in identifying union "agents" for whose actions Taft-Hartley makes the union responsible.

14.22 PREJOB CONFERENCES

When employment conditions pertaining to a given project are out of the ordinary (that is, the conditions are not clearly provided for in the area agreement), it is usual practice for a prejob conference to be held between the contractor and the union or unions involved. This meeting may be held before bidding, so as to establish standard conditions for the bidding contractors, or just before the start of field operations. In either case, the underlying motive is to achieve a meeting of minds between the employer and the unions regarding job conditions of employment. For example, consider a job that is to be located in a remote area. The contractor wishes to man the job in the most economical manner possible, and the unions require that fair standards be maintained. If the project is near a town of any size, the contractor may decide to quarter his men there and furnish transportation back and forth to the site. If this solution is not feasible, temporary barracks or trailers may be provided at the project. At any rate, the contractor and the unions must arrive at a mutually acceptable understanding relative to quarters, subsistence, and transportation. In addition, the locals having jurisdiction must be checked to determine whether they have enough men available to do the job. If not, arrangements must be made to bring workers in from the outside, either by the local or by the contractor.

There is some contractor resistance to the prejob-conference concept, based on the belief that such meetings encourage the unions to make exorbitant demands. Objection or acceptance seems to be a matter of opinion and company policy. However, available evidence seems to indicate that unions are much more reasonable at this stage than they are later on when they detect conditions that lead them to believe that the contractor is trying to get away with something. Obtaining advance union acceptance of his procedure makes it much easier for the contractor to devote his energies to getting the job done without having to combat active union resistance and interference.

15

PROJECT SAFETY

15.1 THE HIGH COST OF ACCIDENTS

The consequences of construction accidents are not expressible in terms of dollars alone. Money loses much of its significance when personal injury and death are involved. Nevertheless, the financial effect of accidents is an important matter to the construction industry and for the individual contractor.

Job accidents impose upon the construction industry a tremendous burden of needless and avoidable expense. The Associated General Contractors of America has estimated that the cost of construction accidents is around two billion dollars per year. It is true that insurance can be purchased to protect the contractor from certain expenses resulting from construction accidents. For example, workmen's compensation insurance provides hospital and medical care, subsistence payments, rehabilitation, and other benefits provided by law for injured workers and their families. However, construction accidents can and do involve substantial costs that are not insurable or that are not included in the usual construction insurance coverage. These are sometimes spoken of as "hidden" or "indirect" costs; examples are damage or destruction of materials, cleanup costs, idle machine time, unproductive labor time, spoiled work, schedule disruptions, loss of trained manpower, work slowdowns, poor public relations, administrative expense, lowered employee morale, and other expensive side effects.

15.2 SAFETY LEGISLATION

The advent of the industrial revolution in the United States was marked by a simultaneous proliferation of unsafe working conditions. Although the employer had certain common-law duties toward his employees, such as to provide a safe place to work, the safeguards to health and safety that are taken for granted today were not customary at that time. As a matter of fact, there was no general acceptance of the notion that employers should be concerned with the welfare and safety of employees while they were on the job. Certainly, no concerted effort was made to render working conditions less hazardous. It was believed by management that most work accidents were caused by the carelessness of the employee himself and that it was the worker's responsibility to avoid accidents. However, the grim loss of life, limb, and livelihood aroused the public conscience, and the latter half of the nineteenth century witnessed a gradual change in the attitude toward work safety.

The primary responsibility for statutory job-safety requirements in the United States has traditionally rested with the state governments. In 1867 Massachusetts took the first legal step toward remedying the dangerous working conditions so characteristic of the time. During the years following many of the states enacted laws pertaining to working conditions in factories, mine safety, machinery operation, inspection of steam boilers and elevators, and fire protection. In 1911 Wisconsin established a state industrial commission which was authorized to develop and issue rules and regulations in the field of industrial health and safety that would have the force of law. Today most of the states have enacted similar legislation to give designated state agencies general rule-making authority in the areas of occupational health and safety.

It is worthy of note that there have been several bills introduced into the Congress that would have established mandatory safety standards on federal construction projects. Although none of these has yet been enacted, it appears probable that some form of federal safety legislation will ultimately be enacted into law.

15.3 STATE SAFETY CODES

Details of safety codes vary somewhat from state to state, but there is a trend toward greater uniformity in the provisions of the regulations through adoption of the standards of nationally recognized codes developed by such bodies as the United States of America Standards Institute. Although some states have established general safety standards applicable to all employments, the tendency has been to develop special codes for particular industries, operations, or hazards. Some specific hazards are regulated in a large majority of the states. Codes now relate to boilers, construction, elevators, mechanical power transmission, cranes and derricks, fire protection, floors and stairways, illumination, sanitation, ventilation, electrical hazards, explosives, ladders, spray painting, welding, and other areas of potential danger. Many states require the provision of first-aid and protective equipment. State safety codes make the employer and his supervisory personnel responsible for compliance with the code and for suitable safety instruction to the worker. In turn, the employee is required to make use of safeguards provided for his protection and to conduct his work in conformance with the established safety rules.

The various state industrial commissions or labor departments have jurisdiction over every employment and place of employment within the state and are authorized to enforce and administer all codes and rules pertaining to the safety and protection of workers. The commission is vested with full power and authority to establish and enforce necessary and reasonable rules and regulations for the purpose of implementing the state law. In general, whenever the commission finds that any employment or place of employment is not safe or that employees are not being adequately protected, it is empowered to order the employer to rectify the situation and to furnish safety devices and other safeguards reasonably required. Violation of the code is usually made a misdemeanor, with each violation constituting a separate offense.

15.4 CONTRACT SAFETY REQUIREMENTS

With increasing frequency, contracts for the construction of public projects include required safety standards that must be maintained on the job. Many state highway department contracts now include a safety code that requires highway contractors to follow uniform and standard safety practices on road projects. Several federal agencies, including the U. S. Corps of Engineers, the U. S. Navy Bureau of Yards and Docks, and the Bureau of Reclamation, include required safety standards in their construction contracts. These standards represent a contractual obligation on the part of the contractor for compliance.

Labor agreements may also impose contractual safety requirements on the contractor. The National Labor Relations Board has ruled that safety regulations, as an essential part of employees' terms and conditions of employment, are mandatory subjects of bargaining whenever either party places the issue on the bargaining table.

15.5 NATIONAL SAFETY MOVEMENT

Soon after the beginning of the industrial safety movement, it became apparent that, to be effective, accident prevention programs required more than rules, laws, safety devices, and mechanical safeguards. Workers continued to have accidents because of unsafe work habits. For this reason, the national safety movement has grown to include and even emphasize the promotion of safety practices among workers and supervisors through educational programs.

The federal government has provided leadership and technical assistance in the campaign against work accidents. The U. S. Department of Labor conducts training courses for state safety inspectors and safety specialists of management and labor. It assists state governments in drafting safety codes and in setting up special safety programs for hazardous occupations. Employer associations, insurance companies, unions, and trade organizations have joined in the general drive to promote safety and reduce accidents.

15.6 WORK INJURY STATISTICS

Fortunately, not all accidents result in personal injury. Nevertheless, statistics pertaining to the frequency and severity of worker injury are widely used to describe the accident problem and to evaluate the efficacy of safety programs. In this regard, the USA Standard Method of Recording and Measuring Work Injury Experience (USA Standard Z16.1) has been generally accepted as a uniform procedure for classifying and recording injuries and computing injury rates. To understand the significance of published accident data compiled according to this method, it is necessary that certain terms be defined.

15.7 WORK INJURY CLASSIFICATIONS

Work injuries are classified according to their severity in accordance with the divisions listed below. The standard method defines a work injury as any injury, including occupational disease and work-connected disability, that arises out of and in the course of employment. Occupational disease is a disease caused by environmental factors that are peculiar to a particular trade and to which an employee is not ordinarily subjected away from such employment.

1. *Death.* Any fatality resulting from a work injury regardless of the time intervening between injury and death.
2. *Permanent total disability.* An injury of this type permanently and totally incapacitates the worker from engaging in any gainful occupation, or results in the loss, or the complete loss of use, of any of the following in one accident:
   (a) Both eyes.
   (b) One eye and one hand, or arm, or foot, or leg.
   (c) Any two of the following not on the same limb: hand, arm, foot, or leg.
3. *Permanent partial disability.* This is an injury that results in the loss, or complete loss of use, of any member or part of a member of the body, or any permanent impairment of functions of the body or part thereof.
4. *Temporary total disability.* Such an injury renders the worker unable to perform his regular duties during the entire time of his regular shift on one or more days subsequent to his injury.
5. *Disabling injury.* This is any work injury classified as one of the preceding four types. These are sometimes referred to as lost-time injuries and are used in calculating the disabling injury frequency rate and the disabling injury severity rate.

As can be seen, minor injuries are excluded in the calculation of the standard injury rates. The reason for this is the difficulty of standardizing minor cases.

15.8 WORK INJURY RATES

There are three measures of injury experience that are commonly used to describe the extent of injuries resulting from work accidents. Two of these are the disabling injury frequency rate, which is the number of disabling injuries per million man-hours worked, and the disabling injury severity rate, which is calculated on the basis of the number of days charged per million man-hours worked.

Disabling injury frequency rate =
$$\frac{\text{Number of disabling injuries} \times 1,000,000}{\text{Employee hours of exposure}}$$

Disabling injury severity rate =
$$\frac{\text{Total days charged} \times 1,000,000}{\text{Employee hours of exposure}}$$

The number of hours of exposure is the total number of hours worked by all employees of the contractor regardless of the nature of their duties.

A third measure included in the standard method shows the average severity of the injuries. It is called the "average days charged per disabling injury" and can be calculated by either of the following:

$$\frac{\text{Total days charged}}{\text{Total disabling injuries}}$$

or

$$\frac{\text{Injury severity rate}}{\text{Injury frequency rate}}$$

15.9 DAYS CHARGED

Time losses caused by work injuries are expressed in terms of days of disability, either actual or potential. These losses are referred to as "days charged." The first three classes of disabling injuries—death, permanent total disability, and permanent partial disability—have associated with them specified and predetermined numbers of days charged that usually exceed the actual time lost but are selected to reflect a potential loss of productive capacity in the future. For each death or permanent total disability, a scheduled charge of 6,000 days is made with no variation. For permanent partial disability, the scheduled charges vary, depending upon the specific loss. Table 15.1 contains a list of scheduled time charges. For fatal, permanent total, and permanent partial injuries, only the scheduled charges are used. The actual days of disability are disregarded.

For temporary total disability, the number of days charged is the total number of full calendar days during which the person was unable to work as a result of the injury. The total does not include the day the injury occurred or the day the person returned to work, but it does include all intervening calendar days.

To illustrate the calculation of the three measures of injury experience, suppose that a contractor has an average force of 350 employees who work 40

TABLE 15.1 Tabulation of Scheduled Charges

Injury	Time Charge (days)
Death	6,000
Permanent total disability	6,000
Loss of member, traumatic or surgical	
Thumb	300-900
Index finger	100-600
Middle finger	75-500
Ring finger	60-450
Little finger	50-400
Hand at wrist	3,000
Great toe	150-600
Other toes	35-350
Foot at ankle	2,400
Arm, above wrist and at or below elbow	3,600
Arm, above elbow	4,500
Leg, above ankle and at or below knee	3,000
Leg, above knee	4,500
One eye, loss of sight	1,800
One ear, complete industrial loss of hearing	600
Both ears, complete industrial loss of hearing, in one accident	3,000
Unrepaired hernia	50

The time charge for loss of fingers and toes depends upon the number of bones involved. In case of multiple amputation of fingers and/or toes, the separate charges for each finger and/or toe are totaled. Special rules apply for loss of use and for injuries not identified in the table. (From USA Standard Z16.1)

---

hours per week, 50 weeks per year. If during a year's time there are 14 disabling injuries:

$$\text{Disabling injury frequency rate} = \frac{14 \times 1,000,000}{350 \times 40 \times 50} = 20.0$$

Let us further assume that these disabling injuries involved a total time loss from work of 221 calendar days. Consider that only one of these injuries involved a scheduled time charge: the injury of a carpenter who cut off his index and middle fingers with an electric saw. Although he was absent from work only 22 calendar days, the scheduled time charge is 375 days. Therefore, the total days charged = 221 − 22 + 375 = 574 days.

$$\text{Disabling injury severity rate} = \frac{574 \times 1,000,000}{350 \times 40 \times 50} = 820$$

$$\text{Average days charged per disabling injury} = \frac{820}{20} = 41$$

15.10 CONSTRUCTION SAFETY STATISTICS

In construction, as elsewhere in industry, the matter of work safety has come to be recognized as a management responsibility. Contractors now expend considerable time and money to maintain effective company safety programs and to educate their employees to be safety conscious. Insurance companies and contractor associations, such as the Associated General Contractors of America, contribute valuable guidance and know-how to these programs. The National Safety Council, supported by private industry, devotes its energies to safety promotion and the elimination of accidents. Organized labor plays an active role and sponsors safety training courses.

Tables 15.2 and 15.3 present accident data for selected major industries, including construction. These data show that the construction industry has one of the worst accident records of all the major American industries. For the past several years, with the construction industry employing about 4 percent of the total labor force, it has accounted for about 11 percent of all disabling work injuries and 18 percent of all deaths resulting from occupational accidents. Construction ranks among the highest in disabling injury frequency rates and severity rates of the forty leading industries in the United States. Table 15.4 presents a breakdown of accident statistics within the construction industry itself.

In retrospect, the construction industry has made great strides in improving its accident record, although, admittedly, much more remains to be done. In 1927, construction had a disabling injury rate of 65.07 and a severity rate of 7,130. By 1937, the frequency rate had dropped to 21.96 and the severity rate to 2,510. Since that time, the rates have fluctuated to some extent and were 13.21 and 1,931, respectively, in 1967.

Notwithstanding the recent lack of appreciable progress, the experience of the U. S. Army Corps of Engineers, which requires that contractors institute and maintain safety standards on their jobs, indicates that construction accidents can be re-

TABLE 15.2   Work Accidents in the Major Industries, 1966*

Industry Group	Deaths		Disabling Injuries	
	Total	Per 100,000 Workers	Total	Per 100,000 Workers
All industries	14,500	20	2,200,000	3,030
Trade	1,300	8	420,000	2,660
Manufacturing	1,900	10	470,000	2,500
Service, government	3,200	13	580,000	2,310
Transportation and public utilities	1,700	40	200,000	4,710
Agriculture	2,900	69	250,000	5,950
Construction	2,800	74	240,000	6,320
Mining, quarrying	700	108	40,000	6,150

* Adapted from data published by the National Safety Council.

TABLE 15.3   Disabling Injury Rates in Selected Industries, 1966*

Industry	Frequency Rate	Severity Rate
All industries	6.91	689
Automobile	1.67	235
Aircraft manufacturing	2.26	184
Electrical equipment	2.30	148
Chemical	3.78	399
Cement	4.10	1,182
Machinery	4.81	329
Sheet metal products	5.21	430
Petroleum	7.55	775
Railroad equipment	9.27	702
Clay and mineral products	9.87	937
Iron and steel products	10.48	631
Foundry	11.73	1,005
Construction	12.24	2,170
Wood products	13.35	1,030
Lumber	16.61	2,311
Marine transportation	20.20	2,541
Mining, underground coal	36.64	5,264

* Adapted from data published by National Safety Council.

TABLE 15.4   Disabling Injury Rates in Construction, 1966*

Category	Frequency Rate	Severity Rate	Death and Permanent Disability
Construction industry	12.24	2,170	0.84
Heavy construction	11.95	3,319	1.04
Highway construction	13.01	1,206	0.54
Concrete, bridge and dam	14.48	2,871	0.93
Structural and ornamental metal work	16.72	2,430	1.61
General building construction	17.47	2,190	0.95
Public utility construction	19.29	2,218	0.69
Marine construction	35.76	5,270	1.80

* Adapted from data published by National Safety Council.

duced. The frequency rate on construction work supervised by the Corps of Engineers has been ranging between 5 and 6, while for contractors generally it has been two or three times as high. The severity rates on Corps of Engineers' projects are substantially less than the rate for the construction industry as a whole.

It should be noted that accident statistics are compiled and reported by both the National Safety Council and the Bureau of Labor Statistics of the U. S. Department of Labor. For any given year, the figures of the Bureau of Labor Statistics invariably indicate higher frequency and severity rates than do those of the National Safety Council, because each set of data represents the experience of a different group. The National Safety Council rates are based primarily on data furnished by the large contractors. The Bureau of Labor Statistics figures are based on a much larger sampling and are probably more representative of the industry as a whole.

To understand the difference in reported safety statistics, it must be remembered that most construction work is carried on by small contractors. Although many small firms are safety conscious and have excellent records, small firms, as a class, are less likely to be able to make long-term investments in equipment, personnel, and training that lead to better safety performance. The relatively short duration of their jobs is another factor working against an effective safety program. In general, the small contractors have no functioning safety program and, consequently, a poorer overall accident record.

15.11 ECONOMIC BENEFITS OF SAFETY

In addition to the humanitarian aspect, there is also a compelling economic motivation in accident prevention. Many financial benefits accrue to the contractor who conducts his field operations in a safe manner and whose accident experience is low. The most immediate and obvious financial benefit is the savings realized because of accidents that do not happen. Mention has already been made of the indirect costs of accidents that are not covered by insurance and that can constitute serious financial loss.

Construction workers appreciate and value job safety even though they sometimes tend to be careless in their work habits. The employee who feels that his employer is genuinely concerned about his safety and who sees tangible evidence about him of this concern is more likely to be a loyal and cooperative worker. The incorporation of safety measures as an integral part of operations, instead of setting them apart to be handled as a necessary evil, is a key factor in obtaining high morale and employee loyalty. Safety is one of the potent forces that makes a man proud of the company he works for, proud of the manner in which he has performed his job, and proud of his personal record in preventing accidents. The fruits of good worker morale are higher production and better workmanship, two economic benefits of no mean proportion.

Another important financial benefit to the contractor that results from fewer accidents is the reduced cost of insurance. As discussed in Chapter 9, the premiums of certain types of insurance are adjusted up or down for the individual contractor in accordance with his loss experience. Workmen's compensation insurance is of this type. Basic workmen's compensation costs are determined by manual rates established for specific businesses and industries. A contractor can obtain his insurance at lower than manual rates by "experience modification," a plan that adjusts his premium on the basis of his actual accident history. Experience modification operates so that the contractor's past loss experience is a determining factor in his present and future compensation costs. The fewer claims the insurance company pays in behalf of a contractor, the lower are his insurance costs. Frequency and severity of accidents are basic elements of the rating formula. Such adjustment of insurance premiums represents substantial economies of operation.

To illustrate the magnitude of possible savings, let us look at what might be achieved in reducing the cost of workmen's compensation insurance. Assume that a building contractor does an annual volume of $10 million worth of work a year. Considering a typical amount of subcontracting and the cost of materials, this general contractor's annual payroll will be of the order of magnitude of $2.5 million. If his present workmen's compensation rate averages about 6 percent, his annual premium will be about $150,000. Now assume that an effective accident prevention program results in an experience-modification rate reduction of 30 percent below the workmen's compensation insurance rates formerly paid. Annual savings of the order of $45,000 are therefore entirely possible on the cost of this one insurance coverage alone. A direct result of such savings is the improved competitive situation of the contractor. Lower insurance premiums mean lower bids.

Also, safety is an important public relations tool, there being few other activities with such great potential for building goodwill. Good public relations have important financial implications for the contractor. A serious job accident can adversely affect a contractor's reputation, and the attendant unfavorable publicity can undo years of good public relations.

15.12 DUTIES OF MANAGEMENT

Top management bears the ultimate responsibility for the company's accident record, and the impetus for improved safety performance must emanate from this level. The attitude of management toward safe work practices will be reflected by the supervisors and workers. A mood of top-level interest and concern keeps everybody safety conscious. Conversely, if the top executives are not genuinely interested in preventing accidents and injuries, no one else is likely to be concerned either. If employee cooperation and participation are to be obtained, the accident control program must start with the demonstrated interest and backing of company management. Additionally, adequate funds must be provided to assure the successful operation of the safety program.

Every level of company management, therefore, must reflect a concern for safety and set a good example of compliance with safety regulations. Management interest must be vocal, visible, and vigorous. The logical beginning is a written company safety policy, announced by management and implemented by rules that are enforced. This policy should be widely publicized so that every employee becomes familiar with it, especially with the aspects that pertain directly to him. A carefully worded safety policy, signed by the company president, that is personally and forcefully brought to the attention of every employee will emphasize management's desire and determination to reduce accidents. In addition, a written policy is very useful in the enforcement of safety rules by supervisors.

Top administrators personally should give timely credit and commendation for good safety performance whenever and wherever it occurs. Attendance of executives at employee safety meetings will impress workers with management's sincere concern for their job safety.

15.13 THE COMPANY SAFETY PROGRAM

A company safety program is just as much a part of a contractor's business as is estimating and cost accounting. Fundamentally, the company plan must be one of identifying specific job hazards and educating the employees to conduct their work in a way that will minimize the risk of injury. The cause of any accident is an unsafe act or an unsafe condition. The objective of the company accident-prevention program is to eliminate both of these from the jobs. Unsafe conditions result from either inadequate safety planning or no planning at all and are a consequence of the way the job is planned or the way it is run. In most cases, unsafe conditions can be corrected by changing job procedures. Unsafe acts result from personal carelessness or lack of safety training. They can be prevented by safety education of the individual worker and enforcement of safety regulations.

Because construction work is inherently hazardous, it is unlikely that disabling injuries and accidents can ever be completely eliminated. Nevertheless, much can be done to reduce the incidence level and the severity. The fact that the work is hazardous and accident prevention is difficult should prompt the contractor to give added attention to his safety program. The mere presence of a dangerous situation cannot be used to justify failure to do everything possible to reduce the waste and suffering caused by construction accidents.

Mechanical safeguards are important in the prevention of job accidents, but the mental attitude of the workers is even more significant. Rules and regulations alone will not guarantee safe work habits. Effective accident prevention in construction is largely a human relations problem and is achieved primarily through education, persuasion, and eternal vigilance. Until an awareness of his individual responsibility and a desire to ensure his personal safety are established the mind of each employee, efforts to reduce accidents will remain ineffective.

Because of differences in organization, type of activity, and scope of operations, each contractor must develop an accident prevention plan that fits his own particular needs. Job hazards differ considerably among housing, building, highway, heavy, and industrial construction, a fact that must be reflected by the detailed workings of the program. Experience indicates that it is good practice to place a capable and interested administrator in overall charge of the company accident prevention program. He is made responsible for safety training, distribution and use of safety equipment, maintenance of first-aid facilities on the projects, investigation of accidents, writing and filing of accident reports, and associated duties. As a member of management, he has the authority to promulgate and enforce safety regulations and policies.

Company safety meetings of supervisory personnel held once or twice a year can be very effective. A formal program consisting of a guest safety speaker or a film may be presented. Information concerning how the company ranked in state and national safety contests can be discussed. Accompanying this could be a tabulation of recent company lost-time accidents with information on how they could have been prevented.

Safety contests between company projects may also be conducted. At a dinner meeting, project superintendents with the best safety records are recognized and presented with cash awards substantial enough to be appreciated. The participation of rank-and-file workers can also be encouraged through the awarding of cash prizes for employees' safety suggestions and slogans.

15.14 PROJECT SAFETY PLAN

Accident prevention aimed at the avoidance of specific happenings must be planned into each construction project. The constantly changing nature of a project under construction does not allow the detection and elimination of hazards purely on an experience basis. The contractor must establish in advance for each project the specific hazards that the proposed methods, procedures, and equipment will create and then devise an accident prevention plan to combat the peculiar risks to be encountered. Analysis of accident experience is a valuable first step. Insurance company engineers can be of great assistance in providing management with continuing technical advice needed to maintain a company safety program at peak performance.

Having established the ground rules of job safety, the commencement of field operations must be accompanied by implementation of the plan. The following steps are suggested for the conduct of the safety program during construction activities:

1. The job superintendent should be given the prime responsibility for accident prevention on his project. Under him, each craft foreman is made responsible for safety measures as applied to his group. It is the foreman who is with his men all of the time, and it is the foreman who must watch for unsafe practices or conditions and who must promote safety by instruction, precept, and example. On large projects, there may be a safety engineer who coordinates the overall plan and devotes his time and energies exclusively to matters of safety, first aid, sanitation, fire prevention, and other such activities.
2. Adequate first-aid facilities should be made available. These facilities may range from a well-supplied first-aid kit on small projects to a nurse-staffed infirmary on very large ones. On the usual job with no professional medical assistance available on the site, first-aid training for supervisors and foremen is desirable. Locations of adjacent hospital facilities and ambulance service telephone numbers should be prominently posted in the job office. First-aid kits should be dustproof, easily available, and checked at frequent intervals for any replenishments needed. Every man on the job should be informed as to where first-aid facilities are available.
3. New employees should be acquainted with the company's safety policy and informed that strict conformance with safety regulations is a condition of employment. Special safety instruction should be given for particularly hazardous work. Every employee should be instructed to report immediately any injury, however trivial, to his foreman and to obtain suitable first-aid treatment.
4. The proper use of personal protective clothing and equipment should be insisted upon, with no exceptions made.
5. Periodic tool-box safety talks should be held for all work gangs. Merely prodding workers "to be careful" is not likely to accomplish much. Information as

to the proper use of tools, handling of materials, building of scaffolds, and operation of equipment can be topics of successful meetings. The material must be specific, practical, and pertinent to current operations. Suggestions for improved safety should be solicited from the workers.

6. Safety posters, safety instruction cards, and warning signs should be utilized to the fullest degree. Prominent display of the project accident record, as well as of notices that remind workers of specific project safety requirements, is very effective.

7. Periodic meetings of the superintendent, craft foremen, and other supervisors are essential to review job safety and make necessary revisions to the program. This group should investigate immediately all lost-time accidents and determine corrective measures to prevent recurrence.

8. Ample fire-fighting means should be provided. Since welding and flame cutting are among the most frequent causes of construction fires, special regulations must apply to these activities. Specific areas should be provided for the storage of flammable, combustible, and explosive materials.

9. Some system of safety inspection should be put into operation in which the job superintendent, in company with the firm's safety man, tours the project periodically to check on safety conditions.

10. Good housekeeping should be required. Designated storage areas for materials, tools, and supplies should be maintained and used. Rubbish and waste material should be removed promptly from the area of operations.

11. All equipment should be maintained in accordance with a definite schedule. This maintenance should include inspection of accident hazards such as frayed cables, bad tires, slipping clutches, and electrical grounds. Inspection and maintenance must not be limited to mechanical equipment but should be extended to scaffolding, towers, ladders, and other nonoperating items.

12. Obtaining the full cooperation of subcontractors is essential. All of the measures previously outlined must include the personnel of subcontractors on the project.

15.15 THE FIELD SUPERVISOR

Top management has the major responsibility for establishing safety policies, procedures, and safe working conditions. However, most of what is planned and established must reach the worker on the job by way of his field supervisor. To be effective, any campaign for the prevention of accidents in construction must be communicated to the worker in a clear, practical, and understandable form. Although the executives of the company may prescribe safe practices, the supervisor, who has the authority to direct the men in the field and is in daily contact with them, plays a dominant role in implementing the company safety policy.

The construction worker mirrors his supervisor's attitude toward safety. For this reason, the wholehearted cooperation of the superintendent and foreman is indispensable to the success of any safety program. The best way for a supervisor to sell accident prevention to his men is to practice what he preaches. A worker is much more likely to follow a supervisor's example than his instructions. If a supervisor breaks a safety rule, he not only reduces the importance of the rule but also loses some of the confidence of his men. If the field supervisor clearly believes in safety and reflects the fact by word and deed, the men under him will be much more cognizant of the advantages of safe work practices and the costly results of any alternative. It is largely up to the supervisor to find and control the potential hazards on his job. He must teach by doing and must be able to demonstrate the safe way to do any particular job. Job instructions to workers should include not only what is to be done but also how it is to be done. Accident potential decreases when the workman is given complete procedural instructions in advance.

Safety regulations must be enforced. The worker must not only be taught safe practices but also be required to follow them. Safety discipline is a delicate area, but it is very important to an accident prevention program. If a rule has been established, the supervisor must always enforce it. An established safety regulation that is not enforced will not be obeyed. If a rule is enforced only some of the time, a man who is reprimanded will feel that he is being "picked on" and singled out for unfair treatment. Those who violate the rule and are not reprimanded will begin to believe that the regulation really isn't very important. The supervisor must, of course, exercise care to keep his personal feelings out of safety discipline.

The objective of safety discipline is to improve the safety performance of the crew. A worker who is convinced that a safety procedure is designed to protect his welfare will support its enforcement. Similarly, workers are more likely to accept a reprimand if they believe that it is for their own protection. A spirit of group responsibility for safety and a sense of safety competition among work crews help to establish a self-disciplining attitude about safety violations. A word to his business agent will usually snap even the most recalcitrant worker back into conformance with safety regulations.

15.16 GROUP SAFETY PROGRAMS

A cooperative plan of accident prevention by a local group of contractors can be very effective. The usual scheme is for the program to be implemented and conducted by the local chapter of a contractors' association. An accident prevention committee can be appointed to determine a general plan of action. Some standard safety manual, such as that of the Associated General Contractors of America, is usually used as a basis for the program. Plans are formulated for the application of the safety provisions to the work of the group. Revisions necessary to reflect local conditions and needs are included as the plan is developed. The safety regulations are then disseminated to the supervisory employees of the member contractors. These people are encouraged to offer suggestions, and occasional meetings are held for the purpose of safety demonstrations, first-aid instructions, explanation of safety rules, and group discussions of safety problems.

Once the group plan is in action, the accident prevention committee can perform other kinds of functions. A safety inspection team can be organized that represents the contractors, insurance companies, and state safety agencies. This team can make periodic inspections of the members' projects and compile a safety check list of detected unsafe acts and conditions. The committee can make a personal on-site inspection of all serious or fatal accidents that occur on the members' projects. In addition, a member of the committee, in company with an official of the contracting firm on whose work the accident occurred and the project superintendent, can conduct a thorough study of why the accident occurred and how similar accidents can be prevented in the future. The resulting report of findings and recommendations can be submitted to both the committee and the contracting firm involved. The mere fact that an investigation of accidents will be made has a powerful psychological influence on supervisors.

15.17 ACCIDENT RECORDS

The compilation of accident records and their analysis are important phases of the company's safety program. These records serve primarily to pinpoint the locations and underlying causes of accidents, information which is vital to the planning of more effective accident prevention programs. Accident records can also be valuable in quite another way. They can be used to arouse the competitive spirit of workmen on the various projects to establish a safety record that compares favorably with the records of other projects or with their own past record.

Every accident resulting in personal injury should be made a matter of record, regardless of how inconsequential the injury may appear to be. On every job a daily record book can be maintained in which the project superintendent or his representative enters each injury in chronological order. For each occurrence, entry should be made of the date, name of the injured worker, nature of the injury, first-aid treatment given on the site, and any further information deemed desirable. This record will prove to be of value in the occasional instance when an injury appears to be trivial on first impression but later proves to be more serious.

The company's safety procedures should require the job superintendent to conduct an investigation of every disabling injury that occurs on his project and to submit a written report of his findings. A company form can be devised for the purpose, although many contractors find the standard form of accident report required by the state workmen's compensation laws to be satisfactory. In any event, specific information pertaining to the accident and its cause is required. Figure 15.1 shows a company accident form that is brief but informative.

A periodic summary of company accident experience should be prepared for the purpose of keeping top management informed. Because safety is an important management function, the executives of a company must keep current as to the efficacy of its safety program. These summary reports can contain information pertaining to the frequency and severity of accidents and the total man-days lost from work. To be of maximum benefit, data should be presented for each of the individual projects together with overall totals for the company.

BLANK CONSTRUCTION COMPANY, INC.

PORTLAND, OHIO

A C C I D E N T   R E P O R T   Date _____

Name of injured worker _____   Project name _____
Approximate age _____   Job location where injury occurred _____
Occupation _____   _____
                                                 Weather _____

Name of injured worker's supervisor   _____
Date and hour of injury _____
Nature and severity of injury _____
Agency actually causing injury _____
                                (saw blade, falling bolt, etc.)
What worker was doing _____
Names of witnesses _____
Accident type _____
                (fall, struck, burned, etc.)
Unsafe act of worker (if any)_____
                             (removed guard from saw, improper lifting position, etc.)
Unsafe behavior of worker (if any)_____
                                  (deliberate chance–taking, refusal to wear hard hat, etc.)
Cause not attributable to worker (if any)_____ __
                                        (guard railing not made sufficiently strong, carelessness of worker above, poor
                                        illumination, etc.)
Recommendations for elimination of accident cause_____
First-aid rendered by _____
Name of doctor or hospital _____
Date injured worker returned to work _____

Signature of project superintendent_____

Figure 15.1   Accident report.

15.18 PROTECTION OF THE PUBLIC

A very important aspect of a company's accident prevention program is the safety of the general public. People are innately curious and are capable of many thoughtless actions in their attempts to observe construction operations. The contractor must reconcile himself to the fact that the public will know what is going on; how they find out is up to him. If an attempt is made to shut people out completely, they will feel compelled to climb over the fences, follow trucks through the gates, or do some other equally human but hazardous thing. Verbal admonitions or warning signs seem to do little good, and positive action must be taken to protect the public against its own unthinking acts. The best scheme is for the contractor to allow the public to view the proceedings from controlled vantage points. The contractor who provides means for the public to see the work and simultaneously be protected from its hazards is using his head, from the standpoint of both safety and public relations.

The problem of protecting the public becomes even more difficult during weekends and at other times when job operations are not in progress. Children in particular seem to find construction projects irresistible, and insurance company records are filled with cases involving the deaths or injuries of youngsters caused by playing on projects during off-hours. On projects located in areas where children are likely to be playing, the job safety plan must make specific provision for this additional hazard. Watchmen or security fences with lockable gates may be required.

15.19 COST OF SAFETY PROGRAM

A company safety program does, of course, cost money. One contractor has estimated that his accident prevention efforts cost him an average of $20 per employee per year. Whether this figure is typical or not is difficult to say, but an important distinction between safety costs and other items of expense must be recognized. The distinction is that the spending of one dollar for safety can save the contractor two dollars in other costs. Although this ratio is only figurative, it has been well demonstrated that the costs of safety programs are more than compensated for by savings on accidents that do not happen. Accident reports make it evident that almost all accidents can be prevented with only moderate if any extra cost. The additional expense involved in building a proper scaffold, tying the top of a ladder, grounding an electric drill, or otherwise doing an assigned task in a safe and sane manner is insignificant compared to the costs of accident or injury. The contractor cannot look upon his safety program as an extra source of expense. Rather, because an effective accident prevention program is necessary to achieve fast-moving, smoothly functioning jobs, any costs entailed should be considered merely as normal operating expenses associated with efficient operation.

TYPICAL SPECIFICATION OUTLINE
FOR BUILDING CONSTRUCTION

INSTRUCTIONS TO BIDDERS
1. Contract documents
2. Proposal form
3. Proposal technicalities
4. Proposal guarantee
5. Acceptance
6. Interpretations
7. Postponement

Division 1. GENERAL CONDITIONS
1. Standard forms
2. Modifications to standard forms
   a. Drawings furnished
   b. Permits
   c. Insurance
   d. Bonds
   e. Building and window cleaning

Division 2. SPECIAL CONDITIONS
1. Scope of work and work not included in construction contract
2. Start and completion
3. Liquidated damages and bonus
4. Examination of site
5. Special site conditions
6. Laying out work
7. Temporary field office
8. Temporary heat
9. Temporary utilities
   a. Water
   b. Sewer
   c. Electrical
   d. Telephone
10. Temporary toilets
11. Watchman
12. Order of construction
13. Maintenance of services

14. Safety requirements
    a. Site protection
    b. Personal injury
15. Temporary enclosures
16. Storage of materials
17. Job signs
18. Progress payments
    a. Basis for payment
    b. Method of payment
    c. Payments for materials properly stored; insurance
19. Cash allowances
20. Predetermined wage schedule
21. Owner occupancy
22. Photographs
23. Guarantees

Division 3. ALTERNATE PROPOSALS

Division 4. DEMOLITION
1. General notes
2. Protection of adjoining property
3. Capping of utilities
4. Salvage material and ownership

Division 5. EXCAVATION AND SITE PREPARATION
1. General notes
2. Subsurface soil data
   a. Borings
   b. Water conditions
3. Clearing site
4. Protection of adjoining property
5. Drainage requirements
6. Stripping topsoil
7. Earth excavation
8. Rock excavation

9. Backfill and compaction
10. Filling and grading
11. Tile subsoil drains
12. Grading for driveways and walks
13. Temporary roads
14. Blasting
15. Shoring and protection
16. Dewatering

Division 6. PILES OR SPECIAL FOUNDATIONS
1. General notes
2. Caissons
3. Piles and test piles
4. Sheathing
5. Shoring
6. Underpinning
7. Cofferdams
8. Dredging

Division 7. CONCRETE
1. General notes
2. Materials, including lightweight concrete
3. Storage of materials
4. Types of forms and finishes
5. Forms, centering, and metal pans
6. Placing tile fillers
7. Inserts and fastening devices for other work
8. Strength, proportions, and mixes of concrete
9. Admixtures
10. Measuring and mixing concrete
11. Tests
12. Placing concrete
13. Construction and expansion joints
14. Removal of forms
15. Patching
16. Protection and curing
17. Floor slabs on earth
18. Cement floor finishes
19. Exposed concrete finishes
20. Concrete sills, lintels poured-in-place
21. Pre-cast structural members
22. Cant strips and crickets
23. Curbs, drives, and sidewalks
24. Hardeners
25. Anchor bolts
26. Manholes
27. Fireproofing
28. Smoke stacks

Division 8. REINFORCING STEEL
1. General notes
2. Material
3. Tests
4. Fabrication
5. Cleaning and storing
6. Supports
7. Steel mesh, metal lath, etc.
8. Placing
9. Shop drawings

Division 9. MASONRY
1. General notes
2. Masonry materials including glass block, terra cotta, gypsum block, and tile
3. Types of mortar
4. Mortar waterproofing
5. Precautions and protections
6. Pre-cast concrete, sills, coping, etc.
7. Laying masonry units
8. Joints and bonding
9. Expansion joints
10. Parging walls
11. Built-in work including anchors
12. Samples and sample wall panels
13. Pointing and caulking
14. Protection and cleaning
15. Manholes
16. Smoke stacks

Division 10. STONE WORK
1. General notes
2. Materials
3. Mortar
4. Cutting
5. Carving and models
6. Anchors, dowels, and cramps
7. Setting
8. Expansion joints
9. Pointing and caulking
10. Shop and setting drawings
11. Samples and sample wall panels
12. Protection and cleaning

Division 11. DAMP-PROOFING AND WATER-PROOFING
1. General notes
2. Materials including chemical, fabric, membrane, and metallic
3. Preparation of surfaces

4. Exterior damp-proofing
5. Interior damp-proofing

Division 12. STRUCTURAL STEEL AND STEEL JOISTS
1. General notes
2. Materials, tests, and inspection
3. Fabrication
4. Loose lintels
5. Erection of steel
6. Shop painting
7. Shop drawings

Division 13. SPECIAL FLOORS AND ROOF DECK
1. General notes
2. Materials
   a. Composition
   b. Concrete
   c. Gypsum
   d. Metal
3. Fabrication
4. Installation
5. Shop painting
6. Shop drawings

Division 14. MISCELLANEOUS METAL CON-STRUCTION
1. General notes
2. Materials
3. Special walls and sidings
4. Metal buildings
5. Light steel sections
6. Custom fabricated items
7. Fabrication
8. Erection
9. Shop painting
10. Shop drawings

Division 15. ORNAMENTAL METALS
1. General notes
2. Materials
   a. Aluminum
   b. Brass
   c. Bronze
   d. Cast iron
   e. Copper
   f. Wrought iron
   g. Lead
   h. Mild steel
   i. Stainless steel
3. Fabrication

4. Finishing
5. Shop painting
6. Erection
7. Samples
8. Shop drawings

Division 16. METAL SPECIALTIES
1. General notes
2. Lockers
3. Mail chutes
4. Metal base and trim
5. Metal fencing
6. Metal louvers
7. Metal shelving
8. Prefabricated chutes
9. Toilet partitions
10. Vault doors
11. Access doors
12. Shop painting
13. Shop drawings

Division 17. METAL DOORS AND TRIM
1. General notes
2. Materials
3. Doors
4. Frames and trim
5. Finishes
6. Hardware
7. Fabrication
8. Installation
9. Underwriter's labels
10. Shop painting
11. Shop drawings

Division 18. METAL SASH AND TRIM
1. General notes
2. Materials
3. Types
4. Hardware
5. Screens
6. Operators
7. Fabrication
8. Installation
9. Underwriter's requirements
10. Shop painting
11. Shop drawings

Division 19. PREFABRICATED WALL PANELS
1. General notes
   a. Window walls
   b. Movable partitions
2. Materials

3. Fabrication
4. Shop finish
5. Design standards
6. Erection
7. Work included in other contracts or branches of general contract
   a. Steel framing
   b. Field painting
8. Shop drawings
9. Cleaning

Division 20. SHEET METAL
1. General notes
2. Materials
3. Building expansion joints
4. Chutes
5. Copings
6. Cornices
7. Flashings
8. Grilles
9. Gutters and down spouts
10. Others
11. Hoods
12. Louvers
13. Skylights
14. Ventilators, gravity only
15. Fabrication
16. Installation
17. Shop drawings

Division 21. ROOFING AND ROOF INSULATION
1. General notes
2. Materials
3. Insulation
4. Built-up roofing
5. Composition, slate, tile, metal
6. Shingles
7. Application
8. Flashings, fabric
9. Bond or guarantee

Division 22. CARPENTRY
1. General notes
2. Materials
3. Storage and protection
4. Rough hardware
5. Framing
6. Prefabricated wood trusses, laminated members, etc.
7. Wood grounds, bucks, furring, and sleepers
8. Sheathing

9. Subflooring
10. Stock wood siding
11. Wood stairs, framing
12. Preservative treatment
13. Back priming

Division 23. MILLWORK
1. General notes
2. Materials
3. Storage and protection
4. Preservative and pressure treatment
5. Special wood siding
6. Window frames
7. Wood sash and screens
8. Special hardware
9. Wood door frames
10. Wood doors
11. Wood louvers
12. Wood stairs
13. Wood handrails
14. Wood seats
15. Wood shelving
16. Cabinets and counters
17. Wood paneling
18. Hook strips
19. Miscellaneous items
20. Shop drawings
21. Back priming

Division 24. CAULKING AND WEATHERSTRIPPING
1. General notes
2. Materials
3. Application
4. Metal thresholds

Division 25. FURRING, LATHING, PLASTER, AND STUCCO
1. General notes
2. Materials
3. Lath and lathing
4. Base screeds, corner beads, etc.
5. Application and finishes
6. Specialties
7. Samples
8. Cleaning
9. Guarantee
10. Patching

Division 26. MARBLE, CERAMIC AND QUARRY TILE
1. General notes
2. Materials

3. Accessories
4. Laying out work
5. Installation
6. Miscellaneous items
7. Samples
8. Shop drawings
9. Cleaning

Division 27. TERRAZZO AND MOSAIC
1. General notes
2. Materials
3. Terrazzo composition and colors
4. Non-slip floors
5. Conductive floors
6. Dividers
7. Installation
8. Cleaning and sealing

Division 28. SPECIAL FINISHES FOR WALLS
AND COUNTER TOPS
1. General notes
2. Materials
   a. Linoleum
   b. Metal tile
   c. Plastic tile
   d. Vinyl coverings
   e. Formica
3. Accessories and mouldings
4. Dry wall
5. Samples
6. Cleaning

Division 29. RESILIENT FLOOR COVERING
1. General notes
2. Materials
3. Preparation of subsurface
4. Installation
5. Samples
6. Cleaning and finishing

Division 30. WOOD FLOORING
1. General notes
2. Materials
3. Installation
4. Finish

Division 31. GLASS AND GLAZING
1. General notes
2. Materials
3. Installation
4. Mirrors
5. Specialties
6. Store front construction

Division 32. ACOUSTICAL TREATMENT
1. General notes
2. Materials
3. Installation methods
   a. Cement
   b. Metal suspension
   c. Nail or screw attachments
4. Application of sprayed treatment

Division 33. FINISH HARDWARE
1. General notes
2. Allowance or schedule
3. Keying instructions
4. Key cabinets
5. Templates
6. Packing and marking
7. Cabinet hardware
8. Installation
9. Name plates and signs
10. Hardware items not included herein

Division 34. PAINTING AND DECORATING
1. General notes
2. Work included
   a. General painting
   b. Decorating
   c. Mechanical
   d. Electrical
   e. Other
3. Materials
4. Mixing and storage
5. Colors and samples
6. Preparation of surfaces
7. Priming and back painting
8. Schedule of painting
9. Application
10. Protection
11. Tests
12. Cleaning and touch-up

Division 35. MISCELLANEOUS EQUIPMENT
1. Blackboards
2. Blinds
3. Book stacks
4. Bulletin boards
5. Cabinets
6. Church furniture
7. Drapes
8. Floor mats
9. Folding doors
10. Fire extinguishers
11. Incinerator

12. Kitchen equipment
13. Laboratory equipment
14. Laundry equipment
15. Library furniture
16. Lightproof shades
17. Refrigeration (packaged units)
18. Seating
19. Sterilizers
20. Gymnasium equipment
21. X-ray equipment
22. Window shades
23. Pneumatic tubes
24. Auditorium and stage equipment

Division 36. OWNER FURNISHED EQUIPMENT
1. General notes
2. Schedule of items
3. Installation

Division 37. TOILET ACCESSORIES
1. General notes
2. Schedule of items
   a. Medicine cabinets
   b. Soap holders and/or dispensers
   c. Towel bars
   d. Robe hooks
   e. Toilet paper holders
   f. Others
3. Installation

Division 38. SITE IMPROVEMENTS
1. General notes
2. Permanent roads and parking areas
   a. Compaction and fine grading
   b. Paving
   c. Tests
3. Landscaping
   a. Soil preparation
   b. Planting
   c. Seeding and/or sodding

Division 39. INSULATION
1. General notes
2. Materials
3. Installation
4. Samples

Division 40. VERTICAL TRANSPORTATION
1. General notes
2. Physical and operational requirements
   a. Passenger elevators

b. Moving stairs
c. Freight elevators
d. Dumb waiters
3. Installation
4. Tests
5. Special guarantees

Division 41. MECHANICAL REQUIREMENTS
1. Scope of work
   a. Plumbing
   b. Heating
   c. Temperature control
   d. Ventilation
   e. Refrigeration
   f. Insulation
   g. Fire protection
2. Drawings
3. Field measurements
4. Salvageable materials and ownership
5. Codes and permits
6. Electrical services
   a. Motor sizes and types, voltage
   b. Motor controls
7. Altitude ratings
8. Protection of materials and equipment
9. Quality of materials and equipment
10. Excavating and backfilling
11. Cutting and repairing
12. Access panels and doors
13. Foundations
14. Shop drawings and submittals
15. Piping installation
16. Labeling of piping
17. Supports and hangers
18. Pipe sleeves
19. Floor, wall, and ceiling plates
20. Flashings
21. Operating and maintenance instructions
22. Owner furnished equipment
23. Lubrication
24. Drives and belt guards
25. Flushing and draining
26. Guarantee

Division 42. PLUMBING
1. General notes
   a. Temporary utilities
   b. Work included
      (1) Cold water
      (2) Hot water
      (3) Gas

(4) Air
(5) Fuel oil
(6) Oxygen
(7) Suction
(8) Acid and chemical
(9) Protective coatings
(10) Sanitary sewer
(11) Storm sewer
(12) Special systems
(13) Alterations and removal work
(14) Connections to equipment furnished by others
  c. Work by others
    (1) Electrical work
    (2) Concrete and masonry work
    (3) Painting
    (4) Insulation
2. Material schedules
3. Utilities
  a. Water service
  b. Gas service
  c. Sewer service
4. Sanitary system
5. Storm water system
6. Special waste systems
7. Water system
8. Special supply systems
9. Equipment and installation
10. Fixtures
11. Tests and approvals
12. Cleaning and lubricating

Division 43. HEATING AND/OR AIR CON-
DITIONING
1. General notes
  a. Temporary heat
  b. Work included
    (1) Steam heat
    (2) Hot water heat
    (3) Process steam
    (4) Alterations and removal work
    (5) Connections to equipment furnished by others
  c. Work by others
    (1) Electrical work
    (2) Plumbing work
    (3) Temperature control work
    (4) Concrete and masonry work
    (5) Ventilation work
    (6) Painting
    (7) Insulation

2. Material schedules
3. Heating system and/or air conditioning
4. Equipment and installation
5. Installation of piping systems
  a. Steam and return piping
  b. Hot water piping
  c. Chilled water piping
  d. Condenser water piping
  e. Drains and overflows
  f. Joints
  g. Welding
  h. Valves
  i. Traps
  j. Expansion joints
  k. Thermometers and gages
6. Tests and approvals
7. Cleaning and lubricating

Division 44. TEMPERATURE CONTROL
1. General notes
  a. Work included
    (1) Pneumatic control
    (2) Electric control
    (3) Electronic control
    (4) Alterations and removal work
    (5) Connections to equipment furnished by others
  b. Work by others
    (1) Electrical work
    (2) Heating work
    (3) Painting
2. Material and equipment
3. Temperature control sequence
4. Air piping
5. Equipment and installation
6. Tests and approvals
7. Cleaning and lubricating

Division 45. VENTILATION (AND AIR CON-
DITIONING)
1. General notes
  a. Work included
    (1) Ventilation units
    (2) Evaporative coolers
    (3) Warm air furnaces
    (4) Warm air heating units
    (5) Coils
    (6) Duct work
    (7) Duct interior insulation
    (8) Roof ventilators
    (9) Alterations and removal work

(10) Connections to equipment furnished by others

b. Work by others
   (1) Electrical work
   (2) Piping work
   (3) Temperature control work
   (4) Refrigeration work
   (5) Concrete and masonry work
   (6) Insulation
2. Material schedules
3. Sheet metal gages
4. Flexible connections
5. Hangers and supports
6. Ventilation system
7. Equipment and installation
8. Tests and approvals
9. Cleaning and lubricating

Division 46. REFRIGERATION
1. General notes
  a. Work included
    (1) Package units
    (2) Central system
    (3) Cooling towers
    (4) Alteration and removal work
    (5) Connections to equipment furnished by others
  b. Work by others
    (1) Electrical work
    (2) Temperature control work
    (3) Plumbing work
    (4) Ventilation and sheet metal work
    (5) Concrete and masonry work
    (6) Painting
    (7) Insulation
2. Material schedules
3. Refrigeration system
4. Equipment and installation
5. Refrigeration piping
6. Tests and approvals
7. Cleaning and lubricating
8. Refrigerant and lubricating oil
9. Evacuation and charging
10. Control sequence

Division 47. THERMAL INSULATION
1. General notes
  a. Work included
    (1) Pipe
    (2) Ducts
    (3) Equipment
  b. Work excluded

    (1) Painting
2. Material schedules
3. Equipment and installation

Division 48. FIRE PROTECTION
1. General notes
  a Work included
    (1) Sprinkler systems
    (2) CO_2 systems
    (3) Stand pipe
    (4) Hose racks and cabinets
    (5) Fire extinguishers in hose cabinets
    (6) Alteration and removal work
    (7) Connections to equipment furnished by others
  b. Work by others
    (1) Electrical work
    (2) Concrete and masonry work
    (3) Painting
2. Material schedules
3. Fire protection system
4. Equipment and installation
  a. Alarm devices
  b. Sprinkler heads
  c. Fire extinguishers in hose cabinets
  d. Cabinets and hose racks
  e. Piping
5. Tests and approvals
6. Cleaning and lubricating

Division 49. ELECTRICAL REQUIREMENTS
1. Scope
  a. Temporary services
  b. Work included
    (1) Lighting
    (2) Power
    (3) Clocks
    (4) Radio system
    (5) Television system
    (6) Telephones
    (7) Intercom and public address system
    (8) Fire alarm system
    (9) Alterations and removal work
    (10) Connections to equipment furnished by others
  c. Work by others
2. Cash allowances for fixtures, etc.
3. Drawings, plans
4. Salvage materials and ownership
5. Codes and permits

6. Service entrance
7. Grounding
8. Substations, power centers, transformers
9. Switches and switch boards
10. Panels
11. Feeders
    a. Conduit
    b. Wire and cable
    c. Bus feeders
    d. Underground and underfloor distribution
12. Branch circuits
    a. Method of wiring
    b. Lighting circuits
    c. Motor circuits
13. Low voltage lighting circuits and equipment
14. Outlet and junction boxes
    a. Locations
    b. Support of boxes
15. Wall switches
16. Receptacles
17. Device plates
18. Emergency lighting systems
19. Signal, communication, and special systems
    a. Clock
    b. Radio
    c. Television
    d. Telephone
    e. Intercom and public address
    f. Fire alarm
    g. Other special systems
20. Lighting fixtures
    a. Types
    b. Supports
    c. Special lighting
21. Motors and motor controls
22. Temperature control wiring
23. Electrical heating systems
24. Cutting, patching
25. Excavation and backfilling
26. Performance tests
27. Guarantee

TYPICAL SPECIFICATION OUTLINE
FOR ENGINEERING CONSTRUCTION

GENERAL PROVISIONS
 1. Definitions and terms
 2. Proposal requirements and conditions
 3. Award and execution of contract
 4. Scope of work
 5. Control of the work
 6. Control of material
 7. Legal relations and responsibility
 8. Prosecution and progress
 9. Measurement and payment

Division 1. OBSTRUCTIONS

Division 2. CLEARING AND GRUBBING

Division 3. EARTHWORK
 1. General
 2. Roadway excavation
 3. Excavation for structures
 4. Ditch and channel excavation
 5. Embankment
 6. Selected rock slope protection
 7. Shoulders
 8. Surplus and borrow excavation
 9. Overhaul

Division 4. EROSION CONTROL AND PREPARATORY LANDSCAPING

Division 5. SUBGRADE
 1. General requirements
 2. Class "A" subgrade
 3. Class "B" subgrade
 4. Class "C" subgrade
 5. Class "D" subgrade
 6. Class "E" subgrade
 7. Class "F" subgrade

Division 6. WATERING

Division 7. FINISH ROADWAY

Division 8. CEMENT-TREATED SUBGRADE

Division 9. ROAD-MIXED CEMENT TREATED BASE

Division 10. PLANT-MIXED CEMENT TREATED BASE

Division 11. UNTREATED ROCK SURFACING

Division 12. CRUSHER RUN BASE

Division 13. PENETRATION TREATMENT

Division 14. SEAL COATS

Division 15. BITUMINOUS SURFACE TREATMENT

Division 16. ARMOR COAT

Division 17. NON-SKID SURFACE TREATMENT

Division 18. ROAD-MIXED SURFACING

Division 19. PLANT-MIXED SURFACING
 1. Description
 2. Materials
 3. Drying, proportioning, and mixing materials
 4. Subgrade
 5. Prime coat
 6. Spreading and compacting equipment
 7. Spreading and compacting mixture
 8. Miscellaneous details
 9. Payment

Division 20. SIDE FORMS

Division 21. BITUMINOUS MACADAM SURFACE

Division 22. ASPHALT CONCRETE PAVEMENT

Division 23. PORTLAND CEMENT CONCRETE PAVEMENT

Division 24. TIMBER STRUCTURES
 1. General requirements
 2. Structural timber
 3. Construction
 4. Payment

Division 25. CONCRETE STRUCTURES

Division 26. STEEL STRUCTURES
 1. General requirements
 2. Materials and testing
 3. Workmanship
 4. Payment

Division 27. PILING
1. General requirements
2. Timber piles
3. Precast concrete piles
4. Cast-in-place concrete piles
5. Steel piles
6. Payment

Division 28. TREATMENT OF TIMBER AND PILES

Division 29. WATERPROOFING

Division 30. PAINTING

Division 31. RUBBLE MASONRY

Division 32. RIPRAP

Division 33. CONCRETE SLOPE PAVING AND APRONS

Division 34. CONCRETE CURBS AND GUTTERS

Division 35. PORTLAND CEMENT CONCRETE SIDEWALKS

Division 36. RIGHT OF WAY MONUMENTS AND FREEWAY ACCESS OPENING MARKERS

Division 37. CONCRETE BARRIER POSTS

Division 38. GUARD RAILING
1. New construction
2. Salvaging and reconstructing guard railing

Division 39. PIPE HANDRAIL

Division 40. CULVERT MARKERS, CLEARANCE MARKERS, AND GUIDEPOSTS
1. New installation
2. Salvaging and resetting

Division 41. FENCES
1. New construction
2. Salvaging and reconstruction

Division 42. REINFORCED CONCRETE PIPE CULVERTS AND SIPHONS
1. General requirements

2. Manufacture
3. Installation
4. Headwalls
5. Payment

Division 43. CORRUGATED METAL PIPE CULVERTS AND SIPHONS

Division 44. FIELD-ASSEMBLED PLATE CULVERTS

Division 45. NON-REINFORCED CONCRETE PIPE LINES
1. General requirements
2. Installation
3. Headwalls
4. Payment

Division 46. SEWER PIPE LINES

Division 47. UNDERDRAINS

Division 48. SPILLWAY ASSEMBLIES AND DOWN DRAINS

Division 49. SALVAGING AND RELAYING EXISTING DRAINAGE FACILITIES

Division 50. REINFORCEMENT

Division 51. PORTLAND CEMENT CONCRETE

Division 52. ASPHALTIC PAINT BINDER

Division 53. PAINT
1. Materials
2. Standard paint for steel work
3. Standard paint for reinforcing bars, drift bolts, and iron hand rails
4. Standard paint for timber
5. Black paint for culvert markers
6. Wood preservative
7. Reflective paints

Division 54. ASPHALTS

Division 55. LIQUID ASPHALTS

Division 56. ASPHALTIC EMULSIONS

Division 57. EXPANSION JOINT FILLER

APPENDIX B

INSTRUCTIONS TO BIDDERS

1. CONTRACT DOCUMENTS. The Notice to Bidders, the Instructions to Bidders, the General Conditions, the Special Conditions, the Drawings and Specifications, the Contractor's Proposal Form, and the Agreement as finally negotiated compose the Contract Documents.

Copies of these documents can be obtained from the office of Jones and Smith, Architect-Engineers, 142 Welsh St., Portland, Ohio, upon deposit of $100.00 for each set thereof, said deposit being refundable upon return of the documents in good order within 10 days after the bidding date.

2. PRINTED FORM FOR PROPOSAL. All proposals must be made upon the Contractor's Proposal Form attached hereto and should give the amounts bid for the work, both in words and in figures, and must be signed and acknowledged by the Contractor. In order to insure consideration, the Proposal should be enclosed in a sealed envelope marked "Proposal for Municipal Airport Terminal Building to be opened at 2:30 P.M., (E.S.T.) May 19, 19—," showing the return address of the sender and addressed to John Doe, City Manager, Portland, Ohio.

If the proposal is made by a partnership, it shall contain the names of each partner and shall be signed in the firm name, followed by the signature of the person authorized to sign. If the proposal is made by a corporation, it shall be signed by the name of the corporation, followed by the written signature of the officer signing, and the printed or typewritten designation of the office he holds in the corporation, together with the corporation seal. All blank spaces in the proposal form shall be properly filled in.

3. ALTERNATES. Each bidder shall submit with his proposal, on forms provided, alternate proposals stating the differences in price (additions or deductions) from the base bid for substituting, omitting, or changing the materials or construction from that shown on the drawings and as specified in a manner as described in the Division "Alternate Proposals" of these specifications.

The difference in price shall include all omissions, additions, and adjustments of all trades as may be necessary because of each change, substitution, or omission as described.

4. PAYMENT OF EMPLOYEES. For work done in the State of Ohio the payment for employees of the Contractor and any and all subcontractors shall comply with the current

minimum wage scale as published by the Labor Commission of the State of Ohio, a copy of which is appended to the Special Conditions.

The Contractor and each of his subcontractors shall pay each of their employees engaged in work on the project under this contract in full, less deductions made mandatory by law, and not less often than once each week. All forms required by local authorities, the State of Ohio, and the United States Government, shall be properly submitted.

5. TELEGRAPHIC MODIFICATION. Any bidder may modify his bid by telegraphic communication at any time prior to the scheduled closing time for receipt of bids provided such telegraphic communication is received by the City Manager prior to said closing time, and provided further, that the City Manager is satisfied that a written confirmation of such telegraphic modification over the signature of the bidder was mailed prior to said closing time. If such written confirmation is not received within two (2) days from said closing time, no consideration will be given to the said telegraphic modification.

6. DELIVERY OF PROPOSALS. It is the bidder's responsibility to deliver his proposal at the proper time to the proper place. The mere fact that a proposal was dispatched will not be considered. The bidder must have the proposal actually delivered. Any proposal received after the scheduled closing time will be returned unopened to the bidder.

7. OPENING OF PROPOSALS. At 2:30 P.M. (E.S.T.), May 19, 19____, in the Office of the City Manager, City Hall, Portland, Ohio, each and every proposal (except those which have been withdrawn in accordance with Item 10, "Withdrawal of Proposals," of this Section) received prior to the scheduled closing time for receipt of proposals, will be publicly opened and read aloud, irrespective of any irregularities or informalities in such proposals.

8. ALTERATIONS IN PROPOSAL. Except as otherwise provided herein, proposals which are incomplete or which are conditioned in any way or which contain erasures not authenticated as provided herein or items not called for in the proposal or which may have been altered or are not in conformity with the law, may be rejected as informal.

The proposal form invites bids on definite plans and specifications. Only the amounts and information asked on the proposal form furnished will be considered as the bid. Each bidder shall bid upon the work exactly as specified and as provided in the proposal.

9. ERASURES. The proposal submitted must not contain erasures, interlineations, or other corrections unless each such correction is suitably authenticated by affixing in the margin immediately opposite the correction the surname or surnames of the person or persons signing the bid.

10. WITHDRAWAL OF PROPOSALS. At any time prior to the scheduled closing time for receipt of proposals, any bidder may withdraw his proposal, either personally or by telegraphic or written request. If withdrawal is made personally, proper receipt shall be given therefor.

After the scheduled closing time for the receipt of proposals and before award of contract, no bidder will be permitted to withdraw his proposal unless said award is delayed for a period exceeding thirty (30) days. Negligence on the part of the bidder in preparing his bid confers no rights for the withdrawal of the proposal after it has been opened.

11. DETERMINATION OF LOW BID. In making award of contract, the owner reserves the right to take into consideration the plant facilities of the bidders and the bidder's ability to complete the contract within the time specified in the proposal. The owner also reserves the right to evaluate factors that in his opinion would affect the final total cost.

12. REJECTION OF PROPOSALS. The owner reserves the right to reject any or all proposals. Without limiting the generality of the foregoing, any proposal which is incomplete, obscure, or irregular may be rejected; any proposal which omits a bid of any one or more items in the price sheet may be rejected; any proposal in which unit prices are omitted or in which unit prices are obviously unbalanced may be rejected; any proposal accompanied by an insufficient or irregular certified check, cashier's check, or bid bond may be rejected.

13. PROPOSAL AND PERFORMANCE GUARANTEES. A certified check, cashier's check, or bid bond for an amount equal to at least five per cent (5%) of the total amount bid, shall accompany each proposal as evidence of good faith and as a guarantee that if awarded the Contract, the bidder will execute the Contract and give bond as required. The successful bidder's check or bid bond will be retained until he has entered into a satisfactory contract and furnished required contract bonds. The owner reserves the right to hold the certified checks, cashier's checks, or bid bonds of the three lowest bidders until the successful bidder has entered into a contract and furnished the required contract bonds.

14. ACCEPTANCE OF PROPOSALS. Within thirty (30) days after receipt of the proposals the owner will act upon them. The acceptance of a proposal will be a Notice of Acceptance in writing signed by a duly authorized representative of the owner and no other act of the owner shall constitute the acceptance of a proposal. The acceptance of a proposal shall bind the successful bidder to execute the Contract. The rights and obligations provided for in the Contract shall become effective and binding upon the parties only upon its formal execution.

15. TIME FOR EXECUTING CONTRACT AND PROVIDING CONTRACT BOND. Any contractor whose proposal shall be accepted will be required to execute the Contract and furnish contract bonds as required within ten (10) days after notice that the Contract has been awarded to him. Failure or neglect to do so shall constitute a breach of the agreement effected by the acceptance of the proposal.

16. PRICES. In the event of a discrepancy between the prices quoted in words and those quoted in figures in the proposal, the words shall control. The prices are to include the furnishing of all materials, plant, equipment, tools, and all other facilities, and the performance of all labor and services necessary or proper for the completion of the work except as may be otherwise expressly provided in the Contract Documents.

17. EXAMINATION OF DRAWINGS. Bidders shall thoroughly examine and be familiar with the drawings and specifications. The failure or omission of any bidder to receive or examine any form, instrument, addendum, or other document shall in no way relieve any bidder from any obligation with respect to his proposal or to the Contract. The submission of a bid shall be taken as prima facie evidence of compliance with this Section.

18. INTERPRETATIONS. No oral interpretations will be made to any bidder as to the meaning of the drawings and specifications or other contract documents. Every request for such an interpretation shall be made in writing and addressed and forwarded to the owner's authorized representative (Architect-Engineer) five (5) or more days before the date fixed for opening of proposals. Every interpretation made to a bidder will be in the form of an addendum to the Contract Documents which, if issued, will be sent as promptly as is practicable to all persons to whom the drawings and specifications have been issued. All such addenda shall become part of the Contract Documents.

19. POSTPONEMENT OF DATE FOR OPENING PROPOSALS. The owner reserves the right to postpone the date of presentation and opening of proposals and will give telegraphic notice of any such postponement to each interested party.

APPENDIX C

GENERAL CONDITIONS OF THE CONTRACT FOR CONSTRUCTION
THE AMERICAN INSTITUTE OF ARCHITECTS

AIA Document A201

General Conditions of the Contract for Construction

TABLE OF ARTICLES

AIA DOCUMENT A 201 • GENERAL CONDITIONS OF THE CONTRACT FOR CONSTRUCTION • ELEVENTH EDITION • AIA ®
SEPTEMBER 1967 © THE AMERICAN INSTITUTE OF ARCHITECTS, 1735 NEW YORK AVENUE, N.W., WASHINGTON, D.C. 20006

1

This document, copyrighted by The American Institute of Architects, is reproduced here with its permission.

INDEX

2   AIA DOCUMENT A 201 • GENERAL CONDITIONS OF THE CONTRACT FOR CONSTRUCTION • ELEVENTH EDITION • AIA ®
SEPTEMBER 1967 © THE AMERICAN INSTITUTE OF ARCHITECTS, 1735 NEW YORK AVENUE, N.W., WASHINGTON, D.C. 20006

AIA DOCUMENT A 201 • GENERAL CONDITIONS OF THE CONTRACT FOR CONSTRUCTION • ELEVENTH EDITION • AIA ®
SEPTEMBER 1967 © THE AMERICAN INSTITUTE OF ARCHITECTS, 1735 NEW YORK AVENUE, N.W., WASHINGTON, D.C. 20006

GENERAL CONDITIONS OF THE CONTRACT FOR CONSTRUCTION

ARTICLE 1

CONTRACT DOCUMENTS

1.1   DEFINITIONS

1.1.1 THE CONTRACT DOCUMENTS
The Contract Documents consist of the Agreement, the Conditions of the Contract (General, Supplementary and other Conditions), the Drawings, the Specifications, all Addenda issued prior to execution of the Agreement, and all Modifications thereto. A Modification is (1) a written amendment to the Contract signed by both parties, (2) a Change Order, (3) a written interpretation issued by the Architect pursuant to Subparagraph 1.2.5, or (4) a written order for a minor change in the Work issued by the Architect pursuant to Paragraph 12.3. A Modification may be made only after execution of the Contract.

1.1.2 THE CONTRACT
The Contract Documents form the Contract. The Contract represents the entire and integrated agreement between the parties hereto and supersedes all prior negotiations, representations, or agreements, either written or oral, including the bidding documents. The Contract may be amended or modified only by a Modification as defined in Subparagraph 1.1.1.

1.1.3 THE WORK
The term Work includes all labor necessary to produce the construction required by the Contract Documents, and all materials and equipment incorporated or to be incorporated in such construction.

1.1.4 THE PROJECT
The Project is the total construction designed by the Architect of which the Work performed under the Contract Documents may be the whole or a part.

1.2   EXECUTION, CORRELATION, INTENT AND
    INTERPRETATIONS

1.2.1 The Contract Documents shall be signed in not less than triplicate by the Owner and Contractor. If either the Owner or the Contractor or both do not sign the Conditions of the Contract, Drawings, Specifications, or any of the other Contract Documents, the Architect shall identify them.

1.2.2 By executing the Contract, the Contractor represents that he has visited the site, familiarized himself with the local conditions under which the Work is to be performed, and correlated his observations with the requirements of the Contract Documents.

1.2.3 The Contract Documents are complementary, and what is required by any one shall be as binding as if required by all. The intention of the Documents is to include all labor, materials, equipment and other items as provided in Subparagraph 4.4.1 necessary for the proper execution and completion of the Work. It is not intended that Work not covered under any heading, section, branch, class or trade of the Specifications shall be supplied unless it is required elsewhere in the Contract Documents or is reasonably inferable therefrom as being necessary to produce the intended results. Words which have well-known technical or trade meanings are used herein in accordance with such recognized meanings.

1.2.4 The organization of the Specifications into divisions, sections and articles, and the arrangement of Drawings shall not control the Contractor in dividing the Work among Subcontractors or in establishing the extent of Work to be performed by any trade.

1.2.5 Written interpretations necessary for the proper execution or progress of the Work, in the form of drawings or otherwise, will be issued with reasonable promptness by the Architect and in accordance with any schedule agreed upon. Such interpretations shall be consistent with and reasonably inferable from the Contract Documents, and may be effected by Field Order.

1.3   COPIES FURNISHED AND OWNERSHIP

1.3.1 Unless otherwise provided in the Contract Documents, the Contractor will be furnished, free of charge, all copies of Drawings and Specifications reasonably necessary for the execution of the Work.

1.3.2 All Drawings, Specifications and copies thereof furnished by the Architect are and shall remain his property. They are not to be used on any other project, and, with the exception of one contract set for each party to the Contract, are to be returned to the Architect on request at the completion of the Work.

ARTICLE 2

ARCHITECT

2.1   DEFINITION

2.1.1 The Architect is the person or organization identified as such in the Agreement and is referred to throughout the Contract Documents as if singular in number and masculine in gender. The term Architect means the Architect or his authorized representative.

2.1.2 Nothing contained in the Contract Documents shall create any contractual relationship between the Architect and the Contractor.

2.2   ADMINISTRATION OF THE CONTRACT

2.2.1 The Architect will provide general Administration of the Construction Contract, including performance of the functions hereinafter described.

2.2.2 The Architect will be the Owner's representative during construction and until final payment. The Architect will have authority to act on behalf of the Owner to the

AIA DOCUMENT A 201 • GENERAL CONDITIONS OF THE CONTRACT FOR CONSTRUCTION • ELEVENTH EDITION • AIA ®
SEPTEMBER 1967 © THE AMERICAN INSTITUTE OF ARCHITECTS, 1735 NEW YORK AVENUE, N.W., WASHINGTON, D.C. 20006

extent provided in the Contract Documents, unless otherwise modified by written instrument which will be shown to the Contractor. The Architect will advise and consult with the Owner, and all of the Owner's instructions to the Contractor shall be issued through the Architect.

2.2.3 The Architect shall at all times have access to the Work wherever it is in preparation and progress. The Contractor shall provide facilities for such access so the Architect may perform his functions under the Contract Documents.

2.2.4 The Architect will make periodic visits to the site to familiarize himself generally with the progress and quality of the Work and to determine in general if the Work is proceeding in accordance with the Contract Documents. On the basis of his on-site observations as an architect, he will keep the Owner informed of the progress of the Work, and will endeavor to guard the Owner against defects and deficiencies in the Work of the Contractor. The Architect will not be required to make exhaustive or continuous on-site inspections to check the quality or quantity of the Work. The Architect will not be responsible for construction means, methods, techniques, sequences or procedures, or for safety precautions and programs in connection with the Work, and he will not be responsible for the Contractor's failure to carry out the Work in accordance with the Contract Documents.

2.2.5 Based on such observations and the Contractor's Applications for Payment, the Architect will determine the amounts owing to the Contractor and will issue Certificates for Payment in such amounts, as provided in Paragraph 9.4.

2.2.6 The Architect will be, in the first instance, the interpreter of the requirements of the Contract Documents and the judge of the performance thereunder by both the Owner and Contractor. The Architect will, within a reasonable time, render such interpretations as he may deem necessary for the proper execution or progress of the Work.

2.2.7 Claims, disputes and other matters in question between the Contractor and the Owner relating to the execution or progress of the Work or the interpretation of the Contract Documents shall be referred initially to the Architect for decision which he will render in writing within a reasonable time.

2.2.8 All interpretations and decisions of the Architect shall be consistent with the intent of the Contract Documents. In his capacity as interpreter and judge, he will exercise his best efforts to insure faithful performance by both the Owner and the Contractor and will not show partiality to either.

2.2.9 The Architect's decisions in matters relating to artistic effect will be final if consistent with the intent of the Contract Documents.

2.2.10 Any claim, dispute or other matter that has been referred to the Architect, except those relating to artistic effect as provided in Subparagraph 2.2.9 and except any which have been waived by the making or acceptance of final payment as provided in Subparagraphs 9.7.5 and 9.7.6, shall be subject to arbitration upon the written demand of either party. However, no demand for arbitra-

tion of any such claim, dispute or other matter may be made until the earlier of:

   .1 the date on which the Architect has rendered his decision, or

   .2 the tenth day after the parties have presented their evidence to the Architect or have been given a reasonable opportunity to do so, if the Architect has not rendered his written decision by that date.

2.2.11 If a decision of the Architect is made in writing and states that it is final but subject to appeal, no demand for arbitration of a claim, dispute or other matter covered by such decision may be made later than thirty days after the date on which the party making the demand received the decision. The failure to demand arbitration within said thirty days' period will result in the Architect's decision becoming final and binding upon the Owner and the Contractor. If the Architect renders a decision after arbitration proceedings have been initiated, such decision may be entered as evidence but will not supersede any arbitration proceedings except where the decision is acceptable to the parties concerned.

2.2.12 The Architect will have authority to reject Work which does not conform to the Contract Documents. Whenever, in his reasonable opinion, he considers it necessary or advisable to insure the proper implementation of the intent of the Contract Documents, he will have authority to require the Contractor to stop the Work or any portion thereof, or to require special inspection or testing of the Work as provided in Subparagraph 7.8.2 whether or not such Work be then fabricated, installed or completed. However, neither the Architect's authority to act under this Subparagraph 2.2.12, nor any decision made by him in good faith either to exercise or not to exercise such authority, shall give rise to any duty or responsibility of the Architect to the Contractor, any Subcontractor, any of their agents or employees, or any other person performing any of the Work.

2.2.13 The Architect will review Shop Drawings and Samples as provided in Subparagraphs 4.13.1 through 4.13.8 inclusive.

2.2.14 The Architect will prepare Change Orders in accordance with Article 12, and will have authority to order minor changes in the Work as provided in Subparagraph 12.3.1.

2.2.15 The Architect will conduct inspections to determine the dates of Substantial Completion and final completion, will receive written guarantees and related documents required by the Contract and assembled by the Contractor, and will issue a final Certificate for Payment.

2.2.16 If the Owner and Architect agree, the Architect will provide one or more full-time Project Representatives to assist the Architect in carrying out his responsibilities at the site. The duties, responsibilities and limitations of authority of any such Project Representative shall be as set forth in an exhibit to be incorporated in the Contract Documents.

2.2.17 The duties, responsibilities and limitations of authority of the Architect as the Owner's representative during construction as set forth in Articles 1 through 14 inclusive of these General Conditions will not be modified or extended without written consent of the Owner and the Architect which will be shown to the Contractor.

2.2.18 The Architect will not be responsible for the acts or omissions of the Contractor, any Subcontractors, or any of their agents or employees, or any other persons performing any of the Work.

2.2.19 In case of the termination of the employment of the Architect, the Owner shall appoint an architect against whom the Contractor makes no reasonable objection, whose status under the Contract Documents shall be that of the former architect. Any dispute in connection with such appointment shall be subject to arbitration.

ARTICLE 3

OWNER

3.1 DEFINITION

3.1.1 The Owner is the person or organization identified as such in the Agreement and is referred to throughout the Contract Documents as if singular in number and masculine in gender. The term Owner means the Owner or his authorized representative.

3.2 INFORMATION AND SERVICES REQUIRED OF THE OWNER

3.2.1 The Owner shall furnish all surveys describing the physical characteristics, legal limits and utility locations for the site of the Project.

3.2.2 The Owner shall secure and pay for easements for permanent structures or permanent changes in existing facilities.

3.2.3 Information or services under the Owner's control shall be furnished by the Owner with reasonable promptness to avoid delay in the orderly progress of the Work.

3.2.4 The Owner shall issue all instructions to the Contractor through the Architect.

3.2.5 The foregoing are in addition to other duties and responsibilities of the Owner enumerated herein and especially those in respect to Payment and Insurance in Articles 9 and 11 respectively.

ARTICLE 4

CONTRACTOR

4.1 DEFINITION

4.1.1 The Contractor is the person or organization identified as such in the Agreement and is referred to throughout the Contract Documents as if singular in number and masculine in gender. The term Contractor means the Contractor or his authorized representative.

4.2 REVIEW OF CONTRACT DOCUMENTS

4.2.1 The Contractor shall carefully study and compare the Agreement, Conditions of the Contract, Drawings, Specifications, Addenda and Modifications and shall at once report to the Architect any error, inconsistency or omission he may discover; but the Contractor shall not be liable to the Owner or the Architect for any damage resulting from any such errors, inconsistencies or omissions.

The Contractor shall do no Work without Drawings, Specifications or interpretations.

4.3 SUPERVISION AND CONSTRUCTION PROCEDURES

4.3.1 The Contractor shall supervise and direct the Work, using his best skill and attention. He shall be solely responsible for all construction means, methods, techniques, sequences and procedures and for coordinating all portions of the Work under the Contract.

4.4 LABOR AND MATERIALS

4.4.1 Unless otherwise specifically noted, the Contractor shall provide and pay for all labor, materials, equipment, tools, construction equipment and machinery, water, heat, utilities, transportation, and other facilities and services necessary for the proper execution and completion of the Work.

4.4.2 The Contractor shall at all times enforce strict discipline and good order among his employees and shall not employ on the Work any unfit person or anyone not skilled in the task assigned to him.

4.5 WARRANTY

4.5.1 The Contractor warrants to the Owner and the Architect that all materials and equipment furnished under this Contract will be new unless otherwise specified, and that all Work will be of good quality, free from faults and defects and in conformance with the Contract Documents. All Work not so conforming to these standards may be considered defective. If required by the Architect, the Contractor shall furnish satisfactory evidence as to the kind and quality of materials and equipment.

4.5.2 The warranty provided in this Paragraph 4.5 shall be in addition to and not in limitation of any other warranty or remedy required by law or by the Contract Documents.

4.6 TAXES

4.6.1 The Contractor shall pay all sales, consumer, use and other similar taxes required by law.

4.7 PERMITS, FEES AND NOTICES

4.7.1 The Contractor shall secure and pay for all permits, governmental fees and licenses necessary for the proper execution and completion of the Work.

4.7.2 The Contractor shall give all notices and comply with all laws, ordinances, rules, regulations and orders of any public authority bearing on the performance of the Work. If the Contractor observes that any of the Contract Documents are at variance therewith in any respect, he shall promptly notify the Architect in writing, and any necessary changes shall be adjusted by appropriate Modification. If the Contractor performs any Work knowing it to be contrary to such laws, ordinances, rules and regulations, and without such notice to the Architect, he shall assume full responsibility therefor and shall bear all costs attributable thereto.

4.8 CASH ALLOWANCES

4.8.1 The Contractor shall include in the Contract Sum all allowances stated in the Contract Documents. These

AIA DOCUMENT A 201 • GENERAL CONDITIONS OF THE CONTRACT FOR CONSTRUCTION • ELEVENTH EDITION • AIA ®
SEPTEMBER 1967 © THE AMERICAN INSTITUTE OF ARCHITECTS, 1735 NEW YORK AVENUE, N.W., WASHINGTON, D.C. 20006

allowances shall cover the net cost of the materials and equipment delivered and unloaded at the site, and all applicable taxes. The Contractor's handling costs on the site, labor, installation costs, overhead, profit and other expenses contemplated for the original allowance shall be included in the Contract Sum and not in the allowance. The Contractor shall cause the Work covered by these allowances to be performed for such amounts and by such persons as the Architect may direct, but he will not be required to employ persons against whom he makes a reasonable objection. If the cost, when determined, is more than or less than the allowance, the Contract Sum shall be adjusted accordingly by Change Order which will include additional handling costs on the site, labor, installation costs, overhead, profit and other expenses resulting to the Contractor from any increase over the original allowance.

4.9 SUPERINTENDENT

4.9.1 The Contractor shall employ a competent superintendent and necessary assistants who shall be in attendance at the Project site during the progress of the Work. The superintendent shall be satisfactory to the Architect, and shall not be changed except with the consent of the Architect, unless the superintendent proves to be unsatisfactory to the Contractor and ceases to be in his employ. The superintendent shall represent the Contractor and all communications given to the superintendent shall be as binding as if given to the Contractor. Important communications will be confirmed in writing. Other communications will be so confirmed on written request in each case.

4.10 RESPONSIBILITY FOR THOSE PERFORMING THE WORK

4.10.1 The Contractor shall be responsible to the Owner for the acts and omissions of all his employees and all Subcontractors, their agents and employees, and all other persons performing any of the Work under a contract with the Contractor.

4.11 PROGRESS SCHEDULE

4.11.1 The Contractor, immediately after being awarded the Contract, shall prepare and submit for the Architect's approval an estimated progress schedule for the Work. The progress schedule shall be related to the entire Project to the extent required by the Contract Documents. This schedule shall indicate the dates for the starting and completion of the various stages of construction and shall be revised as required by the conditions of the Work, subject to the Architect's approval.

4.12 DRAWINGS AND SPECIFICATIONS AT THE SITE

4.12.1 The Contractor shall maintain at the site for the Owner one copy of all Drawings, Specifications, Addenda, approved Shop Drawings, Change Orders and other Modifications, in good order and marked to record all changes made during construction. These shall be available to the Architect. The Drawings, marked to record all changes made during construction, shall be delivered to him for the Owner upon completion of the Work.

4.13 SHOP DRAWINGS AND SAMPLES

4.13.1 Shop Drawings are drawings, diagrams, illustra-
tions, schedules, performance charts, brochures and other data which are prepared by the Contractor or any Subcontractor, manufacturer, supplier or distributor, and which illustrate some portion of the Work.

4.13.2 Samples are physical examples furnished by the Contractor to illustrate materials, equipment or workmanship, and to establish standards by which the Work will be judged.

4.13.3 The Contractor shall review, stamp with his approval and submit, with reasonable promptness and in orderly sequence so as to cause no delay in the Work or in the work of any other contractor, all Shop Drawings and Samples required by the Contract Documents or subsequently by the Architect as covered by Modifications. Shop Drawings and Samples shall be properly identified as specified, or as the Architect may require. At the time of submission the Contractor shall inform the Architect in writing of any deviation in the Shop Drawings or Samples from the requirements of the Contract Documents.

4.13.4 By approving and submitting Shop Drawings and Samples, the Contractor thereby represents that he has determined and verified all field measurements, field construction criteria, materials, catalog numbers and similar data, or will do so, and that he has checked and coordinated each Shop Drawing and Sample with the requirements of the Work and of the Contract Documents.

4.13.5 The Architect will review and approve Shop Drawings and Samples with reasonable promptness so as to cause no delay, but only for conformance with the design concept of the Project and with the information given in the Contract Documents. The Architect's approval of a separate item shall not indicate approval of an assembly in which the item functions.

4.13.6 The Contractor shall make any corrections required by the Architect and shall resubmit the required number of corrected copies of Shop Drawings or new Samples until approved. The Contractor shall direct specific attention in writing or on resubmitted Shop Drawings to revisions other than the corrections requested by the Architect on previous submissions.

4.13.7 The Architect's approval of Shop Drawings or Samples shall not relieve the Contractor of responsibility for any deviation from the requirements of the Contract Documents unless the Contractor has informed the Architect in writing of such deviation at the time of submission and the Architect has given written approval to the specific deviation, nor shall the Architect's approval relieve the Contractor from responsibility for errors or omissions in the Shop Drawings or Samples.

4.13.8 No portion of the Work requiring a Shop Drawing or Sample submission shall be commenced until the submission has been approved by the Architect. All such portions of the Work shall be in accordance with approved Shop Drawings and Samples.

4.14 USE OF SITE

4.14.1 The Contractor shall confine operations at the site to areas permitted by law, ordinances, permits and the Contract Documents and shall not unreasonably encumber the site with any materials or equipment.

AIA DOCUMENT A 201 • GENERAL CONDITIONS OF THE CONTRACT FOR CONSTRUCTION • ELEVENTH EDITION • AIA ®
SEPTEMBER 1967 © THE AMERICAN INSTITUTE OF ARCHITECTS, 1735 NEW YORK AVENUE, N.W., WASHINGTON, D.C. 20006

4.15 CUTTING AND PATCHING OF WORK

4.15.1 The Contractor shall do all cutting, fitting or patching of his Work that may be required to make its several parts fit together properly, and shall not endanger any Work by cutting, excavating or otherwise altering the Work or any part of it.

4.16 CLEANING UP

4.16.1 The Contractor at all times shall keep the premises free from accumulation of waste materials or rubbish caused by his operations. At the completion of the Work he shall remove all his waste materials and rubbish from and about the Project as well as all his tools, construction equipment, machinery and surplus materials, and shall clean all glass surfaces and leave the Work "broom-clean" or its equivalent, except as otherwise specified.

4.16.2 If the Contractor fails to clean up, the Owner may do so and the cost thereof shall be charged to the Contractor as provided in Paragraph 7.6.

4.17 COMMUNICATIONS

4.17.1 The Contractor shall forward all communications to the Owner through the Architect.

4.18 INDEMNIFICATION

4.18.1 The Contractor shall indemnify and hold harmless the Owner and the Architect and their agents and employees from and against all claims, damages, losses and expenses including attorneys' fees arising out of or resulting from the performance of the Work, provided that any such claim, damage, loss or expense **(a)** is attributable to bodily injury, sickness, disease or death, or to injury to or destruction of tangible property (other than the Work itself) including the loss of use resulting therefrom, and **(b)** is caused in whole or in part by any negligent act or omission of the Contractor, any Subcontractor, anyone directly or indirectly employed by any of them or anyone for whose acts any of them may be liable, regardless of whether or not it is caused in part by a party indemnified hereunder.

4.18.2 In any and all claims against the Owner or the Architect or any of their agents or employees by any employee of the Contractor, any Subcontractor, anyone directly or indirectly employed by any of them or anyone for whose acts any of them may be liable, the indemnification obligation under this Paragraph 4.18 shall not be limited in any way by any limitation on the amount or type of damages, compensation or benefits payable by or for the Contractor or any Subcontractor under workmen's compensation acts, disability benefit acts or other employee benefit acts.

4.18.3 The obligations of the Contractor under this Paragraph 4.18 shall not extend to the liability of the Architect, his agents or employees arising out of (1) the preparation or approval of maps, drawings, opinions, reports, surveys, Change Orders, designs or specifications, or (2) the giving of or the failure to give directions or instructions by the Architect, his agents or employees provided such giving or failure to give is the primary cause of the injury or damage.

ARTICLE 5

SUBCONTRACTORS

5.1 DEFINITION

5.1.1 A Subcontractor is a person or organization who has a direct contract with the Contractor to perform any of the Work at the site. The term Subcontractor is referred to throughout the Contract Documents as if singular in number and masculine in gender and means a Subcontractor or his authorized representative.

5.1.2 A Sub-subcontractor is a person or organization who has a direct or indirect contract with a Subcontractor to perform any of the Work at the site. The term Sub-subcontractor is referred to throughout the Contract Documents as if singular in number and masculine in gender and means a Sub-subcontractor or an authorized representative thereof.

5.1.3 Nothing contained in the Contract Documents shall create any contractual relation between the Owner or the Architect and any Subcontractor or Sub-subcontractor.

5.2 AWARD OF SUBCONTRACTS AND OTHER CONTRACTS FOR PORTIONS OF THE WORK

5.2.1 As soon as practicable after bids are received and prior to the award of the Contract, the successful bidder shall furnish to the Architect in writing for acceptance by the Owner and the Architect a list of the names of the subcontractors or other persons or organizations (including those who are to furnish materials or equipment fabricated to a special design) proposed for such portions of the Work as may be designated in the bidding requirements, or, if none is so designated, the names of the Subcontractors proposed for the principal portions of the Work. Prior to the award of the Contract, the Architect shall notify the successful bidder in writing if either the Owner or the Architect, after due investigation, has reasonable objection to any person or organization on such list. Failure of the Owner or Architect to make an objection to any person or organization on the list prior to the award shall constitute acceptance of such person or organization.

5.2.2 If, prior to the award of the Contract, the Owner or Architect has a reasonable and substantial objection to any person or organization on such list, and refuses in writing to accept such person or organization, the successful bidder may, prior to the award, withdraw his bid without forfeiture of bid security. If the successful bidder submits an acceptable substitute with an increase in his bid price to cover the difference in cost occasioned by such substitution, the Owner may, at his discretion, accept the increased bid price or he may disqualify the bid. If, after the award, the Owner or Architect refuses to accept any person or organization on such list, the Contractor shall submit an acceptable substitute and the Contract Sum shall be increased or decreased by the difference in cost occasioned by such substitution and an appropriate Change Order shall be issued; however, no increase in the Contract Sum shall be allowed for any such substitution unless the Contractor has acted promptly and responsively in submitting a name with respect thereto prior to the award.

AIA DOCUMENT A 201 • GENERAL CONDITIONS OF THE CONTRACT FOR CONSTRUCTION • ELEVENTH EDITION • AIA ®
SEPTEMBER 1967 © THE AMERICAN INSTITUTE OF ARCHITECTS. 1735 NEW YORK AVENUE, N.W., WASHINGTON, D.C. 20006

5.2.3 The Contractor shall not contract with any Subcontractor or any person or organization proposed for portions of the Work designated in the bidding requirements or, if none is so designated, with any Subcontractor proposed for the principal portions of the Work who has not been accepted by the Owner and the Architect. The Contractor will not be required to contract with any subcontractor or person or organization against whom he has a reasonable objection.

5.2.4 If the Owner or the Architect requires a change of any proposed Subcontractor or person or organization previously accepted by them, the Contract Sum shall be increased or decreased by the difference in cost occasioned by such change and an appropriate Change Order shall be issued.

5.2.5 The Contractor shall not make any substitution for any Subcontractor or person or organization who has been accepted by the Owner and the Architect, unless the substitution is acceptable to the Owner and the Architect.

5.3   SUBCONTRACTUAL RELATIONS

5.3.1 All work performed for the Contractor by a Subcontractor shall be pursuant to an appropriate agreement between the Contractor and the Subcontractor (and where appropriate between Subcontractors and Subsubcontractors) which shall contain provisions that:

.1 preserve and protect the rights of the Owner and the Architect under the Contract with respect to the Work to be performed under the subcontract so that the subcontracting thereof will not prejudice such rights;

.2 require that such Work be performed in accordance with the requirements of the Contract Documents;

.3 require submission to the Contractor of applications for payment under each subcontract to which the Contractor is a party, in reasonable time to enable the Contractor to apply for payment in accordance with Article 9;

.4 require that all claims for additional costs, extensions of time, damages for delays or otherwise with respect to subcontracted portions of the Work shall be submitted to the Contractor (via any Subcontractor or Sub-subcontractor where appropriate) in the manner provided in the Contract Documents for like claims by the Contractor upon the Owner;

.5 waive all rights the contracting parties may have against one another for damages caused by fire or other perils covered by the property insurance described in Paragraph 11.3, except such rights as they may have to the proceeds of such insurance held by the Owner as trustee under Paragraph 11.3; and

.6 obligate each Subcontractor specifically to consent to the provisions of this Paragraph 5.3.

5.4   PAYMENTS TO SUBCONTRACTORS

5.4.1 The Contractor shall pay each Subcontractor, upon receipt of payment from the Owner, an amount equal to the percentage of completion allowed to the Contractor on account of such Subcontractor's Work. The Contractor shall also require each Subcontractor to make similar payments to his subcontractors.

5.4.2 If the Architect fails to issue a Certificate for Payment for any cause which is the fault of the Contractor and not the fault of a particular Subcontractor, the Contractor shall pay that Subcontractor on demand, made at any time after the Certificate for Payment should otherwise have been issued, for his Work to the extent completed, less the retained percentage.

5.4.3 The Contractor shall pay each Subcontractor a just share of any insurance moneys received by the Contractor under Article 11, and he shall require each Subcontractor to make similar payments to his subcontractors.

5.4.4 The Architect may, on request and at his discretion, furnish to any Subcontractor, if practicable, information regarding percentages of completion certified to the Contractor on account of Work done by such Subcontractors.

5.4.5 Neither the Owner nor the Architect shall have any obligation to pay or to see to the payment of any moneys to any Subcontractor except as may otherwise be required by law.

ARTICLE 6

SEPARATE CONTRACTS

6.1   OWNER'S RIGHT TO AWARD SEPARATE CONTRACTS

6.1.1 The Owner reserves the right to award other contracts in connection with other portions of the Project under these or similar Conditions of the Contract.

6.1.2 When separate contracts are awarded for different portions of the Project, "the Contractor" in the contract documents in each case shall be the contractor who signs each separate contract.

6.2   MUTUAL RESPONSIBILITY OF CONTRACTORS

6.2.1 The Contractor shall afford other contractors reasonable opportunity for the introduction and storage of their materials and equipment and the execution of their work, and shall properly connect and coordinate his Work with theirs.

6.2.2 If any part of the Contractor's Work depends for proper execution or results upon the work of any other separate contractor, the Contractor shall inspect and promptly report to the Architect any apparent discrepancies or defects in such work that render it unsuitable for such proper execution and results. Failure of the Contractor so to inspect and report shall constitute an acceptance of the other contractor's work as fit and proper to receive his Work, except as to defects which may develop in the other separate contractor's work after the execution of the Contractor's Work.

6.2.3 Should the Contractor cause damage to the work or property of any separate contractor on the Project, the Contractor shall, upon due notice, settle with such other contractor by agreement or arbitration, if he will so settle. If such separate contractor sues the Owner on account of any damage alleged to have been so sustained, the Owner shall notify the Contractor who shall defend such proceedings at the Owner's expense, and if any judgment against the Owner arises therefrom the Contractor shall pay or satisfy it and shall reimburse the Owner for all attorneys' fees and court costs which the Owner has incurred.

6.3 CUTTING AND PATCHING UNDER SEPARATE CONTRACTS

6.3.1 The Contractor shall do all cutting, fitting or patching of his Work that may be required to fit it to receive or be received by the work of other contractors shown in the Contract Documents. The Contractor shall not endanger any work of any other contractors by cutting, excavating or otherwise altering any work and shall not cut or alter the work of any other contractor except with the written consent of the Architect.

6.3.2 Any costs caused by defective or ill-timed work shall be borne by the party responsible therefor.

6.4 OWNER'S RIGHT TO CLEAN UP

6.4.1 If a dispute arises between the separate contractors as to their responsibility for cleaning up as required by Paragraph 4.16, the Owner may clean up and charge the cost thereof to the several contractors as the Architect shall determine to be just.

ARTICLE 7

MISCELLANEOUS PROVISIONS

7.1 LAW OF THE PLACE

7.1.1 The Contract shall be governed by the law of the place where the Project is located.

7.2 SUCCESSORS AND ASSIGNS

7.2.1 The Owner and the Contractor each binds himself, his partners, successors, assigns and legal representatives to the other party hereto and to the partners, successors, assigns and legal. representatives of such other party in respect to all covenants, agreements and obligations contained in the Contract Documents. Neither party to the Contract shall assign the Contract or sublet it as a whole without the written consent of the other, nor shall the Contractor assign any moneys due or to become due to him hereunder, without the previous written consent of the Owner.

7.3 WRITTEN NOTICE

7.3.1 Written notice shall be deemed to have been duly served if delivered in person to the individual or member of the firm or to an officer of the corporation for whom it was intended, or if delivered at or sent by registered or certified mail to the last business address known to him who gives the notice.

7.4 CLAIMS FOR DAMAGES

7.4.1 Should either party to the Contract suffer injury or damage to person or property because of any act or omission of the other party or of any of his employees, agents or others for whose acts he is legally liable, claim shall be made in writing to such other party within a reasonable time after the first observance of such injury or damage.

7.5 PERFORMANCE BOND AND LABOR AND MATERIAL PAYMENT BOND

7.5.1 The Owner shall have the right, prior to signing the Contract, to require the Contractor to furnish bonds covering the faithful performance of the Contract and the payment of all obligations arising thereunder in such form and amount as the Owner may prescribe and with such sureties as may be agreeable to the parties. If such bonds are stipulated in the bidding requirements, the premiums shall be paid by the Contractor; if required subsequent to the submission of quotations or bids, the cost shall be reimbursed by the Owner. The Contractor shall deliver the required bonds to the Owner not later than the date of execution of the Contract, or if the Work is commenced prior thereto in response to a notice to proceed, the Contractor shall, prior to commencement of the Work, submit evidence satisfactory to the Owner that such bonds will be issued.

7.6 OWNER'S RIGHT TO CARRY OUT THE WORK

7.6.1 If the Contractor defaults or neglects to carry out the Work in accordance with the Contract Documents or fails to perform any provision of the Contract, the Owner may, after seven days' written notice to the Contractor and without prejudice to any other remedy he may have, make good such deficiencies. In such case an appropriate Change Order shall be issued deducting from the payments then or thereafter due the Contractor the cost of correcting such deficiencies, including the cost of the Architect's additional services made necessary by such default, neglect or failure. The Architect must approve both such action and the amount charged to the Contractor. If the payments then or thereafter due the Contractor are not sufficient to cover such amount, the Contractor shall pay the difference to the Owner.

7.7 ROYALTIES AND PATENTS

7.7.1 The Contractor shall pay all royalties and license fees. He shall defend all suits or claims for infringement of any patent rights and shall save the Owner harmless from loss on account thereof, except that the Owner shall be responsible for all such loss when a particular design, process or the product of a particular manufacturer or manufacturers is specified, but if the Contractor has reason to believe that the design, process or product specified is an infringement of a patent, he shall be responsible for such loss unless he promptly gives such information to the Architect.

7.8 TESTS

7.8.1 If the Contract Documents, laws, ordinances, rules, regulations or orders of any public authority having jurisdiction require any Work to be inspected, tested or approved, the Contractor shall give the Architect timely notice of its readiness and of the date arranged so the Architect may observe such inspection, testing or approval. The Contractor shall bear all costs of such inspections, tests and approvals unless otherwise provided.

7.8.2 If after the commencement of the Work the Architect determines that any Work requires special inspection, testing or approval which Subparagraph 7.8.1 does not include, he will, upon written authorization from the Owner, instruct the Contractor to order such special inspection, testing or approval, and the Contractor shall give notice as in Subparagraph 7.8.1. If such special inspection or testing reveals a failure of the Work to comply (1) with the requirements of the Contract Documents or (2), with respect to the performance of the Work, with laws, ordinances, rules, regulations or orders of any public authority having jurisdiction, the Contractor shall bear all costs thereof, including the Architect's additional services made necessary by such failure; otherwise the Owner shall bear such costs, and an appropriate Change Order shall be issued.

7.8.3 Required certificates of inspection, testing or approval shall be secured by the Contractor and promptly delivered by him to the Architect.

7.8.4 If the Architect wishes to observe the inspections, tests or approvals required by this Paragraph 7.8, he will do so promptly and, where practicable, at the source of supply.

7.8.5 Neither the observations of the Architect in his administration of the Contract, nor inspections, tests or approvals by persons other than the Contractor shall relieve the Contractor from his obligations to perform the Work in accordance with the Contract Documents.

7.9 INTEREST

7.9.1 Any moneys not paid when due to either party under this Contract shall bear interest at the legal rate in force at the place of the Project.

7.10 ARBITRATION

7.10.1 All claims, disputes and other matters in question arising out of, or relating to, this Contract or the breach thereof, except as set forth in Subparagraph 2.2.9 with respect to the Architect's decisions on matters relating to artistic effect, and except for claims which have been waived by the making or acceptance of final payment as provided by Subparagraphs 9.7.5 and 9.7.6, shall be decided by arbitration in accordance with the Construction Industry Arbitration Rules of the American Arbitration Association then obtaining unless the parties mutually agree otherwise. This agreement so to arbitrate shall be specifically enforceable under the prevailing arbitration law. The award rendered by the arbitrators shall be final, and judgment may be entered upon it in accordance with applicable law in any court having jurisdiction thereof.

7.10.2 Notice of the demand for arbitration shall be filed in writing with the other party to the Contract and with the American Arbitration Association, and a copy shall be filed with the Architect. The demand for arbitration shall be made within the time limits specified in Subparagraphs 2.2.10 and 2.2.11 where applicable, and in all other cases within a reasonable time after the claim, dispute or other matter in question has arisen, and in no event shall it be made after institution of legal or equitable proceedings based on such claim, dispute or other matter in question would be barred by the applicable statute of limitations.

7.10.3 The Contractor shall carry on the Work and maintain the progress schedule during any arbitration proceedings, unless otherwise agreed by him and the Owner in writing.

ARTICLE 8

TIME

8.1 DEFINITIONS

8.1.1 The Contract Time is the period of time allotted in the Contract Documents for completion of the Work.

8.1.2 The date of commencement of the Work is the date established in a notice to proceed. If there is no notice to proceed, it shall be the date of the Agreement or such other date as may be established therein.

8.1.3 The Date of Substantial Completion of the Work or designated portion thereof is the Date certified by the Architect when construction is sufficiently complete, in accordance with the Contract Documents, so the Owner may occupy the Work or designated portion thereof for the use for which it is intended.

8.2 PROGRESS AND COMPLETION

8.2.1 All time limits stated in the Contract Documents are of the essence of the Contract.

8.2.2 The Contractor shall begin the Work on the date of commencement as defined in Subparagraph 8.1.2. He shall carry the Work forward expeditiously with adequate forces and shall complete it within the Contract Time.

8.3 DELAYS AND EXTENSIONS OF TIME

8.3.1 If the Contractor is delayed at any time in the progress of the Work by any act or neglect of the Owner or the Architect, or by any employee of either, or by any separate contractor employed by the Owner, or by changes ordered in the Work, or by labor disputes, fire, unusual delay in transportation, unavoidable casualties or any causes beyond the Contractor's control, or by delay authorized by the Owner pending arbitration, or by any cause which the Architect determines may justify the delay, then the Contract Time shall be extended by Change Order for such reasonable time as the Architect may determine.

8.3.2 All claims for extension of time shall be made in writing to the Architect no more than fifteen days after the occurrence of the delay; otherwise they shall be waived. In the case of a continuing cause of delay only one claim is necessary.

8.3.3 If no schedule or agreement is made stating the dates upon which written interpretations as set forth in Subparagraph 1.2.5 shall be furnished, then no claim for delay shall be allowed on account of failure to furnish such interpretations until fifteen days after demand is made for them, and not then unless such claim is reasonable.

8.3.4 This Paragraph 8.3 does not exclude the recovery of damages for delay by either party under other provisions of the Contract Documents.

ARTICLE 9

PAYMENTS AND COMPLETION

9.1 CONTRACT SUM

9.1.1 The Contract Sum is stated in the Agreement and is the total amount payable by the Owner to the Contractor for the performance of the Work under the Contract Documents.

9.2 SCHEDULE OF VALUES

9.2.1 Before the first Application for Payment, the Contractor shall submit to the Architect a schedule of values of the various portions of the Work, including quantities if required by the Architect, aggregating the total Contract Sum, divided so as to facilitate payments to Subcontractors in accordance with Paragraph 5.4, prepared in such form as specified or as the Architect and the Contractor may agree upon, and supported by such data to substantiate its correctness as the Architect may require. Each item in the schedule of values shall include its proper share of overhead and profit. This schedule, when approved by the Architect, shall be used only as a basis for the Contractor's Applications for Payment.

9.3 PROGRESS PAYMENTS

9.3.1 At least ten days before each progress payment falls due, the Contractor shall submit to the Architect an itemized Application for Payment, supported by such data substantiating the Contractor's right to payment as the Owner or the Architect may require.

9.3.2 If payments are to be made on account of materials or equipment not incorporated in the Work but delivered and suitably stored at the site, or at some other location agreed upon in writing, such payments shall be conditioned upon submission by the Contractor of bills of sale or such other procedures satisfactory to the Owner to establish the Owner's title to such materials or equipment or otherwise protect the Owner's interest including applicable insurance and transportation to the site.

9.3.3 The Contractor warrants and guarantees that title to all Work, materials and equipment covered by an Application for Payment, whether incorporated in the Project or not, will pass to the Owner upon the receipt of such payment by the Contractor, free and clear of all liens, claims, security interests or encumbrances, hereinafter referred to in this Article 9 as "liens"; and that no Work, materials or equipment covered by an Application for Payment will have been acquired by the Contractor,' or by any other person performing the Work at the site or furnishing materials and equipment for the Project, subject to an agreement under which an interest therein or an encumbrance thereon is retained by the seller or otherwise imposed by the Contractor or such other person.

9.4 CERTIFICATES FOR PAYMENT

9.4.1 If the Contractor has made Application for Payment as above, the Architect will, with reasonable promptness but not more than seven days after the receipt of the Application, issue a Certificate for Payment to the Owner, with a copy to the Contractor, for such amount as he determines to be properly due, or state in writing his reasons for withholding a Certificate as provided in Subparagraph 9.5.1.

9.4.2 The issuance of a Certificate for Payment will constitute a representation by the Architect to the Owner, based on his observations at the site as provided in Subparagraph 2.2.4 and the data comprising the Application for Payment, that the Work has progressed to the point indicated; that, to the best of his knowledge, information and belief, the quality of the Work is in accordance with the Contract Documents (subject to an evaluation of the Work as a functioning whole upon Substantial Completion, to the results of any subsequent tests required by the Contract Documents, to minor deviations from the Contract Documents correctable prior to completion, and to any specific qualifications stated in his Certificate); and that the Contractor is entitled to payment in the amount certified. In addition, the Architect's final Certificate for Payment will constitute a further representation that the conditions precedent to the Contractor's being entitled to final payment as set forth in Subparagraph 9.7.2 have been fulfilled. However, by issuing a Certificate for Payment, the Architect shall not thereby be deemed to represent that he has made exhaustive or continuous on-site inspections to check the quality or quantity of the Work or that he has reviewed the construction means, methods, techniques, sequences or procedures, or that he has made any examination to ascertain how or for what purpose the Contractor has used the moneys previously paid on account of the Contract Sum.

9.4.3 After the Architect has issued a Certificate for Payment, the Owner shall make payment in the manner provided in the Agreement.

9.4.4 No Certificate for a progress payment, nor any progress payment, nor any partial or entire use or occupancy of the Project by the Owner, shall constitute an acceptance of any Work not in accordance with the Contract Documents.

9.5 PAYMENTS WITHHELD

9.5.1 The Architect may decline to approve an Application for Payment and may withhold his Certificate in whole or in part if in his opinion he is unable to make representations to the Owner as provided in Subparagraph 9.4.2. The Architect may also decline to approve any Applications for Payment or, because of subsequently discovered evidence or subsequent inspections, he may nullify the whole or any part of any Certificate for Payment previously issued to such extent as may be necessary in his opinion to protect the Owner from loss because of:

.1 defective work not remedied,

.2 claims filed or reasonable evidence indicating probable filing of claims,

.3 failure of the Contractor to make payments properly to Subcontractors or for labor, materials or equipment,

.4 reasonable doubt that the Work can be completed for the unpaid balance of the Contract Sum,

.5 damage to another contractor,

.6 reasonable indication that the Work will not be completed within the Contract Time, or

.7 unsatisfactory prosecution of the Work by the Contractor.

9.5.2 When the above grounds in Subparagraph 9.5.1 are removed, payment shall be made for amounts withheld because of them.

9.6 FAILURE OF PAYMENT

9.6.1 If the Architect should fail to issue any Certificate for Payment, through no fault of the Contractor, within seven days after receipt of the Contractor's Application for Payment, or if the Owner should fail to pay the Contractor within seven days after the date of payment established in the Agreement any amount certified by the Architect or awarded by arbitration, then the Contractor may, upon seven additional days' written notice to the Owner and the Architect, stop the Work until payment of the amount owing has been received.

9.7 SUBSTANTIAL COMPLETION AND FINAL PAYMENT

9.7.1 When the Contractor determines that the Work or a designated portion thereof acceptable to the Owner is substantially complete, the Contractor shall prepare for submission to the Architect a list of items to be completed or corrected. The failure to include any items on such list does not alter the responsibility of the Contractor to complete all Work in accordance with the Contract Documents. When the Architect on the basis of an inspection determines that the Work is substantially complete, he will then prepare a Certificate of Substantial Completion which shall establish the Date of Substantial Completion, shall state the responsibilities of the Owner and the Contractor for maintenance, heat, utilities, and insurance, and shall fix the time within which the Contractor shall complete the items listed therein, said time to be within the Contract Time unless extended pursuant to Paragraph 8.3. The Certificate of Substantial Completion shall be submitted to the Owner and the Contractor for their written acceptance of the responsibilities assigned to them in such Certificate.

9.7.2 Upon receipt of written notice that the Work is ready for final inspection and acceptance and upon receipt of a final Application for Payment, the Architect will promptly make such inspection and, when he finds the Work acceptable under the Contract Documents and the Contract fully performed, he will promptly issue a final Certificate for Payment stating that to the best of his knowledge, information and belief, and on the basis of his observations and inspections, the Work has been completed in accordance with the terms and conditions of the Contract Documents and that the entire balance found to be due the Contractor, and noted in said final Certificate, is due and payable.

9.7.3 Neither the final payment nor the remaining retained percentage shall become due until the Contractor submits to the Architect (1) an Affidavit that all payrolls, bills for materials and equipment, and other indebtedness connected with the Work for which the Owner or his

property might in any way be responsible, have been paid or otherwise satisfied, (2) consent of surety, if any, to final payment and (3), if required by the Owner, other data establishing payment or satisfaction of all such obligations, such as receipts, releases and waivers of liens arising out of the Contract, to the extent and in such form as may be designated by the Owner. If any Subcontractor refuses to furnish a release or waiver required by the Owner, the Contractor may furnish a bond satisfactory to the Owner to indemnify him against any such lien. If any such lien remains unsatisfied after all payments are made, the Contractor shall refund to the Owner all moneys that the latter may be compelled to pay in discharging such lien, including all costs and reasonable attorneys' fees.

9.7.4 If after Substantial Completion of the Work final completion thereof is materially delayed through no fault of the Contractor, and the Architect so confirms, the Owner shall, upon certification by the Architect, and without terminating the Contract, make payment of the balance due for that portion of the Work fully completed and accepted. If the remaining balance for Work not fully completed or corrected is less than the retainage stipulated in the Agreement, and if bonds have been furnished as required in Subparagraph 7.5.1, the written consent of the surety to the payment of the balance due for that portion of the Work fully completed and accepted shall be submitted by the Contractor to the Architect prior to certification of such payment. Such payment shall be made under the terms and conditions governing final payment, except that it shall not constitute a waiver of claims.

9.7.5 The making of final payment shall constitute a waiver of all claims by the Owner except those arising from:

.1 unsettled liens,

.2 faulty or defective Work appearing after Substantial Completion,

.3 failure of the Work to comply with the requirements of the Contract Documents, or

.4 terms of any special guarantees required by the Contract Documents.

9.7.6 The acceptance of final payment shall constitute a waiver of all claims by the Contractor except those previously made in writing and still unsettled.

ARTICLE 10

PROTECTION OF PERSONS AND PROPERTY

10.1 SAFETY PRECAUTIONS AND PROGRAMS

10.1.1 The Contractor shall be responsible for initiating, maintaining and supervising all safety precautions and programs in connection with the Work.

10.2 SAFETY OF PERSONS AND PROPERTY

10.2.1 The Contractor shall take all reasonable precautions for the safety of, and shall provide all reasonable protection to prevent damage, injury or loss to:

.1 all employees on the Work and all other persons who may be affected thereby;

.2 all the Work and all materials and equipment to be incorporated therein, whether in storage on or off the site, under the care, custody or control of the Contractor or any of his Subcontractors or Sub-subcontractors; and

.3 other property at the site or adjacent thereto, including trees, shrubs, lawns, walks, pavements, roadways, structures and utilities not designated for removal, relocation or replacement in the course of construction.

10.2.2 The Contractor shall comply with all applicable laws, ordinances, rules, regulations and orders of any public authority having jurisdiction for the safety of persons or property or to protect them from damage, injury or loss. He shall erect and maintain, as required by existing conditions and progress of the Work, all reasonable safeguards for safety and protection, including posting danger signs and other warnings against hazards, promulgating safety regulations and notifying owners and users of adjacent utilities.

10.2.3 When the use or storage of explosives or other hazardous materials or equipment is necessary for the execution of the Work, the Contractor shall exercise the utmost care and shall carry on such activities under the supervision of properly qualified personnel.

10.2.4 All damage or loss to any property referred to in Clauses 10.2.1.2 and 10.2.1.3 caused in whole or in part by the Contractor, any Subcontractor, any Sub-subcontractor, or anyone directly or indirectly employed by any of them, or by anyone for whose acts any of them may be liable, shall be remedied by the Contractor, except damage or loss attributable to faulty Drawings or Specifications or to the acts or omissions of the Owner or Architect or anyone employed by either of them or for whose acts either of them may be liable, and not attributable to the fault or negligence of the Contractor.

10.2.5 The Contractor shall designate a responsible member of his organization at the site whose duty shall be the prevention of accidents. This person shall be the Contractor's superintendent unless otherwise designated in writing by the Contractor to the Owner and the Architect.

10.2.6 The Contractor shall not load or permit any part of the Work to be loaded so as to endanger its safety.

10.3   EMERGENCIES

10.3.1 In any emergency affecting the safety of persons or property, the Contractor shall act, at his discretion, to prevent threatened damage, injury or loss. Any additional compensation or extension of time claimed by the Contractor on account of emergency work shall be determined as provided in Article 12 for Changes in the Work.

ARTICLE 11

INSURANCE

11.1   CONTRACTOR'S LIABILITY INSURANCE

11.1.1 The Contractor shall purchase and maintain such insurance as will protect him from claims set forth below which may arise out of or result from the Contractor's operations under the Contract, whether such operations be by himself or by any Subcontractor or by anyone directly or indirectly employed by any of them, or by anyone for whose acts any of them may be liable:

.1 claims under workmen's compensation, disability benefit and other similar employee benefit acts;

.2 claims for damages because of bodily injury, occupational sickness or disease, or death of his employees, and claims insured by usual personal injury liability coverage;

.3 claims for damages because of bodily injury, sickness or disease, or death of any person other than his employees, and claims insured by usual personal injury liability coverage; and

.4 claims for damages because of injury to or destruction of tangible property, including loss of use resulting therefrom.

11.1.2 The insurance required by Subparagraph 11.1.1 shall be written for not less than any limits of liability specified in the Contract Documents, or required by law, whichever is greater, and shall include contractual liability insurance as applicable to the Contractor's obligations under Paragraph 4.18.

11.1.3 Certificates of Insurance acceptable to the Owner shall be filed with the Owner prior to commencement of the Work. These Certificates shall contain a provision that coverages afforded under the policies will not be cancelled until at least fifteen days' prior written notice has been given to the Owner.

11.2   OWNER'S LIABILITY INSURANCE

11.2.1 The Owner shall be responsible for purchasing and maintaining his own liability insurance and, at his option, may purchase and maintain such insurance as will protect him against claims which may arise from operations under the Contract.

11.3   PROPERTY INSURANCE

11.3.1 Unless otherwise provided, the Owner shall purchase and maintain property insurance upon the entire Work at the site to the full insurable value thereof. This insurance shall include the interests of the Owner, the Contractor, Subcontractors and Sub-subcontractors in the Work and shall insure against the perils of Fire, Extended Coverage, Vandalism and Malicious Mischief.

11.3.2 The Owner shall purchase and maintain such steam boiler and machinery insurance as may be required by the Contract Documents or by law. This insurance shall include the interests of the Owner, the Contractor, Subcontractors and Sub-subcontractors in the Work.

AIA DOCUMENT A 201 • GENERAL CONDITIONS OF THE CONTRACT FOR CONSTRUCTION • ELEVENTH EDITION • AIA ®
SEPTEMBER 1967 © THE AMERICAN INSTITUTE OF ARCHITECTS, 1735 NEW YORK AVENUE, N.W., WASHINGTON, D.C. 20006

11.3.3 Any insured loss is to be adjusted with the Owner and made payable to the Owner as trustee for the insureds, as their interests may appear, subject to the requirements of any applicable mortgagee clause and of Subparagraph 11.3.8.

11.3.4 The Owner shall file a copy of all policies with the Contractor before an exposure to loss may occur. If the Owner does not intend to purchase such insurance, he shall inform the Contractor in writing prior to commencement of the Work. The Contractor may then effect insurance which will protect the interests of himself, his Subcontractors and the Sub-subcontractors in the Work, and by appropriate Change Order the cost thereof shall be charged to the Owner. If the Contractor is damaged by failure of the Owner to purchase or maintain such insurance and so to notify the Contractor, then the Owner shall bear all reasonable costs properly attributable thereto.

11.3.5 If the Contractor requests in writing that other special insurance be included in the property insurance policy, the Owner shall, if possible, include such insurance, and the cost thereof shall be charged to the Contractor by appropriate Change Order.

11.3.6 The Owner and Contractor waive all rights against each other for damages caused by fire or other perils to the extent covered by insurance provided under this Paragraph 11.3, except such rights as they may have to the proceeds of such insurance held by the Owner as trustee. The Contractor shall require similar waivers by Subcontractors and Sub-subcontractors in accordance with Clause 5.3.1.5.

11.3.7 If required in writing by any party in interest, the Owner as trustee shall, upon the occurrence of an insured loss, give bond for the proper performance of his duties. He shall deposit in a separate account any money so received, and he shall distribute it in accordance with such agreement as the parties in interest may reach, or in accordance with an award by arbitration in which case the procedure shall be as provided in Paragraph 7.10. If after such loss no other special agreement is made, replacement of damaged work shall be covered by an appropriate Change Order.

11.3.8 The Owner as trustee shall have power to adjust and settle any loss with the insurers unless one of the parties in interest shall object in writing within five days after the occurrence of loss to the Owner's exercise of this power, and if such objection be made, arbitrators shall be chosen as provided in Paragraph 7.10. The Owner as trustee shall, in that case, make settlement with the insurers in accordance with the directions of such arbitrators. If distribution of the insurance proceeds by arbitration is required, the arbitrators will direct such distribution.

11.4 LOSS OF USE INSURANCE

11.4.1 The Owner, at his option, may purchase and maintain such insurance as will insure him against loss of use of his property due to fire or other hazards, however caused.

ARTICLE 12

CHANGES IN THE WORK

12.1 CHANGE ORDERS

12.1.1 The Owner, without invalidating the Contract, may order Changes in the Work within the general scope of the Contract consisting of additions, deletions or other revisions, the Contract Sum and the Contract Time being adjusted accordingly. All such Changes in the Work shall be authorized by Change Order, and shall be executed under the applicable conditions of the Contract Documents.

12.1.2 A Change Order is a written order to the Contractor signed by the Owner and the Architect, issued after the execution of the Contract, authorizing a Change in the Work or an adjustment in the Contract Sum or the Contract Time. Alternatively, the Change Order may be signed by the Architect alone, provided he has written authority from the Owner for such procedure and that a copy of such written authority is furnished to the Contractor upon request. The Contract Sum and the Contract Time may be changed only by Change Order.

12.1.3 The cost or credit to the Owner resulting from a Change in the Work shall be determined in one or more of the following ways:

    .1 by mutual acceptance of a lump sum properly itemized;

    .2 by unit prices stated in the Contract Documents or subsequently agreed upon; or

    .3 by cost and a mutually acceptable fixed or percentage fee.

12.1.4 If none of the methods set forth in Subparagraph 12.1.3 is agreed upon, the Contractor, provided he receives a Change Order, shall promptly proceed with the Work involved. The cost of such Work shall then be determined by the Architect on the basis of the Contractor's reasonable expenditures and savings, including, in the case of an increase in the Contract Sum, a reasonable allowance for overhead and profit. In such case, and also under Clause 12.1.3.3 above, the Contractor shall keep and present, in such form as the Architect may prescribe, an itemized accounting together with appropriate supporting data. Pending final determination of cost to the Owner, payments on account shall be made on the Architect's Certificate for Payment. The amount of credit to be allowed by the Contractor to the Owner for any deletion or change which results in a net decrease in cost will be the amount of the actual net decrease as confirmed by the Architect. When both additions and credits are involved in any one change, the allowance for overhead and profit shall be figured on the basis of net increase, if any.

12.1.5 If unit prices are stated in the Contract Documents or subsequently agreed upon, and if the quantities originally contemplated are so changed in a proposed Change Order that application of the agreed unit prices to the quantities of Work proposed will create a hardship on the Owner or the Contractor, the applicable unit prices shall be equitably adjusted to prevent such hardship.

AIA DOCUMENT A 201 • GENERAL CONDITIONS OF THE CONTRACT FOR CONSTRUCTION • ELEVENTH EDITION • AIA ®
SEPTEMBER 1967 © THE AMERICAN INSTITUTE OF ARCHITECTS, 1735 NEW YORK AVENUE, N.W., WASHINGTON, D.C. 20006

12.1.6 Should concealed conditions encountered in the performance of the Work below the surface of the ground be at variance with the conditions indicated by the Contract Documents or should unknown physical conditions below the surface of the ground of an unusual nature, differing materially from those ordinarily encountered and generally recognized as inherent in work of the character provided for in this Contract, be encountered, the Contract Sum shall be equitably adjusted by Change Order upon claim by either party made within a reasonable time after the first observance of the conditions.

12.1.7 If the Contractor claims that additional cost or time is involved because of **(1)** any written interpretation issued pursuant to Subparagraph 1.2.5, **(2)** any order by the Architect to stop the Work pursuant to Subparagraph 2.2.12 where the Contractor was not at fault, or **(3)** any written order for a minor change in the Work issued pursuant to Paragraph 12.3, the Contractor shall make such claim as provided in Paragraph 12.2.

12.2   CLAIMS FOR ADDITIONAL COST OR TIME

12.2.1 If the Contractor wishes to make a claim for an increase in the Contract Sum or an extension in the Contract Time, he shall give the Architect written notice thereof within a reasonable time after the occurrence of the event giving rise to such claim. This notice shall be given by the Contractor before proceeding to execute the Work, except in an emergency endangering life or property in which case the Contractor shall proceed in accordance with Subparagraph 10.3.1. No such claim shall be valid unless so made. If the Owner and the Contractor cannot agree on the amount of the adjustment in the Contract Sum or the Contract Time, it shall be determined by the Architect. Any change in the Contract Sum or Contract Time resulting from such claim shall be authorized by Change Order.

12.3   MINOR CHANGES IN THE WORK

12.3.1 The Architect shall have authority to order minor changes in the Work not involving an adjustment in the Contract Sum or an extension of the Contract Time and not inconsistent with the intent of the Contract Documents. Such changes may be effected by Field Order or by other written order. Such changes shall be binding on the Owner and the Contractor.

12.4   FIELD ORDERS

12.4.1 The Architect may issue written Field Orders which interpret the Contract Documents in accordance with Subparagraph 1.2.5 or which order minor changes in the Work in accordance with Paragraph 12.3 without change in Contract Sum or Contract Time. The Contractor shall carry out such Field Orders promptly.

ARTICLE 13

UNCOVERING AND CORRECTION OF WORK

13.1   UNCOVERING OF WORK

13.1.1 If any Work should be covered contrary to the request of the Architect, it must, if required by the Archi-

tect, be uncovered for his observation and replaced. at the Contractor's expense.

13.1.2 If any other Work has been covered which the Architect has not specifically requested to observe prior to being covered, the Architect may request to see such Work and it shall be uncovered by the Contractor. If such Work be found in accordance with the Contract Documents, the cost of uncovering and replacement shall, by appropriate Change Order, be charged to the Owner. If such Work be found not in accordance with the Contract Documents, the Contractor shall pay such costs unless it be found that this condition was caused by a separate contractor employed as provided in Article 6, and in that event the Owner shall be responsible for the payment of such costs.

13.2   CORRECTION OF WORK

13.2.1 The Contractor shall promptly correct all Work rejected by the Architect as defective or as failing to conform to the Contract Documents whether observed before or after Substantial Completion and whether or not fabricated, installed or completed. The Contractor shall bear all costs of correcting such rejected Work, including the cost of the Architect's additional services thereby made necessary.

13.2.2 If, within one year after the Date of Substantial Completion or within such longer period of time as may be prescribed by law or by the terms of any applicable special guarantee required by the Contract Documents, any of the Work is found to be defective or not in accordance with the Contract Documents, the Contractor shall correct it promptly after receipt of a written notice from the Owner to do so unless the Owner has previously given the Contractor a written acceptance of such condition. The Owner shall give such notice promptly after discovery of the condition.

13.2.3 All such defective or non-conforming Work under Subparagraphs 13.2.1 and 13.2.2 shall be removed from the site where necessary, and the Work shall be corrected to comply with the Contract Documents without cost to the Owner.

13.2.4 The Contractor shall bear the cost of making good all work of separate contractors destroyed or damaged by such removal or correction.

13.2.5 If the Contractor does not remove such defective or non-conforming Work within a reasonable time fixed by written notice from the Architect, the Owner may remove it and may store the materials or equipment at the expense of the Contractor. If the Contractor does not pay the cost of such removal and storage within ten days thereafter, the Owner may upon ten additional days' written notice sell such Work at auction or at private sale and shall account for the net proceeds thereof, after deducting all the costs that should have been borne by the Contractor including compensation for additional architectural services. If such proceeds of sale do not cover all costs which the Contractor should have borne, the difference shall be charged to the Contractor and an appropriate Change Order shall be issued. If the payments then or thereafter due the Contractor are not suf-

AIA DOCUMENT A 201 • GENERAL CONDITIONS OF THE CONTRACT FOR CONSTRUCTION • ELEVENTH EDITION • AIA ®
SEPTEMBER 1967 © THE AMERICAN INSTITUTE OF ARCHITECTS, 1735 NEW YORK AVENUE, N.W., WASHINGTON, D.C. 20006

ficient to cover such amount, the Contractor shall pay the difference to the Owner.

13.2.6 If the Contractor fails to correct such defective or non-conforming Work, the Owner may correct it in accordance with Paragraph 7.6.

13.2.7 The obligations of the Contractor under this Paragraph 13.2 shall be in addition to and not in limitation of any obligations imposed upon him by special guarantees required by the Contract Documents or otherwise prescribed by law.

13.3 ACCEPTANCE OF DEFECTIVE OR NON-CONFORMING WORK

13.3.1 If the Owner prefers to accept defective or non-conforming Work, he may do so instead of requiring its removal and correction, in which case a Change Order will be issued to reflect an appropriate reduction in the Contract Sum, or, if the amount is determined after final payment, it shall be paid by the Contractor.

ARTICLE 14

TERMINATION OF THE CONTRACT

14.1 TERMINATION BY THE CONTRACTOR

14.1.1 If the Work is stopped for a period of thirty days under an order of any court or other public authority having jurisdiction, through no act or fault of the Contractor or a Subcontractor or their agents or employees or any other persons performing any of the Work under a contract with the Contractor, or if the Work should be stopped for a period of thirty days by the Contractor for the Architect's failure to issue a Certificate for Payment as provided in Paragraph 9.6 or for the Owner's failure to make payment thereon as provided in Paragraph 9.6,

then the Contractor may, upon seven days' written notice to the Owner and the Architect, terminate the Contract and recover from the Owner payment for all Work executed and for any proven loss sustained upon any materials, equipment, tools, construction equipment and machinery, including reasonable profit and damages.

14.2 TERMINATION BY THE OWNER

14.2.1 If the Contractor is adjudged a bankrupt, or if he makes a general assignment for the benefit of his creditors, or if a receiver is appointed on account of his insolvency, or if he persistently or repeatedly refuses or fails, except in cases for which extension of time is provided, to supply enough properly skilled workmen or proper materials, or if he fails to make prompt payment to Subcontractors or for materials or labor, or persistently disregards laws, ordinances, rules, regulations or orders of any public authority having jurisdiction, or otherwise is guilty of a substantial violation of a provision of the Contract Documents, then the Owner, upon certification by the Architect that sufficient cause exists to justify such action, may, without prejudice to any right or remedy and after giving the Contractor and his surety, if any, seven days' written notice, terminate the employment of the Contractor and take possession of the site and of all materials, equipment, tools, construction equipment and machinery thereon owned by the Contractor and may finish the Work by whatever method he may deem expedient. In such case the Contractor shall not be entitled to receive any further payment until the Work is finished.

14.2.2 If the unpaid balance of the Contract Sum exceeds the costs of finishing the Work, including compensation for the Architect's additional services, such excess shall be paid to the Contractor. If such costs exceed such unpaid balance, the Contractor shall pay the difference to the Owner. The costs incurred by the Owner as herein provided shall be certified by the Architect.

AIA DOCUMENT A 201 • GENERAL CONDITIONS OF THE CONTRACT FOR CONSTRUCTION • ELEVENTH EDITION • AIA ®
SEPTEMBER 1967 © THE AMERICAN INSTITUTE OF ARCHITECTS, 1735 NEW YORK AVENUE, N.W., WASHINGTON, D.C. 20006 **17**

APPENDIX D

MODIFICATIONS TO GENERAL CONDITIONS

1. DRAWINGS FURNISHED. Subparagraph 1.3.1, of General Conditions, shall be changed to read as follows: "The Architect-Engineer shall furnish free of charge 25 sets of working Drawings and 25 sets of Specifications. The Contractor shall pay the cost of reproduction for all other copies of Drawings and Specifications furnished to him."

2. PERMITS. Subparagraph 4.7.1, of General Conditions, shall be modified as follows: "The Owner shall procure the required building permit at no cost to the Contractor."

3. INSURANCE.

a. Subparagraph 11.2.1, of General Conditions, shall be modified as follows: "The Contractor shall procure, maintain, and pay for Owner's contingent liability insurance. The amount of Owner's contingent liability insurance shall be $100,000 for one person and $300,000 for one accident. A certificate of insurance shall be filed with the Architect-Engineer."

b. Subparagraph 11.3.1, of General Conditions, shall be modified as follows: "The Contractor shall procure, maintain, and pay for fire insurance in the amount of 100 percent of the insurable value of the Project and, in addition, shall procure, maintain, and pay for insurance to protect the Owner from damage by hail, tornado, and hurricane upon the entire work in the amount of 100 percent of the insurable value thereof. Certificates of insurance shall be filed with the Architect-Engineer."

4. CLEANING UP. Subparagraph 4.16.1, of General Conditions, shall be modified as follows: "In addition to removal of rubbish and leaving the work broom-clean, the Contractor shall remove stains, spots, marks, and dirt from decorated work; clean hardware; remove paint spots and smears from all surfaces; clean light and plumbing fixtures; and wash all concrete, tile, and terrazzo floors."

APPENDIX E

SPECIAL CONDITIONS

1. LOCATION OF THE PROJECT. The general location of the work covered in this specification is Portland, Ohio.

2. SCOPE OF THE WORK. The work to be performed under this Contract consists of furnishing all plant, materials, equipment, supplies, labor, and transportation, including fuel, power, and water, and performing all work in strict accordance with specifications, schedules, and drawings, all of which are made a part hereof, and including such detail drawings as may be furnished by the Architect-Engineer from time to time during the construction.

3. EXAMINATION OF SITE. Bidders should visit the site of the building, compare the drawings and specifications with any work in place, and inform themselves of all conditions, including other work, if any, being performed. Failure to visit the site will in no way relieve the successful bidder from the necessity of furnishing any materials or performing any work that may be required to complete the work in accordance with drawings and specifications.

4. LAYING OUT WORK. The Contractor shall, immediately upon entering the project site for the purpose of beginning work, locate all Owner-provided reference points and take such action as is necessary to prevent their destruction, lay out his own work and be responsible for all lines, elevations, and measurements of buildings, grading, paving, utilities, and other work executed by him under the Contract.

5. COMMENCEMENT, PROSECUTION, AND COMPLETION.

a. The Contractor will be required to commence work under this Contract within ten (10) calendar days after the date of receipt by him of Notice to Proceed, to prosecute said work with faithfulness and energy and to complete the entire work, ready for use, within 720 calendar days after receipt of Notice to Proceed. The time stated for completion shall include final clean up of the premises.

b. It is mutually agreed that the time for the commencement and completion of the work will materially affect the progress of other work and that the Owner will suffer financial damages in an amount not now possible to ascertain if this work is not completed on schedule, and in view of these facts, it is agreed that the Owner will withhold from the Contractor, as liquidated damages and not as a penalty, the sum of $100.00 per day for each calendar day that the work remains uncompleted beyond the date specified for the completion of the work.

c. If completion of the work to be performed under the terms of this Contract is delayed by reasons of delay in the performance of any work to be performed by the Owner, or other contractors, and which is essential to the work performed under this Contract, such delay shall not constitute a basis for any claim against the Owner, but the time of performance will be extended for a period equal to such delay or as otherwise mutually agreed upon.

6. WATCHMAN. The Contractor shall employ a responsible watchman to guard the site and premises at all times except during regular working hours, from the beginning of work until acceptance by the Owner.

7. OWNER-FURNISHED MATERIALS AND EQUIPMENT. With the following exception there will be no Owner-furnished materials and/or equipment.

a. Hardware consisting of removable cylinders for locks will be Owner-furnished and installed by the Contractor as specified herein.

8. TAXES. Except as may be otherwise provided in this contract, the contract price is to include all applicable federal, state, and local taxes, but does not include any tax from which the Contractor is exempt. Upon request of the Contractor, the Owner shall furnish a tax exemption certificate or similar evidence of exemption with respect to any such tax not included in the contract price pursuant to this provision.

9. RATES OF WAGES.

a. There shall be paid each laborer or mechanic of the Contractor or subcontractor engaged in work on the project under this Contract in the trade or occupation listed below, not less than the hourly wage rate opposite the same, regardless of any contractual relationship which may be alleged to exist between the Contractor or any subcontractor and such laborers and mechanics.

Classification	Wage Rates per Hour
Asbestos workers	$6.45
Bricklayers	6.55
Carpenters	6.35
Cement masons	6.30
Electricians	6.525
Glaziers	5.97
Ironworkers	6.20
Lathers	6.25
Linoleum layers	5.70
Marble setters	6.55
Mosiac and terrazzo workers	5.85
Painters	5.675
Plasterers	6.38
Plumbers	6.65
Roofers	6.34
Sheet metal workers	6.52
Steamfitters	6.65
Stonemasons	6.55
Tile setters	5.85
Waterproofers	6.34
LABORERS	
Air and power tool operator	4.80
Cement mason tender	4.80
Power buggy operator	4.90
Sandblaster, potman, nozzleman	4.90
Mason tender	4.90

Classification	Wage Rates per Hour
Pipe layers, nonmetallic, sewer and drainage	5.05
Pumpcrete nozzle placementman	4.67
Carpenter tender	4.50
Unskilled and common laborers	4.50
Concrete buggy operator	4.50
Concrete puddler	4.90
Vibrator operator	4.90

POWER EQUIPMENT OPERATORS

Air compressor, power plant, pump operators	5.44
Gunite and pumpcrete machine	5.77
Concrete mixers over 1 cu. yd.	5.77
Concrete batching plants	5.44
Cranes, hysters, side boom tractors	5.60
Winch truck	5.60
Hoists:	
One drum	5.95
Two or more drums	6.35
Guy and stiff leg derricks	6.35
Loaders:	
Front end	4.95
Elevating belt, fork lift	5.44
Pile driver	5.75
Sheeps foot rollers	4.90
Rubber tired rollers	4.90
Shovel, backhoe, clamshell, dragline, under ¾ cu. yd.	5.44
Shovel, backhoe, clamshell, dragline, over ¾ cu. yd.	5.70
Loaders, bulldozers, patrol, scraper	5.85
Trenching machine	5.44

TRUCK DRIVERS

Dumpster	4.95
Dump trucks:	
Batch and under 8 cu. yd.	4.70
8 and over cu. yd.	4.82
Lowboy, heavy equipment	5.25
Lowboy, light equipment	4.90
Flat bed truck, under ½ ton	4.70
Pickup truck	4.60
Transit mix	4.95
Tank truck, no trailer	4.75
Tank truck, with trailer	4.85
Swamper or riding helper	4.60

Welders: receive rate prescribed for craft performing operation to which welding is incidental.

b. The foregoing specified wage rates are minimum rates only, and the Owner will not consider any claims for additional compensation made by the Contractor because of payment by the Contractor of any wage rate in excess of the applicable rate contained in this Contract. All disputes in regard to the payment of wages in excess of those specified in this Contract shall be adjusted by the Contractor.

10. TEMPORARY FACILITIES. The Contractor shall furnish materials and labor to build all temporary buildings on the project site for use during the construction of the project. All such buildings and/or utilities shall remain the property of the Contractor and shall be removed by him, at his expense, upon completion of the work under this Contract.

a. Sanitary Facilities. The Contractor shall provide and maintain ample toilet accommodations for all workmen employed on the project under this Contract. The latrines shall be weather tight, fly-proof, and shall conform to the standards established by the Owner. Toilets shall be flush-type water closets connected to the sewer, and/or chemical type. Toilet facilities shall be maintained in sanitary condition as approved by the Architect-Engineer at all times during the work on this project.

b. Temporary Enclosures. The Contractor shall provide protection against entry, rain, wind, frost, and heat, at all times, and shall maintain all materials, apparatus, equipment, and fixtures free from damage and injury.

c. Temporary Heat. The Contractor shall provide temporary heat at all times when weather conditions are such that good construction will be hampered and delayed. Uniform temperature, not lower than 50° F. shall be maintained at all times, including Saturdays, Sundays, and holidays, in that portion of the building where plastering, ceramic tile work, resilient flooring, and painting are being performed. When the permanent heating system can be operating under temporary heat requirements, all costs of operation shall be at the expense of the Contractor.

d. Water Supply. Water supply for all trades for construction uses and domestic consumption shall be provided and paid for by the Contractor. Temporary lines and connections shall be removed in a manner satisfactory to the Architect-Engineer before final acceptance of work under this Contract.

e. Electricity. Electric current required for power and light for all trades, for construction uses, and temporary lines, lamps, and equipment as required, shall be provided, connected, and maintained by the Contractor at his expense and shall be removed in like manner at the completion of construction work.

f. Telephone. The Contractor shall provide and pay for such telephone service as he may require.

11. SHOP DRAWINGS. The Contractor shall submit to the Architect-Engineer for approval five copies of all shop drawings as may be required. These drawings shall be complete and shall contain all required detailed information. If approved by the Architect-Engineer, each copy of the drawings will be identified as having received such approval by being so stamped and dated. The Contractor shall make any corrections required by the Architect-Engineer. Two sets of all shop drawings will be retained by the Architect-Engineer and three sets will be returned to the Contractor. The approval of the drawings by the Architect-Engineer shall not be construed as a complete check but will indicate only that the general method of construction and detailing is satisfactory. Approval of such drawings will not relieve the Contractor of the responsibility of any error which may exist as the Contractor shall be responsible for the dimensions and design of adequate connections, details, and satisfactory construction of all work.

12. PLAN OF OPERATIONS. The Contractor shall coordinate his work with the operations and work of the Owner and other contractors, as directed by the Architect-Engineer.

13. REPORTING OF COST INFORMATION. The Owner will need cost information regarding certain items of property which will be furnished or installed under this Contract. Accordingly, at the written request of the Architect-Engineer, the Contractor shall furnish to the Owner, cost information pertaining to such items of property furnished or installed under this Contract as the Architect-Engineer may designate, in such form and in such detail as may be required.

14. FIELD OFFICE. The Contractor shall provide adequate facilities for inspection of the project, including office space of not less than 100 square feet of floor space, properly heated, ventilated, and lighted, on the site of the project, for the exclusive use of the Architect-Engineer's representative. The Contractor shall construct a built-in work table

approximately 3' 6" wide by 6' 0" long in the field office and plan racks as directed by the Architect-Engineer.

15. PAYMENT. Partial payments under the Contract shall be made at the request of the Contractor once each month, based upon partial estimates to be furnished by the Contractor and approved by the Architect-Engineer. In making such partial payments, there shall be retained 10 per cent of the estimated amounts until final completion and acceptance of all work covered by the Contract; provided, however, that the Architect-Engineer at any time after 50 per cent of the work has been completed, if he finds that satisfactory progress is being made, with written consent of surety, shall recommend that the remaining partial payments be paid in full. Payments for work, under subcontracts of the Contractor, shall be subject to the above conditions applying to the Contract after the work under a subcontract has been 50 per cent completed. In preparing estimates for partial payments, the material delivered on the site and preparatory work done may be taken into consideration.

16. CONSTRUCTION SCHEDULE. Immediately after execution and delivery of the Contract, and before the first partial payment is made, the Contractor shall deliver to the Architect-Engineer an estimated construction progress schedule showing the proposed dates of commencement and completion of each of the various subdivisions of the work required under the Contract, and the anticipated amount of each monthly payment that will become due the Contractor in accordance with the progress schedule. The Contractor shall also furnish on forms to be supplied by the Owner (*a*) a detailed estimate giving a complete breakdown of the contract price and (*b*) periodical itemized estimates of work done for the purpose of making partial payments thereon.

17. SAFETY AND ACCIDENT PREVENTION.

a. The Contractor shall take all reasonable precautions in the performance of the work under this Contract to protect the health and safety of employees and the public and to minimize danger from all hazards to life and property, and shall comply with all health, safety, and fire protection regulations and requirements. In the event the Contractor fails to comply with the said safety provisions or with the directions of the Architect-Engineer, the Architect-Engineer, without prejudice to any other rights of the Owner, may issue an order stopping all or any part of the work; thereafter, a start order for resumption of work may be issued at the discretion of the Architect-Engineer. No extension of time or compensation for damages by reason of, or in connection with, such work stoppage will be allowed.

b. Accident and Fire Prevention Plan. The Contractor will, prior to commencement of work, furnish the Architect-Engineer, in writing, an outline of his proposed accident prevention and fire prevention plan for all work contemplated under the Contract.

c. Safety Meetings. The Contractor shall conduct at least one safety meeting each week for each shift and require the attendance of all supervisors at such meetings, including those of subcontractors.

d. First-Aid. The provisions of Section 3 of the "Manual of Accident Prevention in Construction" of the Associated General Contractors of America shall apply.

APPENDIX F

PROPOSAL FOR LUMP-SUM CONTRACT

_____Portland, Ohio_____
(Place)
May 19, 19____
(Date)

PROPOSAL of ___The Blank Construction Company, Inc.___ , a corporation organized
and existing under the laws of the State of _____Ohio_____ , a partnership
consisting of _____

_____ ,

an individual doing business as _____.

TO: The City of Portland, Ohio

PROJECT: Municipal Airport Terminal Building
         For the City of Portland, Ohio

Gentlemen:

    The Undersigned, in compliance with your invitation for bids for the General Construction of the above-described project, having examined the drawings and specifications with related contract documents carefully, with all addenda thereto, and the site of the work, and being familiar with all of the conditions surrounding the construction of the proposed project, hereby proposes to furnish all plant, labor, equipment, appliances, supplies, and materials and to perform all work for the construction of the project as required by and in strict accordance with the contract documents, specifications, schedules, and drawings with all addenda issued by the Architect-Engineer, at the prices stated below.

    The Undersigned hereby acknowledges receipt of the following Addenda:

Addendum No. 1 dated April 28, 19____.

Addendum No. 2 dated May 6, 19____.

BASE PROPOSAL: For all work described in the detailed specifications and shown on the

334

contract drawings for the building, I (or We) agree to perform all the work for the sum of Three million, six hundred sixty-eight thousand, eight hundred sixty-one and no/100 ($3,668,861.00) dollars. (Amount shall be shown in both written form and figures. In case of discrepancy between the written amount and the figures, the written amount will govern.)

The above stated compensation covers all expenses incurred in performing the work, including premium for contract bonds, required under the contract documents, of which this proposal is a part.

ALTERNATE NO. 1: QUARRY TILE IN PLACE OF TERRAZZO: If the substitutions specified under this alternate are made, you may (deduct from) (add to) the base proposal the sum of Nine thousand, seven hundred fourteen and no/100 ($9,714.00) dollars.

ALTERNATE NO. 2: CHANGE STRUCTURAL GLAZED TILE TO BRICK IN CONCOURSE: If the substitutions specified under this alternate are made, you may (deduct from) (add to) the base proposal the sum of Four thousand, two hundred eighty and no/100 ($4,280.00) dollars.

ALTERNATE NO. 3: OMIT KITCHEN EQUIPMENT: If the substitutions specified under this alternate are made, you may (deduct from) (add to) the base proposal the sum of Sixty-six thousand, seven hundred twenty-three and no/100 ($66,723.00) dollars.

BID SECURITY: Attached cashier's check (certified check) (Bid Bond) payable without condition, in the sum of 5% of maximum possible bid amount ($_____) dollars (equal to 5% of the largest possible combination) is to become the property of the City of Portland, Ohio, in the event the Contract and contract bonds are not executed within the time set forth hereinafter, as liquidated damages for the delay and additional work caused thereby.

CONTRACT SECURITY: The Undersigned hereby agrees, if awarded the contract, to furnish the contract bonds, as specified, with the Hartford Accident and Indemnity Company Surety Company of Hartford, Connecticut.

Upon receipt of notice of the acceptance of this bid, the Undersigned hereby agrees that he will execute and deliver the formal written Contract in the form prescribed, in accordance with the bid as accepted and that he will give contract bonds, all within ten days after the prescribed forms are presented to him for signature.

If awarded the Contract, the Undersigned proposes to commence work within 10 calendar days after receipt of notice to proceed and to fully complete all of the work under his Contract, ready for occupancy, within 720 calendar days thereafter.

Respectfully submitted,

The Blank Construction Company, Inc.

By   K. O. Acme

Vice-President

(Title)

1938 Cranbrook Lane

Portland, Ohio

(Business Address)

216-344-5507

(Telephone Number)

SEAL:

(If bid is by a

Corporation)

APPENDIX G

BID FORM
UNIT-PRICE CONTRACT

DECEMBER 1965 EDITION
GENERAL SERVICES ADMINISTRATION
FED. PROC. REG. (41 CFR) 1-16.401

BID FORM
(CONSTRUCTION CONTRACT)

REFERENCE

Serial No. Eng. 33-9-69

Read the Instructions to Bidders (Standard Form 22)
This form to be submitted in one copy

DATE OF INVITATION
9 July 19___

NAME AND LOCATION OF PROJECT

Taxiways and Aprons
Holloman Air Force Base
New Mexico

NAME OF BIDDER *(Type or print)*

The Excello Company, Inc.
Albuquerque, New Mexico

9 August 19___
(Date)

TO: District Engineer
Albuquerque District
Corps of Engineers
Albuquerque, New Mexico 87101

In compliance with the above-dated invitation for bids, the undersigned hereby proposes to perform all work for construction of Taxiways and Aprons
Holloman Air Force Base
New Mexico

in strict accordance with the General Provisions (Standard Form 23-A), Labor Standards Provisions Applicable to Contracts in Excess of $2,000 (Standard Form 19-A), specifications, schedules, drawings, and conditions, for the following amount(s)

Unit prices as set forth in the attached

Unit Price Schedule.

21-108

(Continue on other side)

336

The undersigned agrees that, upon written acceptance of this bid, mailed or otherwise furnished within calendar days (60 calendar days unless a different period be inserted by the bidder) after the date of opening of bids, he will within 10 calendar days (unless a longer period is allowed) after receipt of the prescribed forms, execute Standard Form 23, Construction Contract, and give performance and payment bonds on Government standard forms with good and sufficient surety.

The undersigned agrees, if awarded the contract, to commence the work within
    10 calendar days after the date of receipt of notice to proceed, and to complete the work within
            360   calendar days after the date of receipt of notice to proceed.

RECEIPT OF AMENDMENTS: *The undersigned acknowledges receipt of the following amendments of the invitation for bids, drawings, and/or specifications, etc. (Give number and date of each):*

    None

The representations and certifications on the accompanying STANDARD FORM 19-B are made a part of this bid.

ENCLOSED IS BID GUARANTEE, CONSISTING OF	IN THE AMOUNT OF
Bid Bond	5 percent

NAME OF BIDDER (*Type or print*)	FULL NAME OF ALL PARTNERS (*Type or print*)
The Excello Company, Inc.	
BUSINESS ADDRESS (*Type or print*) (*Include "ZIP Code"*) 2000 Random Road N.W. Albuquerque, New Mexico 87107	
BY (*Signature in ink. Type or print name under signature*) V. J. Excello	
TITLE (*Type or print*) President	

DIRECTIONS FOR SUBMITTING BIDS: *Envelopes containing bids, guarantee, etc., must be sealed, marked, and addressed as follows:*

In the upper left corner, enter: "Bid under Serial No. Eng. 33-9-69 to be opened 9 August 19___ ."

Address to: District Engineer
            Albuquerque District
            Corps of Engineers
            Albuquerque,
                New Mexico

CAUTION—Bids should not be qualified by exceptions to the bidding conditions.

☆ U.S. GOVERNMENT PRINTING OFFICE : 1966 O—225-630

Unit Price Schedule

Serial No. Eng. 33-9-69

Item No.	Description	Estimated Quantity	Unit	Unit Price	Estimated Amount
1	Clearing	Job	Lump sum	$13,000.00	$ 13,000
2	Demolition	Job	Lump sum	9,800.00	9,800
3	Excavation	127,000	Cu. yd.	0.55	69,850
4	Base course	160,000	Sq. yd.	1.10	176,000
5	Concrete pavement, 9 in.	90,000	Sq. yd.	4.65	418,500
6	Concrete pavement, 11 in.	70,000	Sq. yd.	6.00	420,000
7	Asphaltic concrete surface	150	Ton	13.60	2,040
8	Concrete pipe, 12 in.	1,000	Lin. ft.	6.80	6,800
9	Concrete pipe, 36 in.	300	Lin. ft.	16.70	5,010
10	Inlet	2	Each	300.00	600
11	Fiber duct, 4 way	600	Lin. ft.	6.00	3,600
12	Fiber duct, 8 way	1,200	Lin. ft.	16.00	19,200
13	Electrical manhole	6	Each	400.00	2,400
14	Underground cable	34,000	Lin. ft.	1.00	34,000
15	Taxiway lights	120	Each	120.00	14,400
16	Apron lights	70	Each	150.00	10,500
17	Taxiway marking	Job	Lump sum	4,000.00	4,000
18	Fence	26,000	Lin. ft.	0.65	16,900

TOTAL ESTIMATED AMOUNT $ 1,226,600

APPENDIX H

STANDARD FORM OF AGREEMENT BETWEEN OWNER AND CONTRACTOR STIPULATED SUM

THE AMERICAN INSTITUTE OF ARCHITECTS

AIA Document A101

Standard Form of Agreement Between Owner and Contractor

where the basis of payment is a
STIPULATED SUM

Use only with the latest Edition of AIA Document A201, General Conditions of the Contract for Construction.

AGREEMENT

made this   **Sixteenth**   day of   **June**   in the year of Nineteen
Hundred and

BETWEEN

The City of Portland, Ohio   the Owner, and

The Blank Construction Company, Inc.   the Contractor.
Portland, Ohio

The Owner and the Contractor agree as set forth below.

This Document, copyrighted by The American Institute of Architects, is reproduced here with its permission.

ARTICLE 1

THE CONTRACT DOCUMENTS

The Contract Documents consist of this Agreement, Conditions of the Contract (General, Supplementary and other Conditions), Drawings, Specifications, all Addenda issued prior to execution of this Agreement and all Modifications issued subsequent thereto. These form the Contract, and all are as fully a part of the Contract as if attached to this Agreement or repeated herein. An enumeration of the Contract Documents appears in Article 8.

ARTICLE 2

THE WORK

The Contractor shall perform all the Work required by the Contract Documents for
(Here insert the caption descriptive of the Work as used on other Contract Documents.)

A Municipal Airport Terminal Building for the City of Portland, Ohio.

ARTICLE 3

ARCHITECT

The Architect for this Project is

Jones and Smith, Architect-Engineers, Portland, Ohio.

ARTICLE 4

TIME OF COMMENCEMENT AND COMPLETION

The Work to be performed under this Contract shall be commenced within ten days after receipt of Notice to Proceed,
and completed within 720 calendar days after receipt of Notice to Proceed
(Here insert any special provisions for liquidated damages relating to failure to complete on time.)

It is mutually agreed that the Owner shall withhold from the Contractor, as liquidated damages and not as a penalty, the sum of one hundred dollars ($100.00) per day for each calendar day that the work remains uncompleted beyond this date.

ARTICLE 5

CONTRACT SUM

The Owner shall pay the Contractor for the performance of the Work, subject to additions and deductions by Change Order as provided in the Conditions of the Contract, in current funds, the Contract Sum of

the lump-sum amount of $3,602,138.00

(State here the lump sum amount, unit prices, or both, as desired.)

Base Proposal	$3,668,861.00
Alternate No. 1: Add $9,714.00 (not accepted)	
Alternate No. 2: Deduct $4,280.00 (not accepted)	
Alternate No. 3: Deduct $66,723.00 (accepted)	
Total Alternates Accepted, deduct	66,723.00
Total Contract Amount	$3,602,138.00

ARTICLE 6

PROGRESS PAYMENTS

Based upon Applications for Payment submitted to the Architect by the Contractor and Certificates for Payment issued by the Architect, the Owner shall make progress payments on account of the Contract Sum to the Contractor as provided in the Conditions of the Contract as follows:

On or about the **tenth** day of each month **ninety** per cent of the proportion of the Contract Sum properly allocable to labor, materials and equipment incorporated in the Work and **ninety** per cent of the portion of the Contract Sum properly allocable to materials and equipment suitably stored at the site or at some other location agreed upon in writing by the parties, up to the **first** day of that month, less the aggregate of previous payments in each case; and upon Substantial Completion of the entire Work, a sum sufficient to increase the total payments to **ninety** per cent of the Contract Sum, less such retainages as the Architect shall determine for all incomplete Work and unsettled claims.

(Here insert any provisions made for limiting or reducing the amount retained after the Work reaches a certain stage of completion.)

provided, however, that the Architect-Engineer at any time after fifty (50) percent of the work has been completed, if he finds that satisfactory progress is being made, with written consent of surety, shall recommend that the remaining progress payments be paid in full.

ARTICLE 7

FINAL PAYMENT

Final payment, constituting the entire unpaid balance of the Contract Sum, shall be paid by the Owner to the Contractor **thirty** days after Substantial Completion of the Work unless otherwise stipulated in the Certificate of Substantial Completion, provided the Work has then been completed, the Contract fully performed, and a final Certificate for Payment has been issued by the Architect.

ARTICLE 8

MISCELLANEOUS PROVISIONS

8.1 Terms used in this Agreement which are defined in the Conditions of the Contract shall have the meanings designated in those Conditions.

8.2 The Contract Documents, which constitute the entire agreement between the Owner and the Contractor, are listed in Article 1 and, except for Modifications issued after execution of this Agreement, are enumerated as follows:

(List below the Agreement, Conditions of the Contract (General, Supplementary, other Conditions), Drawings, Specifications, Addenda and accepted Alternates, showing page or sheet numbers in all cases and dates where applicable.)

All Drawings and Specifications entitled "A Municipal Airport Terminal Building for The City of Portland, Ohio", and dated March 6, 19___.

```
Drawings:   Sheets A-1 through A-44
                   S-1 through S-18
                   P-1 through P-6
                   M-1 through M-8
                   E-1 through E-11
Specifications:  General Conditions
                 Modifications to General Conditions
                 Special Conditions
                 Technical Sections 1 through 24
Addendum No. 1, dated April 28, 19___
Addendum No. 2, dated May 6, 19___
Alternate No. 3, Omit Kitchen Equipment
Agreement, dated June 16, 19___
```

This Agreement executed the day and year first written above.

OWNER _____ CONTRACTOR _____

APPENDIX I

STANDARD FORM OF AGREEMENT BETWEEN OWNER AND CONTRACTOR COST OF THE WORK PLUS A FEE

THE AMERICAN INSTITUTE OF ARCHITECTS

AIA Document A111

Standard Form of Agreement Between Owner and Contractor

where the basis of payment is the

COST OF THE WORK PLUS A FEE

Use only with the latest edition of AIA Document A201, General Conditions of the Contract for Construction.

AGREEMENT

made this   day of   in the year of Nineteen
Hundred and

BETWEEN

the Owner, and

the Contractor.

The Owner and the Contractor agree as set forth below.

This Document, copyrighted by The American Institute of Architects, is reproduced here with its permission.

ARTICLE 1

THE CONTRACT DOCUMENTS

The Contract Documents consist of this Agreement, Conditions of the Contract (General, Supplementary and other Conditions), Drawings, Specifications, all Addenda issued prior to execution of this Agreement and all Modifications issued subsequent thereto. These form the Contract, and all are as fully a part of the Contract as if attached to this Agreement or repeated herein. An enumeration of the Contract Documents appears in Article 17. If anything in the General Conditions is inconsistent with this Agreement, the Agreement shall govern.

ARTICLE 2

THE WORK

The Contractor shall perform all the Work required by the Contract Documents for

(Here insert the caption descriptive of the Work as used on other Contract Documents.)

ARTICLE 3

ARCHITECT

The Architect for this Project is

ARTICLE 4

THE CONTRACTOR'S DUTIES AND STATUS

The Contractor accepts the relationship of trust and confidence established between him and the Owner by this Agreement. He covenants with the Owner to furnish his best skill and judgment and to cooperate with the Architect in furthering the interests of the Owner. He agrees to furnish efficient business administration and superintendence and to use his best efforts to furnish at all times an adequate supply of workmen and materials, and to perform the Work in the best and soundest way and in the most expeditious and economical manner consistent with the interests of the Owner.

ARTICLE 5

TIME OF COMMENCEMENT AND COMPLETION

The Work to be performed under this Contract shall be commenced

and completed

(Here insert any special provisions for liquidated damages relating to failure to complete on time.)

ARTICLE 6

COST OF THE WORK AND GUARANTEED MAXIMUM COST

6.1 The Owner agrees to reimburse the Contractor for the Cost of the Work as defined in Article 9. Such reimbursement shall be in addition to the Contractor's Fee stipulated in Article 7.

6.2 The maximum cost to the Owner, including the Cost of the Work and the Contractor's Fee, is guaranteed not to exceed the sum of
dollars ($); such Guaranteed Maximum Cost shall be increased or decreased for Changes in the Work as provided in Article 8.

(Here insert any provision for distribution of any savings. Delete Paragraph 6.2 if there is no Guaranteed Maximum Cost.)

ARTICLE 7

CONTRACTOR'S FEE

7.1 In consideration of the performance of the Contract, the Owner agrees to pay the Contractor in current funds as compensation for his services a Contractor's Fee as follows:

7.2 For Changes in the Work, the Contractor's Fee shall be adjusted as follows:

7.3 The Contractor shall be paid   per cent (%) of the proportionate amount of his Fee with each progress payment, and the balance of his Fee shall be paid at the time of final payment.

ARTICLE 8

CHANGES IN THE WORK

8.1 The Owner may make Changes in the Work in accordance with Article 12 of the General Conditions insofar as such Article is consistent with this Agreement. The Contractor shall be reimbursed for Changes in the Work on the basis of Cost of the Work as defined in Article 9.

8.2 The Contractor's Fee for Changes in the Work shall be as set forth in Paragraph 7.2, or in the absence of specific provisions therein, shall be adjusted by negotiation on the basis of the Fee established for the original Work.

ARTICLE 9

COSTS TO BE REIMBURSED

9.1 The term Cost of the Work shall mean costs necessarily incurred in the proper performance of the Work and paid by the Contractor. Such costs shall be at rates not higher than the standard paid in the locality of the Work except with prior consent of the Owner, and shall include the items set forth below in this Article 9.

9.1.1 Wages paid for labor in the direct employ of the Contractor in the performance of the Work under applicable collective bargaining agreements, or under a salary or wage schedule agreed upon by the Owner and Contractor, and including such welfare or other benefits, if any, as may be payable with respect thereto.

9.1.2 Salaries of Contractor's employees when stationed at the field office, in whatever capacity employed. Employees engaged, at shops or on the road, in expediting the production or transportation of materials or equipment, shall be considered as stationed at the field office and their salaries paid for that portion of their time spent on this Work.

AIA DOCUMENT A111 • OWNER-CONTRACTOR AGREEMENT • SEPTEMBER 1967 EDITION • AIA® ©1967
THE AMERICAN INSTITUTE OF ARCHITECTS, 1735 NEW YORK AVENUE, N.W., WASHINGTON, D. C. 20006   **4**

9.1.3 Cost of contributions, assessments or taxes for such items as unemployment compensation and social security, insofar as such cost is based on wages, salaries, or other remuneration paid to employees of the Contractor and included in the Cost of the Work under Subparagraphs 9.1.1 and 9.1.2.

9.1.4 The proportion of reasonable transportation, traveling and hotel expenses of the Contractor or of his officers or employees incurred in discharge of duties connected with the Work.

9.1.5 Cost of all materials, supplies and equipment incorporated in the Work, including costs of transportation thereof.

9.1.6 Payments made by the Contractor to Subcontractors for Work performed pursuant to subcontracts under this Agreement.

9.1.7 Cost, including transportation and maintenance, of all materials, supplies, equipment, temporary facilities and hand tools not owned by the workmen, which are consumed in the performance of the Work, and cost less salvage value on such items used but not consumed which remain the property of the Contractor.

9.1.8 Rental charges of all necessary machinery and equipment, exclusive of hand tools, used at the site of the Work, whether rented from the Contractor or others, including installation, minor repairs and replacements, dismantling, removal, transportation and delivery costs thereof, at rental charges consistent with those prevailing in the area.

9.1.9 Cost of premiums for all bonds and insurance which the Contractor is required by the Contract Documents to purchase and maintain.

9.1.10 Sales, use or similar taxes related to the Work and for which the Contractor is liable imposed by any governmental authority.

9.1.11 Permit fees, royalties, damages for infringement of patents and costs of defending suits therefor, and deposits lost for causes other than the Contractor's negligence.

9.1.12 Losses and expenses, not compensated by insurance or otherwise, sustained by the Contractor in connection with the Work, provided they have resulted from causes other than the fault or neglect of the Contractor. Such losses shall include settlements made with the written consent and approval of the Owner. No such losses and expenses shall be included in the Cost of the Work for the purpose of determining the Contractor's Fee. If, however, such loss requires reconstruction and the Contractor is placed in charge thereof, he shall be paid for his services a Fee proportionate to that stated in Paragraph 7.1.

9.1.13 Minor expenses such as telegrams, long distance telephone calls, telephone service at the site, expressage, and similar petty cash items in connection with the Work.

9.1.14 Cost of removal of all debris.

9.1.15 Costs incurred due to an emergency affecting the safety of persons and property.

9.1.16 Other costs incurred in the performance of the Work if and to the extent approved in advance in writing by the Owner.

ARTICLE 10

COSTS NOT TO BE REIMBURSED

10.1 The term Cost of the Work shall not include any of the items set forth below in this Article 10.

10.1.1 Salaries or other compensation of the Contractor's officers, executives, general managers, estimators, auditors, accountants, purchasing and contracting agents and other employees at the Contractor's principal office and branch offices, except employees of the Contractor when engaged at shops or on the road in expediting the production or transportation of materials or equipment for the Work.

10.1.2 Expenses of the Contractor's Principal and Branch Offices other than the Field Office.

10.1.3 Any part of the Contractor's capital expenses, including interest on the Contractor's capital employed for the Work.

10.1.4 Overhead or general expenses of any kind, except as may be expressly included in Article 9.

10.1.5 Costs due to the negligence of the Contractor, any Subcontractor, anyone directly or indirectly employed by any of them, or for whose acts any of them may be liable, including but not limited to the correction of defective Work, disposal of materials and equipment wrongly supplied, or making good any damage to property.

10.1.6 The cost of any item not specifically and expressly included in the items described in Article 9.

10.1.7 Costs in excess of the Guaranteed Maximum Cost, if any, as set forth in Article 6 and adjusted pursuant to Article 8.

ARTICLE 11

DISCOUNTS, REBATES AND REFUNDS

All cash discounts shall accrue to the Contractor unless the Owner deposits funds with the Contractor with which to make payments, in which case the cash discounts shall accrue to the Owner. All trade discounts, rebates and refunds, and all returns from sale of surplus materials and equipment shall accrue to the Owner, and the Contractor shall make provisions so that they can be secured.

(Here insert any provisions relating to deposits by the Owner to permit the Contractor to obtain cash discounts.)

ARTICLE 12

SUBCONTRACTS

12.1 All portions of the Work that the Contractor's organization has not been accustomed to perform shall be performed under subcontracts. The Contractor shall request bids from subcontractors and shall deliver such bids to the Architect. The Architect will then determine, with the advice of the Contractor and subject to the approval of the Owner, which bids will be accepted.

12.2 All Subcontracts shall conform to the requirements of Paragraph 5.3 of the General Conditions. Subcontracts awarded on the basis of the cost of such work plus a fee shall also be subject to the provisions of this Agreement insofar as applicable.

ARTICLE 13

ACCOUNTING RECORDS

The Contractor shall check all materials, equipment and labor entering into the Work and shall keep such full and detailed accounts as may be necessary for proper financial management under this Agreement, and the system shall be satisfactory to the Owner. The Owner shall be afforded access to all the Contractor's records, books, correspondence, instructions, drawings, receipts, vouchers, memoranda and similar data relating to this Contract, and the Contractor shall preserve all such records for a period of three years after the final payment.

ARTICLE 14

APPLICATIONS FOR PAYMENT

The Contractor shall, at least ten days before each progress payment falls due, deliver to the Architect a statement, sworn to if required, showing in complete detail all moneys paid out or costs incurred by him on account of the Cost of the Work during the previous month for which he is to be reimbursed under Article 6 and the amount of the Contractor's Fee due as provided in Article 7, together with payrolls for all labor and all receipted bills for which payment has been received.

ARTICLE 15

PAYMENTS TO THE CONTRACTOR

15.1 The Architect will review the Contractor's statement of moneys due as provided in Article 14 and will promptly issue a Certificate for Payment to the Owner for such amount as he approves, which Certificate shall be payable on or about the   day of the month.

15.2 Final payment, constituting the unpaid balance of the Cost of the Work and of the Contractor's Fee, shall be paid by the Owner to the Contractor when the Work has been completed, the Contract fully performed and a final Certificate for Payment has been issued by the Architect. Final payment shall be due
days after the date of issuance of the final Certificate for Payment.

ARTICLE 16

TERMINATION OF THE CONTRACT

16.1 The Contract may be terminated by the Contractor as provided in Article 14 of the General Conditions.

16.2 If the Owner terminates the Contract as provided in Article 14 of the General Conditions, he shall reimburse the Contractor for any unpaid Cost of the Work due him under Article 6, plus (1) the unpaid balance of the Fee computed upon the Cost of the Work to the date of termination at the rate of the percentage named in Article 7, or (2) if the Contractor's Fee be stated as a fixed sum, such an amount as will increase the payments on account of his Fee to a sum which bears the same ratio to the said fixed sum as the Cost of the Work at the time of termination bears to the adjusted Guaranteed Maximum Cost, if any, otherwise to a reasonable estimated Cost of the Work when completed. The Owner shall also pay to the Contractor fair compensation, either by purchase or rental at the election of the Owner, for any equipment retained. In case of such termination of the Contract the Owner shall further assume and become liable for obligations, commitments and unsettled claims that the Contractor has previously undertaken or incurred in good faith in connection with said Work. The Contractor shall, as a condition of receiving the payments referred to in this Article 16, execute and deliver all such papers and take all such steps, including the legal assignment of his contractual rights, as the Owner may require for the purpose of fully vesting in him the rights and benefits of the Contractor under such obligations or commitments.

ARTICLE 17

MISCELLANEOUS PROVISIONS

17.1 Terms used in this Agreement which are defined in the Conditions of the Contract shall have the meanings designated in those Conditions.

17.2 The Contract Documents, which constitute the entire agreement between the Owner and the Contractor, are listed in Article 1 and, except for Modifications issued after execution of this Agreement, are enumerated as follows:

(List below the Agreement, Conditions of the Contract, (General, Supplementary, other Conditions), Drawings, Specifications, Addenda and accepted Alternates, showing page or sheet numbers in all cases and dates where applicable.)

This Agreement executed the day and year first written above.

OWNER   CONTRACTOR

APPENDIX J
SUBCONTRACT FORM

SUBCONTRACT FORM

(Developed as a guide by The Associated General Contractors of America, The National Electrical Contractors Association, The Mechanical Contractors Association of America, The Sheet Metal and Air Conditioning Contractors National Association and the National Association of Plumbing - Heating - Cooling Contractors © 1966 by the Associated General Contractors of America and the Council of Mechanical Specialty Contracting Industries, Inc.)

THIS AGREEMENT made this   day of   in the year Nineteen

Hundred and   by and between

hereinafter

called the Subcontractor and

hereinafter called the Contractor.

WITNESSETH, That the Subcontractor and Contractor for the consideration hereinafter named agree as follows:

ARTICLE I. The Subcontractor agrees to furnish all material and perform all work as described in

Article II hereof for

(Here name the project.)

for

(Here name the Contractor.)

at

(Here insert the location of the work and name of Owner.)

in accordance with this Agreement, the Agreement between the Owner and Contractor, and in accordance with the General Conditions of the Contract, Supplementary General Conditions, the Drawings and Specifications and addenda prepared by   ,

hereinafter called the Architect or Owner's authorized agent, all of which documents, signed by the parties thereto or identified by the Architect or Owner's authorized agent, form a part of a Contract

between the Contractor and the Owner dated   , 19   , and hereby become a part of this contract, and herein referred to as the Contract Documents, and shall be made available to the Subcontractor upon his request prior to and at anytime subsequent to signing this Subcontract.

ARTICLE II. The Subcontractor and the Contractor agree that the materials and equipment to be furnished and work to be done by the Subcontractor are: (Here insert a precise description of the work, preferably by reference to the numbers of the drawings and the pages of the specifications including addenda and accepted alternates.)

(Page One of 5)

ARTICLE III. Time is of the essence and the Subcontractor agrees to commence and to complete the work as described in Article II as follows: (Here insert any information pertaining to the method of notification for commencement of work, starting and completion dates, or duration, and any liquidated damage requirements.)

(a) No extension of time of this contract will be recognized without the written consent of the Contractor which consent shall not be withheld unreasonably consistent with Article X-4 of this Contract, subject to the arbitration provisions herein provided.

ARTICLE IV. The Contractor agrees to pay the Subcontractor for the performance of this work the sum of   ($)
in current funds, subject to additions and deductions for changes as may be agreed upon in writing, and to make monthly payments on account thereof in accordance with Article X, Sections 20-23 inclusive. (Here insert additional details—unit prices, etc., payment procedure including date of monthly applications for payment, payment procedure if other than on a monthly basis, consideration of materials safely and suitably stored at the site or at some other location agreed upon in writing by the parties—and any provisions made for limiting or reducing the amount retained after the work reaches a certain stage of completion which should be consistent with the Contract Documents.)

ARTICLE V. Final payment shall be due when the work described in this contract is fully completed and performed in accordance with the Contract Documents, and payment to be consistent with Article IV and Article X, Sections 18, 20-23 inclusive of this contract.

Before issuance of the final payment the Subcontractor if required shall submit evidence satisfactory to the Contractor that all payrolls, material bills, and all known indebtedness connected with the Subcontractor's work have been satisfied.

(Page Two of 5)

ARTICLE VI. Performance and Payment Bonds.

(Here insert any requirement for the furnishing of performance and payment bonds.)

ARTICLE VII. Temporary Site Facilities.

(Here insert any requirements and terms concerning temporary site facilities, i.e., storage, sheds, water, heat, light, power, toilets, hoists, elevators, scaffolding, cold weather protection, ventilating, pumps, watchman service, etc.)

ARTICLE VIII.   Insurance.

Unless otherwise provided herein, the Subcontractor shall have a direct liability for the acts of his employees and agents for which he is legally responsible, and the Subcontractor shall not be required to assume the liability for the acts of any others.

Prior to starting work the insurance required to be furnished shall be obtained from a responsible company or companies to provide proper and adequate coverage and satisfactory evidence will be furnished to the Contractor that the Subcontractor has complied with the requirements as stated in this Section.

(Here insert any insurance requirements and Subcontractor's responsibility for obtaining, maintaining and paying for necessary insurance, not less than limits as may be specified in the Contract Documents or required by laws. This to include fire insurance and extended coverage, consideration of public liability, property damage, employer's liability, and workmen's compensation insurance for the Subcontractor and his employees. The insertion should provide the agreement of the Contractor and the Subcontractor on subrogation waivers, provision for notice of cancellation, allocation of insurance proceeds, and other aspects of insurance.)

(It is recommended that the AGC Insurance and Bonds Checklist (AGC Form No. 29) be referred to as a guide for other insurance coverages.)

(Page Three of 5)

ARTICLE IX. Job Conditions.

(Here insert any applicable arrangements and necessary cooperation concerning labor matters for the project.)

ARTICLE X. In addition to the foregoing provisions the parties also agree:

That the Subcontractor shall:

(1) Be bound to the Contractor by the terms of the Contractor Documents and this Agreement, and assume toward the Contractor all the obligations and responsibilities that the Contractor, by those documents. assumes toward the Owner, as applicable to this Subcontract. (a) Not discriminate against any employee or applicant for employment because of race, creed, color, or national origin.

(2) Submit to the Contractor applications for payment at such times as stipulated in Article IV so as to enable the Contractor to apply for payment.

If payments are made on valuations of work done, the Subcontractor shall, before the first application, submit to the Contractor a schedule of values of the various parts of the work, aggregating the total sum of the Contract, made out in such detail as the Subcontractor and Contractor may agree upon, or as required by the Owner, and, if required, supported by such evidence as to its correctness as the Contractor may direct. This schedule, when approved by the Contractor, shall be used as a basis for Certificates for Payment, unless it be found to be in error. In applying for payment, the Subcontractor shall submit a statement based upon this schedule.

If payments are made on account of materials not incorporated in the work but delivered and suitably stored at the site, or at some other location agreed upon in writing, such payments shall be in accordance with the terms and conditions of the Contract Documents.

(3) Pay for all materials and labor used in, or in connection with, the performance of this contract, through the period covered by previous payments received from the Contractor, and furnish satisfactory evidence when requested by the Contractor, to verify compliance with the above requirements.

(4) Make all claims for extras, for extensions of time and for damage for delays or otherwise, promptly to the Contractor consistent with the Contract Documents.

(5) Take necessary precaution to properly protect the finished work of other trades.

(6) Keep the building and premises clean at all times of debris arising out of the operation of this subcontract. The Subcontractor shall not be held responsible for unclean conditions caused by other contractors or subcontractors, unless otherwise provided for.

(7) Comply with all statutory and/or contractual safety requirements applying to his work and/or initiated by the Contractor, and shall report within 3 days to the Contractor any injury to the Subcontractor's employees at the site of the project.

(8) (a) Not assign this subcontract or any amounts due or to become due thereunder without the written consent of the contractor. (b) Nor subcontract the whole of this subcontract without the written consent of the contractor. (c) Nor further subcontract portions of this subcontract without written notification to the contractor when such notification is requested by the contractor.

(9) Guarantee his work against all defects of materials and/or workmanship as called for in the plans, specifications and addenda, or if no guarantee is called for, then for a period of one year from the dates of partial or total acceptance of the Subcontractor's work by the Owner.

(10) And does hereby agree that if the Subcontractor should neglect to prosecute the work diligently and properly or fail to perform any provision of this contract, the Contractor, after three days written notice to the Subcontractor, may, without prejudice to any other remedy he may have, make good such deficiencies and may deduct the cost thereof from the payment then or thereafter due the Subcontractor, provided, however, that if such action is based upon faulty workmanship the Architect or Owner's authorized agent, shall first have determined that the workmanship and/or materials is defective.

(11) And does hereby agree that the Contractor's equipment will be available to the Subcontractor only at the Contractor's discretion and on mutually satisfactory terms.

(12) Furnish periodic progress reports of the work as mutually agreed including the progress of materials or equipment under this Agreement that may be in the course of preparation or manufacture.

(13) Make any and all changes or deviations from the original plans and specifications without nullifying the original contract when specifically ordered to do so in writing by the Contractor. The Subcontractor prior to the commencement of this revised work, shall submit promptly to the Contractor written copies of the cost or credit proposal for such revised work in a manner consistent with the Contract Documents.

(14) Cooperate with the Contractor and other Subcontractors whose work might interfere with the Subcontractor's work and to participate in the preparation of coordinated drawings in areas of congestion as required by the Contract Documents, specifically noting and advising the Contractor of any such interference.

(15) Cooperate with the Contractor in scheduling his work so as not conflict or interfere with the work of others. To promptly submit shop drawings, drawings, and samples, as required in order to carry on said work efficiently and at speed that will not cause delay in the progress of the Contractor's work or other branches of the work carried on by other Subcontractors.

(16) Comply with all Federal, State and local laws and ordinances applying to the building or structure and to comply and give adequate notices relating to the work to proper authorities and to secure and pay for all necessary licenses or permits to carry on the work as described in the Contract Documents as applicable to this Subcontract.

(17) Comply with Federal, State and local tax laws, Social Security laws and Unemployment Compensation laws and Workmen's Compensation Laws insofar as applicable to the performance of this subcontract.

(Page Four of 5)

(18) And does hereby agree that all work shall be done subject to the final approval of the Architect or Owner's authorized agent, and his decision in matters relating to artistic effect shall be final, if within the terms of the Contract Documents. That the Contractor shall—

(19) Be bound to the Subcontractor by all the obligations that the Owner assumes to the Contractor under the Contract Documents and by all the provisions thereof affording remedies and redress to the Contractor from the Owner insofar as applicable to this Subcontract.

(20) Pay the Subcontractor within seven days, unless otherwise provided in the Contract Documents, upon the payment of certificates issued under the Contractor's schedule of values, or as described in Article IV herein. The amount of the payment shall be equal to the percentage of completion certified by the Owner or his authorized agent for the work of this Subcontractor applied to the amount set forth under Article IV and allowed to the Contractor on account of the Subcontractor's work to the extent of the Subcontractor's interest therein.

(21) Permit the Subcontractor to obtain direct from the Architect or Owner's authorized agent, evidence of percentages of completion certified on his account.

(22) Pay the Subcontractor on demand for his work and/or materials as far as executed and fixed in place, less the retained percentage, at the time the payment should be made to the Subcontractor if the Architect or Owner's authorized agent fails to issue the certificate for any fault of the Contractor and not the fault of the Subcontractor or as otherwise provided herein.

(23) And does hereby agree that the failure to make payments to the Subcontractor as herein provided for any cause not the fault of the Subcontractor, within 7 days from the Contractor's receipt of payment or from time payment should be made as provided in Article X, Section 22, or maturity, then the Subcontractor may upon 7 days written notice to the Contractor stop work without prejudice to any other remedy he may have.

(24) Not issue or give any instructions, order or directions directly to employees or workmen of the Subcontractor other than to the persons designated as the authorized representative(s) of the Subcontractor.

(25) Make no demand for liquidated damages in any sum in excess of such amount as may be specifically named in the subcontract, provided, however, no liquidated damages shall be assessed for delays or causes attributable to other Subcontractors or arising outside the scope of this Subcontract.

(26) And does hereby agree that no claim for services rendered or materials furnished by the Contractor to the Subcontractor shall be valid unless written notice thereof is given by the Contractor to the Subcontractor during the first ten days of the calendar month following that in which the claim originated.

(27) Give the Subcontractor an opportunity to be present and to submit evidence in any arbitration involving his rights.

(28) Name as arbitor under arbitration proceedings as provided in the General Conditions the person nominated by the Subcontractor, if the sole cause of dispute is the work, materials, rights or responsibilities of the Subcontractor; or if, of the Subcontractor and any other Subcontractor jointly, to name as such arbitrator the person upon whom they agree. That the Contractor and the Subcontractor agree—

(29) That in the matter of arbitration, their rights and obligations and all procedure shall be analogous to those set forth in the Contract Documents provided, however, that a decision by the Architect or Owner's authorized agent, shall not be a condition precedent to arbitration.

(30) This subcontract is solely for the benefit of the signatories hereto.

ARTICLE XI.

IN WITNESS WHEREOF the parties hereto have executed this Agreement under seal, the day and year first above written.

Attest:

_____   Subcontractor _____

(Seal)   By _____ (Title)

Attest:

_____   Contractor _____

(Seal)   By _____ (Title)

(Page Five of 5)

APPENDIX K

GENERAL LEDGER ACCOUNTS

10.   Petty Cash
11.   Bank Deposits
   .1   General Bank Account
   .2   Payroll Bank Account
   .3   Project Bank Accounts
   .4
12.   Accounts Receivable
   .1
   .2   Parent, Associated, or Affiliated Companies
   .3   Notes Receivable
   .4   Employees' Accounts
   .5   Sundry Debtors
   .6
13.   Deferred Receivables
   All construction contracts are charged to this account, being diminished by progress payments as received. This account is offset by Account 48.0, Deferred Income.
14.   Property, Plant, and Equipment

Property and General Plant

   .100   Real Estate and Improvements
   .200   Leasehold Improvements
   .300   Motor Vehicles
   .400   Shops and Yards

Mobile Equipment

   .500   Power Shovels
   .510   Tractors
   .520   Bottom Dumps
   .525

Stationary Equipment

.530   Concrete Mixing Plant
.540   Concrete Pavers
.550   Air Compressors
.560

Small Power Tools and Portable Equipment

.600   Welders
.610   Concrete Power Buggies
.620   Electric Drills
.630

Marine Equipment

.700

Miscellaneous Construction Equipment

.800   Scaffolding
.810   Concrete Forms
.820   Wheelbarrows
.830

Office and Engineering Equipment

.900   Office Equipment
.910   Office Furniture
.920   Engineering Instruments
.930

15.   Reserve for Depreciation

16.   Amortization for Leasehold

17.   Inventory of Materials and Supplies
.1   Lumber
.2   Hand Shovels
.3   Spare Parts
.4

These accounts show the values of all expendable materials and supplies. Charges against these accounts are made by authenticated requisitions showing project where used.

18.   Returnable Deposits
.1   Plan Deposits
.2   Utilities
.3

19.   Prepaid Expenses
.1   Insurance
.2   Bonds
.3

LIABILITIES

40.   Accounts Payable
41.   Subcontracts Payable
42.   Notes Payable
43.   Interest Payable
44.   Contracts Payable
45.   Taxes Payable

.1   Old-Age, Survivors, and Disability Insurance (withheld from employees' pay)

.2   Federal Income Taxes (withheld from employees' pay)

.3   State Income Taxes (withheld from employees' pay)

.4

46.   Accrued Expenses

.1   Wages and Salaries

.2   Old-Age, Survivors, and Disability Insurance (employer's portion)

.3   Federal Unemployment Tax

.4   State Unemployment Tax

.51   Payroll Insurance (public liability and property damage)

.52   Payroll Insurance (workmen's compensation)

.6   Interest

.7

47.   **Payrolls Payable**

48.   Deferred Income

49.   Advances by Clients

NET WORTH

50.   Capital Stock

51.   Earned Surplus

52.   Paid-in Surplus

53.

INCOME

70.   Income Accounts

.101   Project Income

.102

.2   Cash Discount Earned

.3   Profit or Loss from Sale of Capital Assets

.4   Equipment Rental Income

.5   Interest Income

.6   Other Income

EXPENSE

80.   Project Expense (Expenses directly chargeable to the projects. See Figure 11.1.)

.100   Project Work Accounts

.500   Plant and Equipment Operation Accounts

.700   Overhead Expense Accounts

          These are control accounts for the detail project cost accounts that are maintained in the detail cost ledgers.

81.   Office Expense

.10   Officer Salaries

.11   Insurance on Property and Equipment

.20   Donations

.21   Utilities

.22   Telephone and Telegraph

.23   Postage

.30   Repairs and Maintenance

82.   Yard and Warehouse Expense (not assignable to a particular project)

.10   Yard Salaries

.11   Yard Supplies

83.   Estimating Department Expense Accounts
.10   Estimating Salaries
.11   Estimating Supplies
.12   Estimating Travel

84.   Engineering Department Expense Accounts
.10

85.   Cost of Equipment Ownership
.1   Depreciation
.2   Interest
.3   Taxes and Licenses
.4   Insurance
.5   Storage

86.   Loss on Bad Debts

87.   Interest

90.   Expense on Office Employees
.1   Workmen's Compensation Insurance
.2   Old-Age, Survivors, and Disability Insurance
.3   Employees' Insurance
.4   Other Insurance
.5   Federal and State Unemployment Taxes
.6

91.   Taxes and Licenses
.1   Sales Taxes
.2   Compensating Taxes
.3   State Income Taxes
.4   Federal Income Taxes

APPENDIX L

A STRATEGY OF BIDDING

L.1 MARKUP

When a contractor is bidding on a new job, one of the final actions taken is adding the markup to the estimated cost of the construction. This markup is customarily determined as a percentage of the cost. Although markup can include certain cost items as well as an allowance for profit, the term, as used in this appendix, is construed to be profit only. It is assumed that all items of job expense, including project and office overhead, are included in the contractor's estimate of cost.

Customarily, the contractor will select a markup that hopefully will enable him to bid the largest amount possible and still be the low bidder. By minimizing the difference between his bid and the second lowest, he will realize the maximum profit possible if he actually becomes the successful bidder. How the contractor goes about selecting his markup figure to accomplish this objective is normally a very inexact process and is based more on his subjective judgment than on any rational procedure. Using his past experience as a guide, he attempts to evaluate several bidding variables such as the competition, the type of work, the geographical area, the architect-engineer, and the terms of the contract documents. Although these variables cannot be precisely defined, they indicate in a general way whether high or low markups are in order.

This is not to say that the selection of a markup figure in such an intuitive fashion is altogether wrong or that more objective criteria can be devised which will suit all bidding conditions. Nevertheless, under the right circumstances, there are ways in which markup percentages can be selected that could increase the contractor's profits over the long term. One such circumstance may exist when a contractor's bidding is largely confined to a specific type of work in the same general geographical area.

The customary basis for most construction bidding is to bid each job essentially as an independent entity, attempting to maximize the potential profit on a particular project with little systematic attention being given to how it may relate to the panorama of past and future projects. Where a history of bidding experience has been built up, competitive patterns in past biddings can be used as a guide for future ones. There are a number of ways in which this can be done, these procedures being known as "bidding strategies." It is the purpose of this appendix to discuss one such method. Although this discussion is oriented to lump-sum projects, the procedures are adaptable to unit-price biddings.

L.2 EXPECTED PROFIT

When a contractor bids a lump-sum job, he can anticipate a "potential profit" of $(b - c)$, where b is the amount of his bid and c is the actual cost of the work. The bid b is the sum of the estimated cost of the work and the markup, which is a variable. However, the contractor does not get every job on which he bids. Obviously, his chances of being the successful bidder are related to the amount of his bid, b. He can make his bid so high that his chances of being the low bidder would be zero. Here is a case in which the potential profit is large but the chances of actually realizing it are zero. To use slightly different terms, the "probability" p of being the low bidder is said to be zero when there is no chance of this occurrence. On the other hand, the contractor could bid so low that his winning would be a certainty (probability, $p = 1$), but the potential profit would be very small or even negative (loss). In between, of course, there are many possible bids with the probability of success varying inversely with the size of the bid; that is, the higher the bid the smaller the probability of success. Clearly, there is some optimum bid between the two extremes.

To determine this optimum bid, the concept of expectation or "expected profit" is useful. Expected profit is defined as $p(b - c)$, where p is the probability of the contractor's being the low bidder when his submitted bid is equal to b. As previously explained, p can vary between 0 (no chance) and 1 (certainty), with higher values indicating higher probability or better chances of winning. If the probability, p, is equal to 0.4, this indicates that the contractor's chances of being the low bidder are 4 out of 10.

To illustrate by a simple example the idea of expected profit, let us consider a project whose actual cost, c, will be $50,000. Suppose that a contractor is able to determine that a bid of $56,000 has a probability of 0.3 of being low and that a bid of $53,000 has a probability of 0.8. The objective is to determine which of the two bids is better with respect to expected profit.

When $b = \$56,000$:

Expected profit $= p(b - c) = 0.3(\$56,000 - \$50,000) = \$1,800$

When $b = \$53,000$:

Expected profit $= p(b - c) = 0.8(\$53,000 - \$50,000) = \$2,400$

The bid of $53,000 is the better of the two because it yields the larger expected profit. The reasoning behind maximizing expected profit is based upon long-term considerations. If the $56,000 bid were used, the potential profit would be $6,000. However, there are only 3 chances out of 10 that our contractor will get the job if he uses this bid. If it were possible to bid this same job 10 times and our contractor submitted a bid of $56,000 each time, he would expect to be, on the average, the successful bidder 3 times and would realize a total actual profit of $3(\$6,000) = \$18,000$ from the series of biddings. This is an average profit of $1,800 per bidding. On the other hand, the $53,000 bid would be successful 8 times out of the 10 and would produce a total actual profit of $24,000 or an average profit of $2,400 per bid.

As can now be seen, expected profit represents the *average return per bid* if the biddings were to be repeated a large number of times. Biddings for the same project are, of course, not repeated, but the concept of increasing a contractor's actual profits by maximizing the expected profit for each bid submitted is still valid when utilized over a span of many biddings. It amounts to what might be described as "playing the odds." Our bidding strategy is based upon the concept of maximizing expected profit.

L.3 COST OF CONSTRUCTION

The cost, c, as used herein is the actual cost of the work, a quantity that cannot possibly be known until the construction has been completed. Unfortunately, c is an important element in our bidding strategy, and bidding strategies are designed for use when the job is just being bid and long before c is known. A common assumption is that the actual cost, c, will be equal to the contractor's estimate of cost used in his bid.

Whether or not this is a valid assumption depends upon the accuracy of the contractor's past bids. It is not difficult for a contractor to compute the ratio of the actual construction cost to his original estimated cost for each of his past projects. If these ratios are grouped together into equal intervals (in a manner similar to the first two columns of Table L.2), a histogram and frequency polygon can be plotted. If the smoothed frequency polygon of past biddings resembles a normal distribution of small variance and with its mode at or very near ratio of 1.0, such as that shown by curve A in Figure L.1, the overall bidding accuracy of the contractor has been consistently good. Although curve B has its mode at 1.0, the large dispersion of the values indicates loose estimating with a serious tendency to both under- and overestimate. A biased distribution such as curve C is indicative of systematic estimating errors that result in a pronounced tendency to consistently either under- or overestimate a majority of the jobs bid.

There are statistical ways to make allowance for the bias and variability of past cost estimates. However, it is believed that the bidding records of most succesful contractors will generally resemble curve A. In this case, the assumption that the actual cost, c,

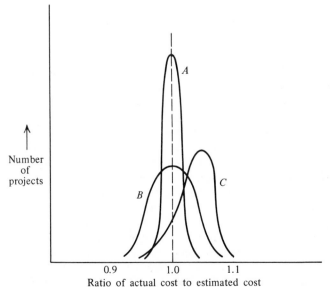

Ratio of actual cost to estimated cost

Figure L.1 Analysis of estimated and actual construction costs.

will be equal to the cost as estimated is statistically acceptable and the bidding strategy will be developed on this basis. Notice that this does not say that the costs of one contractor will necessarily equal those of another competing contractor.

L.4 MAXIMIZING EXPECTED PROFIT

To illustrate how a bid is selected to maximize expected profit, consider the bidding of a project whose estimated cost is $200,000. Assume for the moment that the probability of success for each of several different bids is known and is as shown in the second column of Table L.1. How these probability values are obtained will be discussed subsequently. For the figures shown in Table L.1, a bid of $210,000, or a markup of 5 percent, yields the maximum expected profit and is the best bid.

TABLE L.1   Maximizing Expected Profit

Bid, b	Probability, p	Expected Profit, $p(b - c)$	
$195,000	1.00	$1.00(\$195,000 - \$200,000) =$	$-$5,000 (loss)
200,000	0.97	$0.97(\$200,000 - \$200,000) =$	0
205,000	0.81	$0.81(\$205,000 - \$200,000) =$	4,050
210,000	0.50	$0.50(\$210,000 - \$200,000) =$	5,000
215,000	0.30	$0.30(\$215,000 - \$200,000) =$	4,500
220,000	0.18	$0.18(\$220,000 - \$200,000) =$	3,600
225,000	0.05	$0.05(\$225,000 - \$200,000) =$	1,250
230,000	0.00	$0.00(\$230,000 - \$200,000) =$	0

L.5 CASE I — SINGLE KNOWN COMPETITOR

Before our bidding strategy can be developed further, we must determine how to find the values of probability of bidding success. As we shall see, these values are derived from an analysis of the historical bidding experience of our contractor and his competitors. For simplicity of explanation, let us first confine our discussion to bidding against a single, known competitor called Competitor A. Identification as a "known" competitor implies that our contractor has reason to believe that this competitor will be bidding the project and that our contractor has had past bidding experience with him.

Because bids are customarily opened and read aloud to all attendees at a bid opening, the past bids of competitors are known. In addition, area trade magazines publish the results of most biddings. Suppose that our contractor, using these past bidding records, compiles the information shown in Table L.2 concerning Competitor A, against whom he has bid 62 times during recent years. It is suggested that only comparatively recent biddings be included, say within the past 5 or 6 years. The reason is that the bidding behavior of most contractors changes with time, reflecting economic conditions, changes of company policy, and other temporal factors. Consequently, it is judged that recent bidding data reflect more accurately the probable temper of competitors at present biddings. In Table L.2, $R = b_A/c$, where b_A is Competitor A's bid and c is our contractor's estimate of construction cost.

TABLE L.2   Bidding History of Competitor A

$R = \dfrac{b_A}{c}$	Number of Times
$R < 0.98$	0
$0.98 \leqq R < 1.00$	1
$1.00 \leqq R < 1.02$	3
$1.02 \leqq R < 1.04$	5
$1.04 \leqq R < 1.06$	13
$1.06 \leqq R < 1.08$	18
$1.08 \leqq R < 1.10$	14
$1.10 \leqq R < 1.12$	5
$1.12 \leqq R < 1.14$	2
$1.14 \leqq R < 1.16$	1
$1.16 \leqq R$	0
	Total $= \overline{62}$

The data in Table L.2 now enable us to compute the probabilities, p_A, shown in Table L.3 that various bids by our contractor will be lower than the bid submitted by Competitor A. To illustrate, if our contractor bids a ratio of b/c of 0.98 (2 percent less than his estimated cost), the probability that he will underbid Competitor A is 1.00 because at no time in the past has Competitor A ever bid this low. If our contractor bids the job at cost ($b/c = 1.00$), there is 1 chance in 62 that Competitor A will bid lower. Another way of stating the same thing is to say that our contractor has 61 chances out of 62, or a probability of $61/62 = 0.98$, of being the low bidder. Table L.2 shows that, in the past, Competitor A has bid a value of b_A/c less than 1.02 four times. If our contractor submits a bid-to-cost ratio of 1.02 (markup $= 2$ percent), the probability is $58/62$ or 0.94 that he will be the low bidder. Continuing this process will yield the values of p_A shown in Table L.3.

The values of b/c in Table L.3 are the ratios of our contractor's bid to his estimated cost. The expected profit has been computed in terms of c, the estimated cost. When $b/c = 1.08$ (a markup of 8 percent), then $b = 1.08c$, the probability of success is 0.36, and the expected profit is $0.029c$. The values of expected profit in the last column of Table L.3 indicate that a bid of $1.06c$, or a markup of 6 percent, is optimum when Competitor A is the only other bidder. If our contractor's estimated cost, c, is \$200,000, his bid would be \$212,000. Some additional accuracy in determining the optimum bid can be achieved by plotting the results of Table L.3, as shown in Figure L.2. This figure shows that the optimum markup would be closer to 5.5 than to 6 percent. Whether this kind of accuracy is significant is problematical.

It is interesting to note that the optimum markup percentage is independent of estimated cost and can be determined in advance of bidding. The result is that the optimum markup will be the same for a small project as for a large one. This statement may well run contrary to actual bidding practice, and the answer is to analyze Competitor A's bidding record separately for small jobs and for large ones. For example, probability values could be obtained for all projects less than \$500,000 and for all projects over this amount. It should be obvious that probability values must be updated each time our contractor bids another job against Competitor A.

It may be well as this point to emphasize the fact that any bidding strategy attempts to predict future bidding behavior on the basis of past performance. The entire strategy

TABLE L.3   Maximizing Expected Profit When Bidding Against Competitor A

$\dfrac{b}{c}$	p_A	Expected Profit, $p_A(b-c)$
0.98	$\dfrac{62}{62}=1.00$	$1.00(0.98c-c)=-0.020c$
1.00	$\dfrac{61}{62}=0.98$	$0.98(1.00c-c)=0$
1.02	$\dfrac{58}{62}=0.94$	$0.94(1.02c-c)=0.019c$
1.04	$\dfrac{53}{62}=0.85$	$0.85(1.04c-c)=0.034c$
1.06	$\dfrac{40}{62}=0.65$	$0.65(1.06c-c)=0.039c$
1.08	$\dfrac{22}{62}=0.36$	$0.36(1.08c-c)=0.029c$
1.10	$\dfrac{8}{62}=0.13$	$0.13(1.10c-c)=0.013c$
1.12	$\dfrac{3}{62}=0.05$	$0.05(1.12c-c)=0.006c$
1.14	$\dfrac{1}{62}=0.02$	$0.02(1.14c-c)=0.003c$
1.16	$\dfrac{0}{62}=0.00$	$0.00(1.16c-c)=0$

is based upon the supposition that competitors will continue to follow the same general bidding patterns as they have in the past. What changes in a competitor's future bidding habits might result from the use of a bidding strategy by our contractor is an open question.

L.6 CASE II — MULTIPLE KNOWN COMPETITORS

Now, let us assume that our contractor is going to bid against two known bidders, Competitors A and B. Our contractor must first, by analyzing the past bidding record of Competitor B, determine the same kind of cumulative probability distribution for this competitor as he obtained for Competitor A in the second column of Table L.3. Assume that the results of his analysis are shown in Table L.4.

Table L.4 discloses that if our contractor uses a markup of 8 percent, there is a probability of 0.36 of beating Competitor A, a probability of 0.52 of beating Competitor B, and a probability of 0.19 of beating both of them. For any given value of b/c the probability of beating both Competitors A and B, p_{AB}, is found as the product of the values of p_A and p_B. This applies because the probability of the simultaneous occurrence of a number of independent events is the product of their separate probabilities.

Table L.5 reveals that the optimum markup for our contractor to use when bidding against both Competitors A and B is 6 percent. The extension of the process to include any number of known competitors should be obvious. The inclusion of more com-

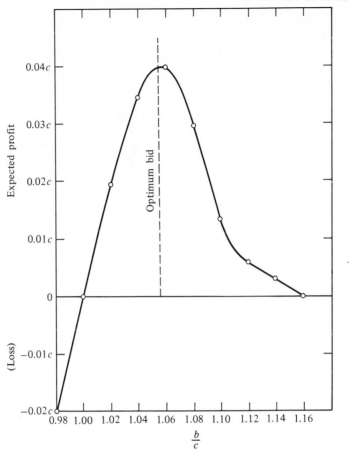

Figure L.2   Plot of data from Table L.3.

TABLE L.4   Probability Values of Known Competitors A and B

$\dfrac{b}{c}$	p_A	p_B	p_{AB}
0.98	1.00	1.00	1.00
1.00	0.98	0.99	0.97
1.02	0.94	0.96	0.90
1.04	0.85	0.90	0.76
1.06	0.65	0.84	0.55
1.08	0.36	0.52	0.19
1.10	0.13	0.31	0.04
1.12	0.05	0.14	0.01
1.14	0.02	0.03	0.00
1.16	0.00	0.00	0.00

petitors invariably reduces the value of the optimum markup. In addition, more competitors reduce the values of the expected profit such that to have enough significant figures the computations must be carried out to more decimal places.

L.7 CASE III — THE AVERAGE COMPETITOR

The preceding discussion has been based on the supposition that the competing contractors are all known; that is, our contractor knows who his competitors will be and that he possesses past bidding information about each of them. Consideration is now given to the case in which some or all of the bidders are not known. It is in this regard that the concept of "average bidder" is useful.

TABLE L.5   Maximizing Expected Profit When Bidding Against Competitors A and B

$\dfrac{b}{c}$	p_{AB}	Expected Profit, $p_{AB}(b - c)$
0.98	1.00	$1.00(0.98c - c) = -0.020c$
1.00	0.97	$0.97(1.00c - c) = \quad 0$
1.02	0.90	$0.90(1.02c - c) = \quad 0.018c$
1.04	0.76	$0.76(1.04c - c) = \quad 0.030c$
1.06	0.55	$0.55(1.06c - c) = \quad 0.033c$
1.08	0.19	$0.19(1.08c - c) = \quad 0.015c$
1.10	0.04	$0.04(1.10c - c) = \quad 0.004c$
1.12	0.01	$0.01(1.12c - c) = \quad 0.001c$
1.14	0.00	$0.00(1.14c - c) = \quad 0$
1.16	0.00	$0.00(1.16c - c) = \quad 0$

An average bidder is a hypothetical competitor whose bidding behavior is a statistical composite of the behaviors of our contractor's competitors. The collective bidding pattern of his competitors can be obtained by combining all of the competitors into one probability distribution. The procedure here is exactly the same as that followed for Competitor A except that all competitors are included with no differentiation made between them.

For illustrative purposes, suppose that the result of this all-inclusive analysis is as shown in the second column of Table L.6, where p_{av} is the probability that our contractor will submit a lower bid than any single, unspecified competitor. If only one unknown competitor is anticipated, an optimum markup of 6 percent is indicated, although the use of 7 or 8 percent might be equally in order, because the difference in expected profit is small and the methods used are not this precise.

In the event that our contractor expects three unknown competitors, the same procedure is followed as with multiple known competitors except that all competitors are the same. That is, each is an average competitor. To illustrate, Table L.6 shows that a probability of 0.51 is associated with a markup of 8 percent and a single, unknown competitor. If there were three such competitors, the probability would be $(0.51)(0.51)(0.51) = (0.51)^3 = 0.13$ for a markup of 8 percent. In other words, if our contractor uses a markup of 8 percent, there is a probability of 0.13 that he will underbid all three

TABLE L.6   Maximizing Expected Profit When Bidding Against a
Single Average Competitor

$\dfrac{b}{c}$	p_{av}	Expected Profit, $p_{av}(b-c)$
0.98	1.00	$-0.020c$
1.00	0.98	0
1.02	0.95	$0.019c$
1.04	0.89	$0.036c$
1.06	0.72	$0.043c$
1.08	0.51	$0.041c$
1.10	0.30	$0.030c$
1.12	0.12	$0.014c$
1.14	0.05	$0.007c$
1.16	0.00	0

unknown competitors. Table L.7 discloses that the optimum markup when three unknown competitors are anticipated is between 4 and 5 percent. This example illustrates
the variation of optimum markup with the number of competitors. For this reason,
accuracy in estimating the number of competing firms is important.

L.8 USE OF BIDDING STRATEGIES

Bidding stratagems of one kind or another have been in use since the concept of competitive bidding began. Every bidding involves a complex game of trying to out-guess
and out-smart the opposition. The application of bidding procedures based on a
systematic analysis of past bidding experience, however, is not common in the construction industry. Nevertheless, available evidence indicates that such methods are now
catching on, although their practitioners are understandably reticent to divulge procedures or results.

TABLE L.7   Maximizing Expected Profit When Bidding Against
Three Average Competitors

$\dfrac{b}{c}$	p_{3av}	Expected Profit, $p_{3av}(b-c)$
0.98	$(1.00)^3 = 1.00$	$-0.020c$
1.00	$(0.98)^3 = 0.94$	0
1.02	$(0.95)^3 = 0.86$	$0.017c$
1.04	$(0.89)^3 = 0.70$	$0.028c$
1.06	$(0.72)^3 = 0.37$	$0.022c$
1.08	$(0.51)^3 = 0.13$	$0.010c$
1.10	$(0.30)^3 = 0.03$	$0.003c$
1.12	$(0.12)^3 = 0.00$	0
1.14	$(0.05)^3 = 0.00$	0
1.16	$(0.00)^3 = 0.00$	0

The probabilistic procedure discussed in this appendix is basic and is easily applied. Refinements of the procedure are possible, such as computing probabilities for different categories of projects. For example, the past projects could be subdivided into different ranges of construction cost and into different types of construction. The reason for this refinement is that different markups are commonly applied to jobs, depending upon their size and type. Another modification could be to give greater weight to recent bidding information than to that from older projects.

Several other forms of bidding models have been devised, many of which involve relatively sophisticated statistical procedures. Whether or not these more refined methods have any real advantage over the simple and straightforward procedure discussed in this appendix is not yet clear.

INDEX